BRICKMAKING IN SUSSEX
A History and Gazetteer

M. Beswick

for the
SUSSEX INDUSTRIAL ARCHAEOLOGY SOCIETY

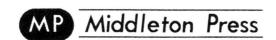
MP Middleton Press

To Wilfrid
who set the ball rolling and has given constant support

First published August 1993
Updated and reprinted July 2001

ISBN 1 873 793 197

© *M. Beswick 2001*

Published by   *Middleton Press*
                    Easebourne Lane
                    Midhurst
                    West Sussex
                    GU29 9AZ
                    Tel (01730) 813169

Typeset and printed by David Brown, Maynards Green, Heathfield, Sussex

CONTENTS

ILLUSTRATIONS

Front cover: Ashburnham. brickyard in about 1900

Back cover: Advertisement of 1886

Permission to reporduce documents, drawings and photographs has been kindly granted as follows:

11, 13	the County Archivist for East Sussex
30, 31	by courtesy of the Rt Rev the Bishop of Chichester and with acknowledgement to the County Archivist for West Sussex
7, 12	the Trustees of the Battle Abbey Estate
32	G.H.W. Comber
16	Mrs E.W. O'Shea
41, 42	John de Havilland
10, 25, 38	the Sussex Archaeological Society
14	F.W. Gregory
23, 35, 45	John Whitehouse
24	Ron Ireland
33	P. G. Lucas
36	R.B.G. Williams
front cover	from the Calvert Local History Collection

Other photographs were taken by:

4, 6, 27	D.A. Calvert
5	David Rudling (Field Archaeology Unit UCL)
20	D.H. Cox
39, 40, 43	W.R. Beswick
44	Peter Longley

Drawings 9, 17, 18 and 21 were made by R.G. Martin
Graph 28 by T. Amherst-Clark
Maps 1, 44 and 47 by Susan Rowland (Geography Laboratory, University of Sussex)

PREFACE

Both my grandfather and great-grandfather were builders and so I suppose that bricks must run in the blood. My own interest in the subject dates from 1977, when I was tracing the history of the house in which we live and discovered that it was built in the mid-19th century for a brickmaker whose yard lay nearby. My husband, who was at that time Chairman of the Sussex Industrial Archaeology Society, suggested that I should contribute an article about it to the Society's *Newsletter*. This evoked a response from a number of members and we became aware that brickmaking was a major industry in the county, which had hitherto received very little attention.

The result was the establishment of a Brick Study Group, under the Chairmanship of the late E.W. O'Shea, which met annually from 1978 to 1986. At this point, it was decided that enough material had been collected to justify publication and the task of collating the information and completing the research fell to me, as Secretary of the Study Group.

Even now, seven years later, I am aware that the job has not been finished: some 750 brickmaking sites have been noted across the counties of East and West Sussex but more are still coming to light. Furthermore, West Sussex has received less detailed coverage than the eastern part of the county, in which I live, but that leaves the way open for further investigation and I hope that this book will provide a foundation on which others can build.

Inevitably, in piecing together the evidence, some mistakes will have been made but I hope that these have been kept to the minimum. Any reader who can supply corrections or new information, is requested to communicate either with the author, or with one of the archivists at the appropriate County Record Office, where a copy of the gazetteer will be lodged.

M.B.
Turners House
Turners Green
Heathfield
May 1993

PREFACE TO THE SECOND EDITION

In the eight years which have elapsed since the publication of the first edition, a number of correspondents have supplied me with additional information and more archive material has become available. As a result, it has been decided to produce this enlarged and revised edition, the new material being incorporated mainly in the gazetteer section. In response principally to requests from family historians, the index has been augmented to include the surnames of brickmakers listed in Part II.

My thanks are due to all those who have contributed in any way but especially to Christopher Whittick of the East Sussex Record Office and David Brown, who has reset the text and seen this edition through the press.

M.B.
Halcyon
Punnetts Town
Heathfield
June 2001

ACKNOWLEDGEMENTS

Many people have given me help and encouragement during the time that this book has been in preparation and I should like to thank all of them for the time and trouble they have expended on my behalf.

In particular, the assistance of the following is gratefully acknowledged: the County Archivists of East and West Sussex and the staff of the two Record Offices at Lewes and Chichester; the Librarian of the Sussex Archaeological Society, the Local History Librarian at Hastings Reference Library and the staff of the Hastings Museum and Art Gallery; the managers and staff, past and present, of Redland Brick, Ibstock Brick Hudsons, W.T. Lamb & Sons, Rudgwick Brickworks, Freshfield Lane Brickworks, Keymer Tiles, Ashpark Brickworks and Aldershaw Tiles, who have allowed me to visit their premises and responded to requests for information; fellow members of the Sussex Industrial Archaeology Society, both those who formed part of the original Brick Study Group and others who have contributed material and checked gazetteer entries subsequently; members of Local History, Family History, Archaeological and Museum Societies in various parts of Sussex, who have supplied copies of their publications or allowed me to make use of unpublished research.

Many of the foregoing will find their individual contributions recorded in the *Notes* relating to the chapters of Part I or in the *References* which conclude each entry in the Gazetteer.

I should like to single out for special thanks:

Christopher Whittick, for drawing my attention to countless maps and documents which I should not otherwise have discovered, for instruction and help in the translation of Latin accounts and, not least, for reading my manuscript and suggesting a number of improvements; Gerald Brodribb, Jeremy Goring, Vic Mitchell and Stewart Morton, for reading and commenting on individual chapters; Ron Martin, not only for his meticulous drawings but also for noting all the brickmaking sites on the 2nd edition Ordnance Survey maps; Geoffrey Mead, for searching newspaper files and archives in the Brighton and Hove Reference Libraries; Kate Cosway, for help in examining maps at the West Sussex Record Office; Gwen Baker and Helen McCurdy for listing details of brickmakers and their families in the decennial census returns; Paul Sowan for details of mining records; David Calvert for the expert copying of old photographs; Ann Hudson for compiling the index.

PART I
BRICKMAKING IN SUSSEX

INTRODUCTION

Sussex has abundant supplies of material for making bricks and tiles but, in spite of this, the local brickmakers have, almost invariably, been followers rather than leaders in developments in the industry. The reasons for this are twofold. Firstly, the Weald was a rich source of timber, which was the primary building material until well into the 18th century. Secondly, except in the 16th century, when the wealden iron industry was at its height, Sussex was never in the vanguard of industrial progress. Therefore brick production was geared, not to the demands of industry, as in the Midlands and the North, but almost entirely to the requirements of the housing market. For this, cheapness was the main consideration. Bricks of great strength and high quality were not essential and, with certain exceptions, which will be examined in the course of this study, brickmaking operations remained, until quite recently, local, small-scale and 'low-tech'.

For the industrial archaeologist and the local historian this has advantages. Examples of traditional practices have been preserved, whereas in other parts of the country they either died out entirely at the end of the 19th century or else were swept away in the wholesale transformation of the industry in the present century. The practice of burning hand-made bricks in open clamps was still widely used in Sussex until the outbreak of World War 2 and it has been possible to interview a number of former brickmakers with clear recollections of the processes involved. An even older tradition is exemplified by the brickyard at Ashburnham, which closed only in 1968. This was the last one, not just in Sussex but in the whole country, to burn hand-made bricks in a wood-fired kiln and a detailed record was made of operations during the final season.[1]

Searching the records for evidence of brickmaking led to an increasing awareness of the people involved and of the lives they led. At the time of writing we are very conscious that the building industry is subject to peaks and troughs and this has been the case throughout history. Brickmakers have always encountered problems in meeting the demand for their products in times of prosperity and then in making ends meet when the demand fell away again. Their experiences in the past and how successful they were in surmounting these problems form the subject of two of the following chapters.

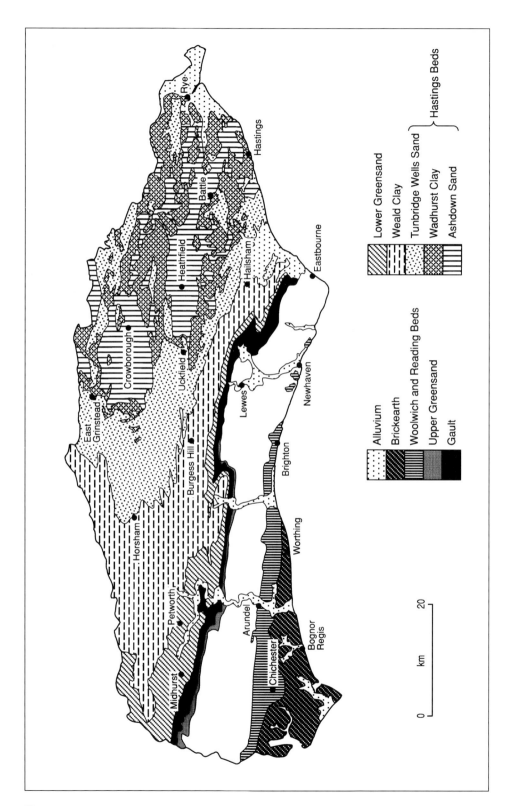

1. Sussex: the main geological strata exploited for brickmaking

Legend:

Lower Greensand
Weald Clay
Tunbridge Wells Sand ⎫
Wadhurst Clay   ⎬ Hastings Beds
Ashdown Sand   ⎭

Alluvium
Brickearth
Woolwich and Reading Beds
Upper Greensand
Gault

Rye
Hastings
Battle
Heathfield
Hailsham
Eastbourne
Crowborough
Uckfield
Lewes
Newhaven
East Grinstead
Burgess Hill
Brighton
Horsham
Worthing
Petworth
Arundel
Midhurst
Chichester
Bognor Regis

km
0   20

1. RAW MATERIALS

Almost anywhere in Sussex, except on the tops of the chalk Downs, if a shallow layer of topsoil is stripped away, the subsoil will consist of material suitable for making bricks. So it is hardly surprising that in the 19th century, when brickmaking in the county reached its peak, practically every parish had at least one brickyard. Brickmaking was not only widespread but was characterised by the variety of its products. The reason is to be found in the different properties of the brick earths and clays produced by the different geological strata which underlie the various parts of the county; some consideration of these at the outset will help in understanding the way in which the industry developed.

Brick earth, clay and sand

The geological formations exploited for brickmaking were the product of the weathering of harder rocks, which were first eroded and then re-deposited as sediment on the beds of ancient lakes. Their main constituent is quartz, in the form of sand or silt, which gives the material its strength but they also contain clay minerals, complex aluminium silicates, which consist of very fine particles that cling together when moist and give the material its plasticity. Also present are small quantities of other compounds, such as the minerals of iron, calcium, magnesium, sodium and potassium. All of these contribute to the quality, durability and appearance of the finished brick.

The proportions of sand and clay present in this raw material vary. This has given rise, at different times and in different parts of Sussex, to the use of terms to distinguish between the coarser brick earths and the finer clays. A satisfactory brick earth, which contains up to 75% of sandy material, was formerly referred to in West Sussex as 'earth' and in East Sussex as 'loam'. This yields a brick which is hard, strong and has good heat resistance and does not shrink excessively on firing. The term 'clay' was at one time reserved for the finer-textured, silty material with a higher alumina content. This is easily moulded but has a tendency to crack in drying and shrink and warp during the burning process and so is more suited to the manufacture of tiles, agricultural drainpipes and other ceramic products. However, it can also be used for brickmaking if the correct proportion of sand is added and nowadays the word clay is often used indiscriminately to denote both the coarser and the finer material.[1]

The **Hastings Beds**, which form the High Weald, or forest ridges, at the core of the wealden district and extend to the coast in the area between Hastings and Bexhill, provide perhaps the best example of the variety of materials available. This is the oldest geological formation exploited for brickmaking in Sussex and consists of a series of deposits of clays and sands, which often outcrop quite close together. The lowest of these, the Ashdown Sand, constitutes an ideal brickmaking material. The Wadhurst Clay, which lies immediately above it, is eminently suitable for tilemaking and the Tunbridge Wells Sand, the highest stratum in the series, is a soft rock which can be ground to provide sand for use in the moulding process. Intermingled with these three main strata are subsidiary deposits such

3

as Fairlight Clay and Grinstead Clay, which can also be exploited.

Given this variety of material, it is not surprising that many of the brickyards in this part of Sussex regularly produced not only bricks but also tiles and sometimes agricultural drainpipes and domestic pottery as well. Maps of the late 19th and early 20th centuries reveal almost as many 'Brick & Tile Works' as simple 'Brick Works' in the area and in a number of places, such as Brede, Hastings, Bexhill and Uckfield, there were 'Brick, Tile & Pottery Works' as well. These latter works were all situated on deposits of Wadhurst or Fairlight Clay but, in general, brickyards would be sited on a suitable bed of loam, the tile clay and sand being carted from pits a short distance away. This was the case, for example, in the estate brickyard at Ashburnham, where loam for brickmaking was dug from a pit on the edge of the yard, clay for making tiles, drainpipes and flower pots was brought from a pit half a mile to the south and sand for moulding was obtained from a nearby outcrop of Tunbridge Wells Sand.

The broad band of **Weald Clay**, which forms the Low Weald to the south and west of the forest ridges, is also a very versatile material, as can be seen from a report produced in 1925 on the subsoil of the land adjoining the Dicker Pottery in Hellingly. This stated:

Clays are found within a relatively small area for nearly every type of clay-ware from common and facing bricks to sanitary pipes.... Field one: beautiful dark red clean plastic clay – suitable for highest class red wares (pottery, facing bricks, roofing and floor tiles and terracotta). In field adjoining: similar clay but not quite so deep, accompanied by rougher texture clay suitable for common bricks. In third field: clean but more sandy clay is found, suitable for common or facing bricks. Below, at one point, a bed of greenish-grey clay is found, believed to go to a considerable depth. This burns to an excellent buff colour: should make good salt-glazed

2. Claypit at North Corner, Horam, in the 1920s

stoneware pipes. There is enough clay for 100 million bricks or equivalent.

Boreholes were sunk to a depth of 15ft (4.5m) only and so give no indication of the potential of the underlying strata, which have never been exploited in this locality.[2]

The great depth of the Weald Clay is the reason why more bricks have been made from this formation than from any other. In 1975, 80% of the bricks produced in Sussex were made of Weald Clay and this figure has probably now been exceeded. In the past, when clay was dug by hand and carted in barrows, claypits might extend over quite a wide area but were rarely more than one or two metres deep. With the advent of modern machinery, however, it became possible to exploit the lower strata which, when weathered and mixed, produce brick earth of the desired texture. At Southwater near Horsham, some of this material was found to be suitable for the production of bricks of engineering quality. Yet even before the era of mechanical extraction, the greatest concentrations of brickyards and potteries were to be found on the Weald Clay belt, from Hailsham in the south, through Burgess Hill in mid-Sussex to Horsham in the north of the county.[3]

Between the Weald and the Downs lie the bands of **Greensand** and **Gault Clay**, which also provided material for brickmaking, although on a much smaller scale. In the Pulborough area, the bottom strata of the Lower Greensand, known as the Atherfield and Marehill Clays, were exploited until quite recently at brickyards in Stopham and North Heath respectively.

Also sand from the quarries at Pulborough was dispatched by rail to brickworks as far afield as Berwick in East Sussex, where it was used in the production of sand-faced bricks. The Gault could be used on its own for making tiles, as was the case in the medieval period in Wilmington, Alciston and Ringmer in East Sussex. In West Sussex, where the bands of Gault and Greensand are very much wider than they are further east, a number of brickyards were sited at the junction of the two formations to take advantage of both materials. One of these small yards is still active at Pitsham, in the parish of Cocking south of Midhurst. Here the Gault provides the main brickmaking material but the adjacent Greensand is mixed with it to give the desired texture and also, until recently, supplied the sand required for moulding.

South of the Downs, from Brighton westwards, the coastal plain gradually widens and here, too, are to be found a range of materials suitable for brickmaking. The **Woolwich and Reading Beds** which outcrop in small patches in Aldrington and Portslade but more extensively west of Worthing, again provide material from which both bricks and tiles could be produced, as was the case at the brickyard on the Goodwood estate at Westhampnett. In the early 1800s this yard was selling 'earth' bricks for building purposes and 'clay' bricks for paving. In fact there were two brickyards in existence simultaneously on opposite sides of the road and it seems probable that each was exploiting a different type of subsoil, one using a sandy earth to make building bricks and the other a finer, silty clay to make not only paving

5

bricks but also a wide variety of tiles and agricultural drainpipes. There were a number of other 'multi-product' yards on this formation, from Poling Pottery, east of Arundel, to Westbourne on the Hampshire border.[4]

The subsoil of the rest of the coastal plain consists mainly of the geological formation known as **Brickearth** which, as its name implies, is suitable for brickmaking. This deposit has been exploited in the Selsey peninsula and along the narrow coastal strip between Brighton and Bognor, where large quantities of bricks were manufactured to meet the demands of the developing coastal resorts. Indeed in Brighton itself, where the Brickearth lay to no great depth, the demand for bricks was such that the deposits were totally exhausted by the middle of the 19th century.

The **Alluvial Clay** of the river valleys, although again offering suitable material for brickmaking, has not been widely used in Sussex. This is principally because most valley-bottom sites were liable to flooding and therefore not worth exploiting, particularly as there was so much material available elsewhere. There were, however, a few short-lived brickfields in the 19th century on the brookland of the Arun and Lower Ouse Valleys, alongside the Cuckmere at Alfriston and at Rye Harbour and a longer span of life was enjoyed by the brickyard on the bank of the Ouse at Piddinghoe.

Finally, the chalk Downs are the one part of Sussex where one would not expect to find bricks being made at all and yet, even here, a few small brickyards once existed, on shallow clay deposits of post-glacial age, which overlay the chalk. Brickyard Farm in the Chilgrove Valley in the parish of West Dean indicates the existence of one such yard and another was in operation on Lye Common in Up Marden in the middle of the 19th century.

Iron and other minerals

The various mineral compounds found naturally in all of the foregoing formations also make their contribution to the texture and, more particularly, the colour of the bricks produced. This is the case with the iron oxide which is present in most Sussex clays and results in the attractive red coloration of the bricks, especially those made in the Weald. The iron is mostly dispersed evenly throughout the brick earth as a thin coating on the sandy particles but concretions do occur, particularly in the lower levels of the Wadhurst Clay. These then appear as black patches within the fabric of the burnt brick. Occasionally, they are also found on the outer surface, where they take on a hard, slag-like appearance, having served to lower the melting point of the silica and then combine with it in the high temperature of the kiln.[5]

Although the majority of the bricks made in Sussex were red, this was not universally the case. Even within the Weald Clay there are occasional strata which burn to a paler red or even a buff colour, particularly when fired in a reducing atmosphere. This is also true of the Gault, if enough calcium is present to cancel out the iron content of the clay. South of the Downs, especially in Worthing and Littlehampton, 'white' bricks were made in the late 18th and early 19th centuries, exploiting natural deposits of suitable material. Later in

3. Polychrome brickwork and terracotta: All Souls' Church, Eastbourne, built in the 1880s

the 19th century, in some yards near the coast, chalk was deliberately incorporated with the brick earth before moulding, in imitation of the methods practised in the brickfields of north Kent. Clamp-burnt bricks, varying in colour from cream to dark yellow, were produced from a mixture consisting of about 64% clay, 11 % chalk and 25% fine ash (the residue from coal fires). These can be seen in many buildings, particularly in the Eastbourne area, where they were also used in the polychrome brickwork fashionable in the Victorian period. Two brickyards which are known to have used chalk in this way were the ones at Westham Station, where chalk was brought in by rail, and at East Blatchington near Seaford.[6]

Fuel

So far only the raw materials for the bricks themselves have been considered. The other essential requirement was, of course, fuel for burning them. Wood, which was in plentiful supply in most parts of Sussex, was the only fuel used until the 18th century and even after the introduction of coal in brickyards near the coast, wood was still the preferred fuel for wealden brick-kilns, where it continued to be used well into the present century.

Brickyards were not generally in competition with other industries, such as ironmaking or shipbuilding, for the available fuel because they used the 'lop and top' which remained when the heavy timber required by the latter and the cordwood needed for charcoal by the former had been removed. This was gathered up into bundles, known as faggots, which burned fiercely in the kilns. An alternative source of wood for faggots was the brushwood which grew on the commons and heathlands and even furze was used in some districts, especially near the coast where wood was scarce. Maps of the late 18th and early 19th centuries show Furze Fields alongside brickyards on Bosham Hoe, at Westhampnett and on Sayers Common in Hurstpierpoint. Even so, as the volume of brick production rose, many brickmakers began to run short of fuel and in parts of the Weald recourse was had to coppiced wood, mainly hornbeam, which was grown specifically for the purpose.[7]

A legacy of the extensive use of wood-fired kilns in the past is the number of grey/blue headers to be seen in the brickwork of buildings, especially

7

in the Weald, where grey and red bricks were mingled in diaper and chequerboard patterns, giving them a very distinctive character. This colouring resulted from the reaction which took place at high temperature within the kiln between the iron oxide in the bricks and the potassium in the wood smoke. In kilns where furze was used, greenish glazed headers were occasionally produced.

When the shortage of wood, particularly in the coastal districts, forced the brickmakers to use coal for their kilns, supplies had to be imported. At first these came by sea from the north-east of England and were landed on the beach. Breeze from the coke ovens on Tyneside was also available by the late 18th century and was being used in the Hastings area in the 1790s. It was probably also used in the bricks which were made on coastal sites for the building of the Martello Towers in 1806-7. With the advent of the railways it became possible to bring in larger quantities of coal more cheaply and, later in the 19th century when coke and breeze from local gasworks became available, these were widely employed in the burning of clamp bricks.

As the towns expanded in the 19th century, the disposal of household refuse became a problem. At this date it consisted mainly of the cinders from coal-fired grates, which brickmakers were glad to purchase for use in the manufacture of clamp bricks. Country brickmakers delivering bricks to the nearby town often returned with a cartload of this 'town ash'. The fine ash was incorporated with the brick earth and the coarser cinders used as fuel to fire the clamp. Clamp-burnt bricks display different characteristics from the traditional products of the wood-fired kiln. Air is largely excluded by casing the clamp with bricks from a previous firing and so burning takes place in a reducing atmosphere, which is responsible for colour variations in the bricks, known in the trade as 'multis'.[8]

In the second half of the 20th century, many changes were introduced. Gas (liquid petroleum gas, natural gas and even methane) was widely substituted for coal and coke in both kilns and clamps. Chemical additives were employed for various purposes. Barium carbonate was added to the clay to counteract the effects of salts such as magnesium sulphate, which can cause efflorescence on the surface of the brick. This problem arose from the exploitation of deeper beds of clay, from which these salts had not been eliminated by the normal leaching process that occurs in the shallower deposits. Other chemicals were added to the sand used for moulding, to achieve variations in the colour of the finished brick.

Yet, in its essentials, the brick has changed little over the centuries and its popularity as a building material seems likely to be maintained.

2. EARLY BRICKS AND TILES

Brickmaking was first introduced to Britain by the Romans after the conquest in AD 43. The techniques they used had already been highly developed in their Mediterranean homelands and so it is not surprising that bricks and a wide variety of tiles were produced in Sussex over the next 300 years, for use in the building of army camps and fortifications as well as a number of villas.

Roman building materials

Roman bricks and tiles were both made from the same type of material: fine-textured, high-alumina clay which, as we have seen, was widely available in Sussex. The bricks bore little resemblance to modern ones, being up to 500mm long and 300mm wide but generally not more than about 40mm thick. It is assumed that they were moulded flat, the clay having first been mixed to the correct consistency with water and then spread as evenly as possible on a level piece of ground, which had previously been sanded. The clay would then have been cut into rectangular pieces and left to dry until the bricks were hard enough, first to be turned to ensure all-round drying and then to be lifted and carried to the kiln. If that was the method employed, it would account for the animal footprints occasionally found on the flat surface of the bricks and also for the fact that the thickness of the bricks varied, not only between one brick and another but also across a single brick.[1]

The structural uses to which they were put also differed from the way in which bricks are used today. Few Roman buildings were constructed entirely of brick. Instead, the bricks were laid in bonding courses, to tie together and strengthen walls built of stone or flint, as can be seen in the walls of the Roman fort at Pevensey. Smaller bricks, also about 40mm thick and anything from 150mm to 300mm square, were used for floors and for the construction of hypocaust pillars, to support the floors and allow hot air to circulate beneath them. Examples of

4. Brick bonding courses in the walls of the Roman fort at Pevensey

these have been found on most of the Roman sites excavated in Sussex and they can be seen still in place at the Roman Palace at Fishbourne.

Sites of Roman villas and bath-houses have also yielded numbers of box-flue tiles, which were an essential part of this type of heating system. These were formed by wrapping a flat slab of sanded clay, about 16mm thick, round a square or rectangular wooden block and making an overlapping joint down the middle of one side. A combed, or roller-stamped, pattern was then applied to two of the opposing sides. This served as a key for the plaster, which would cover the internal walls of the building, of which these flue-tiles formed a part. When the shaping and decorating of the tile was complete, the wooden block was withdrawn and the tile allowed to dry before firing.[2]

Roofing tiles were more precisely moulded probably using wooden moulds, the method still employed for hand-made tiles. A 'standard' carved in stone, against which the dimensions of fired tiles could be measured, can still be seen in the Roman market place in Athens, and it seems probable that the authorities exercised the same control elsewhere. The tiles were similar in shape to the ones still seen in Mediterranean countries today. A flat tile with flanged edges (*tegula*) alternated with a half-round tile (*imbrex*) in every course of tiles on the roof. The effect was to create a series of ridges and gulleys which enabled the rain to run off the roof, in the way that pantiles do. *Tegulae* generally measured about 450mm x 340mm, with 50mm flanges on each side, although larger ones have been found. Fewer complete

examples of *imbrices* have survived but examination of these suggests that they were formed in slightly tapering moulds. This would allow for a small overlap when the tiles were in position on the roof.[3]

The military authorities were probably responsible for much of the Roman brick- and tilemaking in Sussex. Roads, such as Stane Street, were constructed across the region and camps or posting stations built alongside them. The sites of at least two of these, at Hardham and at Alfoldean, have yielded samples of tile and it seems likely that the latter were made at Itchingfield, where an area of burnt earth and a quantity of wasters were discovered in 1964. By the second century, large iron-smelting operations had been established in the Weald to supply military requirements. The slag heaps at the ironworking site at Chitcombe in the parish of Brede have yielded samples of Roman tile, as have the sites at Bardown in Ticehurst and Garden Hill in Hartfield. By far the largest quantities of both brick and tile were found at the site of a Roman bath-house near the ironworks in Beauport Park, between Hastings and Battle, when this was excavated in the 1970s. Contrary to the usual practice, these seem not to have been made on site, as their fabric is quite unlike the local Wadhurst Clay from which the iron ore was obtained. Many of the tiles bear the stamp CL BR, standing for *Classis Britannica* (the British Fleet), the agency responsible for their manufacture and transport to Beauport.[4]

The Romans even found a use for the waste material from their tile kilns. Small pieces were sometimes employed as the red-coloured material required for mosaic floors and tile debris was frequently ground up and used as an ingredient in mortar, giving it a characteristic pinkish tinge. This type of mortar was particularly strong and durable and no doubt contributed to the survival of structures such as the massive walls of the fort at Pevensey.

The kilns

As bricks and tiles were heavy and not easily transported, it was always preferable to make them as close as possible to the site at which they were required. Unfortunately few traces have been found so far of the kilns used during the Roman period. This may be, in part, because archaeologists in the past tended to concentrate on artefacts rather than the contexts in which they were found and may have ignored, or misinterpreted, evidence of the manufacturing process. The footings of a kiln found at Wiston in 1848 were not recognised as such at the time, although details of the construction were recorded and no attempt was made to describe another kiln found at Bignor. However, kiln sites may be inferred from the discovery of large quantities of brick and tile wasters in association with burnt earth, as at Itchingfield. Similar finds were made near Fernhurst in 1976 and more recently at Dell Quay, near Chichester. This latter site was surveyed but not fully excavated, as it was not immediately threatened by either erosion or development and it is possible that a kiln may be revealed at some future date.[5]

Coastal erosion may have been responsible for the destruction of some Roman tilery sites and others have probably disappeared under modern housing developments. It is not surprising, therefore, that the two kilns discovered this century have been at inland locations. Work in a sand pit at Hassocks in the 1920s revealed the site of a Roman cemetery and at about the same time a kiln was found nearby in Hurstpierpoint. This was said to have measured 6ft (I.7m) x 4ft (l.2m) and to have been paved with 8in (203mm)-square red tiles but no detailed report was produced.[6]

The most recent discovery, and the most thorough excavation of a Roman tile kiln so far made, was the one on Great Cansiron Farm north of Hartfield. This lies just to the west of the Roman road from Lewes to London and was evidently associated with ironworking sites nearby. The kiln was built into

5. Roman tile kiln at Hartfield

sloping ground. At the lowest level were a stoke hole and a firing tunnel, leading into the combustion chamber, which had been hollowed out of the bank of earth. The firing tunnel was 2.8m long x 800mm wide and was itself built of bricks, or flat tiles. The combustion chamber measured 3m x 2.4m. Within it were five parallel cross walls, each 300mm wide, with 150mm spaces between them. Clay arches carried these over the firing tunnel, which extended the full length of the kiln. The hot air was thus drawn through the firing tunnel, under the kiln, up through the flues created by the spaces between the cross walls in the combustion chamber and into the main kiln chamber above, where the tiles were stacked for firing. Little remained of the floor of the kiln, but this was probably formed from tiles laid to bridge the spaces between the cross walls, but with gaps left between them to allow hot air to pass through. The walls of the kiln would have been built up vertically to a height of one or two metres with unburnt clay 'bricks', a number of which were found on the site, and a temporary cover of turf placed over the top whilst firing was taking place.[7]

This kiln has been described in detail because it bears a remarkable similarity to the kind of intermittent updraught kiln subsequently used by brickmakers in the Weald, in some cases right up to the present century.

Medieval tiles

Very little permanent building seems to have taken place during the period of unrest which followed the end of the Roman occupation. When the Saxon settlers finally became established, they built in their own tradition, using timber which was plentiful in Sussex. As a result, no more bricks were made in this part of the country for around a thousand years. The first churches, like the houses, were wooden structures but by the 10th century stone had begun to replace timber for church building and pieces of brick and tile from ruined Roman buildings were sometimes incorporated into the new fabric. Examples of this can be seen at Arlington, Clayton, Walberton, Westhampnett and Bosham. Houses and farm buildings, however, continued to be timber-framed, with roofs of thatch or shingles.

The re-introduction of tiles to Sussex was brought about by the monastic foundations, which wielded great influence especially in the 12th and 13th centuries. Most of the abbeys and priories which flourished under Norman rule had regular contacts with France, where the crafts of brick- and tilemaking were already re-established. It is not surprising therefore that the earliest known tilery in Sussex, mentioned in a charter of the second half of the 13th century, was on land belonging to Battle Abbey. References to the abbey tilery and its products appear intermittently in the Cellarers' accounts between 1279 and 1466. Throughout this period it seems to have been administered directly by the abbey, with a tiler and other men hired to do the work. The abbey also had tileries on its estates at Wye in Kent and at Alciston in Sussex, about which more will be said later.[8]

The tilery at Battle Abbey, like the ones established subsequently at

Robertsbridge Abbey and at Michelham Priory, seems to have been used solely for the manufacture of roofing tiles and not of ceramic floor tiles, as was formerly believed. Unlike Roman roofing tiles, the majority of the ones used in the medieval period were flat, oblong tiles, very similar to the plain tiles still in use today. Dimensions varied quite widely to begin with but a need for standardisation must have been felt as, in 1477, a statute decreed that burnt tiles should measure 10½in (266mm) x 6¼in (158mm) x ⅝in (16mm), probably regularising what had become accepted as the most convenient size. Tiles were hung on wooden battens on the roof by means of wooden pegs or nails, and holes for these were punched in each tile with a blunt-ended stick when it was moulded. These holes could be either round or square. Some tiles also had a single nib, made by pinching up a small amount of clay which had been allowed to protrude through a gap at one end of the mould. Some glazed and crested ridge tiles have been found but these seem to have been the products of potteries rather than of the main monastic tileries, the majority of whose ridge tiles were undecorated.[9]

The documents in which tileries were mentioned were written in Latin but English words were occasionally inserted. Thus the main building of the tilery was generally referred to as *domus tegularia* but this sometimes appeared in English as 'tilehouse'. When specific reference was made to the kiln, however, this was almost invariably rendered in English as 'hoste' or 'oste', a word which was in common use up to the end of the 16th century for any kind of kiln but which now survives only in 'oasthouse', the name given to a building in which hops are dried. As for the hired craftsmen, the term 'tiler' could equally well be applied to the man who manufactured the tiles and to the one who laid them on the roof. Indeed the same person often performed both tasks. Like the stonemasons who contracted for work on a building site, hewing the stone, shaping and carving it and being responsible for erecting the building as well, tilers, and later brickmakers, were itinerant craftsmen, performing all the tasks from digging the clay to laying the tiles. Then, when the job was finished, they moved on to their next assignment. However, when a distinction was made between the tile-maker and the tile-layer, it was generally the former who was called a tiler (*tegulator*), whereas the latter was referred to as a roofer (*cubator* or *cooperator*).

There are isolated instances of tiles being used on some secular buildings as early as the 13th century. Nib tiles found on the site of a grange of this date at Drigsell in Salehurst were, in all probability, made at a nearby kiln where similar tile wasters have been discovered. However, the use of tiles was confined mainly to the more important buildings on a few of the larger estates. For example, 6,000 tiles were used on the roof of the hall at Pevensey Castle in 1301. These may well have come from Willingdon, where Joan, daughter of Ralph the tiler, surrendered land in the same year. Indeed the Lord of the Rape of Pevensey may have granted the land to her father in the first place on the understanding that he would exercise his craft in the

Lord's demesnes and not move away. Further payments were made for roofing with tiles at Pevensey in 1366. On this occasion a possible source was the tilehouse at Ashburnham seven miles away, which was in existence by 1362.[10]

In the west of the county, there were tilers living in places as widely separated as Harting and Littlehampton in 1332 and another working in Binsted near Arundel in 1336. The Poll Tax returns of 1380 show that there was a tiler called Thomas Thetcher living in Chichester at that date. His name is interesting as it suggests that he, or his forebears, had originally been thatchers but had changed trades when tiles began to assume greater importance. This tiler evidently had a well-established business: he himself paid 2s in tax and he also had a servant, or assistant, who paid 4d.[11]

By the 15th century the use of tiles had become much more widespread. The church authorities led the way in Chichester, where Bishop Patrington left money in 1417 to tile the roofs of the chapel and the hall of the bishop's palace and, in 1474, 2,000 tiles were bought to repair the steeple of the cathedral at a cost of 12s. In Mayfield the Archbishop of Canterbury had a residence, for which tiles were made in the 1450s. The accounts show that tiles were also used for repairs on the estate and that the surplus, when there was any, was sold for profit. Accounts also survive for the Manor of Pebsham, east of Bexhill, where tiles were being made in the summer of 1426 for use on the roof of the grange. First, payments were made for felling wood for the tile oast, then Laurence Tiler, who was probably

designated in this way because the steward only knew him by his trade, was paid for making tiles. Some bricks also appear to have been produced, as two men were paid for loading brick. Here, as at Mayfield, more tiles were made than were required on the estate. The account roll for Michaelmas in the same year includes receipts for tiles sold to the Manor of Buckholt, north of Bexhill, to the churchwardens of All Saints in Hastings and to three separate individuals in the town. Quantities ranged from 1,000 to 6,000 tiles.[12]

The Alciston tilery

Few written records of tileries in Sussex survive from this period. However the establishment of one tilery is well documented: the one which was built on Battle Abbey's extensive Manor of Alciston in the early 15th century. The manor was situated on good agricultural land, part chalk, part gault clay and part greensand, between the valleys of the Ouse and the Cuckmere. It was self-contained and administered by a steward, who kept detailed accounts. When the church at Alciston had been tiled in the 1350s, the tiles had not been locally-made but had been brought from a kiln on land owned by Battle Abbey at Snape in Wadhurst some 18 miles away. In about 1418, however, when improvements were being made on the manor, it was decided to establish a tilery on the premises. Accordingly a man called John Whiteberd was brought in to be responsible for the construction work. It is not clear whether he was a master builder, a tiler, or both but he lived on the manor for 14 weeks in 1419, building what was at first called a brickyard (*latustrina*) but was subsequently always referred to as a tilehouse (*domus tegularia*). He had two other men working with him that year, one for nine weeks and the other for five weeks, and in addition John Soley, a tiler, spent three weeks digging clay in readiness for making tiles the following year. All four were outsiders, as they were given board and lodging on the manor during the time that they were working there.[13]

The new tilehouse, which was completed in 1420, was quite a substantial building. The workshop area was of timber-framed construction, with a stone-built kiln at one end. Two carpenters and a mason were employed in addition to Whiteberd, who supervised the building of the kiln. As no tiles had yet been made at Alciston, a supply was brought in from Battle for the roof but, as soon as the building was finished, tilemaking got under way and 18,000 tiles had been produced by the end of the season. The detailed tilehouse building accounts were as follows:[14]

By agreement made with 2 carpenters for building a new tilehouse at Alcyston and for other workshops (*domus operar'*) belonging to the tilery, in all . . .£6 13s 4d

By agreement made with 1 mason for building the kiln (*le hoste*) of the said tilehouse and for underpinning the sill (*sullion pynnand'*) 66s 2d

For stone from Bourne bought for the same 46s 8d

For felling and trimming timber for the same 10s 5½d

For sawing timber for the same 29s

For hiring 30 carts to carry the timber from Battle to the said house @ 20d per cart 50s

For 21 cartloads of tiles carried from Battle to the said house @ 20d per load 35s

For laying 21,000 tiles on the said tilehouse @ 12d per thousand 21s

For 12,000 nails bought for the same . . 11s

By agreement made with 1 roofer (*cooperatore*) for roofing on the workshop there, in all 8s

For plastering (*dawbend'*) the walls of the said house .8s 4d

For buying gudgeons and pintles (*gumphis & vertinellis*) .9s 2d

For making 18,000 tiles in the said tilehouse @ 2s per thousand 36s

For digging clay for the same 6s 9d

Subsequently there were several references to the tilehouse and its products in the general accounts. Two years later four arches of the tilekiln needed repair, probably because the sandstone with which it was built was not really adequate to withstand high temperatures. Plain roofing tiles and a small number of ridge tiles seem to have been the only products. 36,000 tiles were made in the year that the kiln was repaired, for use on the hall, chapel and dovecote. Three years later 85,000 tiles were made, some of which were used on the barn and some on the roof of the tilehouse itself. As at other tileries, surplus tiles were sold in the neighbourhood, especially to the manor of Lullington, where 15th-century tiles were found during excavations at the church in the 1960s.[15]

Floor tiles and other products

It might have been expected that floor tiles, which were widely used from the 13th century onwards in monasteries and in some churches, would have been fired in the same kilns as roofing tiles but this does not often seem to have been the case. A kiln at Hastings, probably associated with the Priory of the Holy Trinity, was used for the manufacture of floor tiles in the 13th century but many of the decorated tiles found at sites in Sussex are now thought to have been imported from Normandy. It was only after trade between France and England was disrupted by the outbreak of the Hundred Years' War in 1338, that floor tiles were, of necessity, made locally. Floor-tile wasters have been found at the site of Lewes Friary, indicating a kiln nearby, and kilns have been excavated at two other sites: Shulbrede Priory and St Bartholomew's Hospital, Rye. The remains of the kiln at Shulbrede Priory, in Linchmere near to the Surrey border, were discovered in 1928 by the owner, Lord Ponsonby, not far from the site of the priory church. Unfortunately it appeared that the kiln was not in its original condition but had been re-used at a later date as a brick kiln. A quantity of fragments of both plain and decorated floor tiles were found in the vicinity of the kiln but Lord Ponsonby concluded that 'the output of the Shulbrede kiln was too small for anything but domestic consumption and indeed seems to have been used late in their [the monks'] history, probably only for repairs'.[16]

The operation at Rye was on a much larger scale but in this case tile and pottery manufacture were combined on the same site. The remains of four kilns were found in the 1930s together with pottery wasters, some decorated floor tiles and a few roofing tiles. Other medieval potteries, for example the ones at Ringmer, made some roofing tiles, using them occasionally to line their kilns. Fragments of green-glazed tile, which have been found at Battle Abbey and also on sites excavated in West Sussex, notably at Chithurst church and at West Tarring, were probably also the products of potteries. It was possible to combine the production of pottery and tiles in this way, using quite a small kiln, because the number of tiles required at any one time was never very large. The 76 ridge tiles purchased for use on the manor house at Wiston in 1357-8 and the small quantities of ridge tiles bought by the churchwardens of Arlington a century later may well have been for use on shingled roofs, as no mention was made of plain tiles in either case.[17]

Finally there was one other kind of tile in use in the medieval period. This resembled a thin brick but, like Roman bricks, was made of the same dense, fine-grained material as tiles and had heat-resistant properties. Fireplaces built with such tiles, laid horizontally or herringbone-fashion, have been found in buildings dating from as early as 1200, for example in the guesthouse at Boxgrove Priory. Bodiam Castle, which was built in the 1380s, has tile-lined fireplaces in the outer walls of many of the rooms and the two large fireplaces in the Great Kitchen are backed with tiles laid flat. However, the 2in-thick bricks in one of the fireplaces in the south-east Drum Tower suggest that this must have been re-lined at a later date.[18]

3. THE REINTRODUCTION OF BRICKS

The word 'brick' did not come into common use until about the middle of the 15th century, although bricks, in small quantities, were being used in Sussex from the early 14th century onwards. The scant evidence available is frequently from Latin documents, in which the writers did not always differentiate clearly between bricks and tiles, the word *tegula* being used to refer to both indifferently. An alternative word *laterus*, however, may be taken to refer unambiguously to brick. Accounts written in English, or in Latin with English words inserted, hesitated between several different terms. 'Wall tile' was current for a time and 'bakestone' (cf German: *Backstein*) was in use in the 1390s before eventually giving way to 'brick' (cf French: *brique*). The hybrid word 'brickstone' appeared in a Rye court document of 1483, in which William Belle agreed to settle a debt in 'brickstonys' or in money and was still in use as late as the 1670s in connection with imports of building materials to Brighton.[1]

The uncertainty about terminology probably derived from the fact that bricks were not made locally in the 14th century but were being imported only sporadically from Flanders and the Netherlands. The port of Winchelsea had a flourishing trade with that part of the continent, exporting wool and firewood, and bricks occasionally formed part of the cargo, or were carried as ballast, on the return journey. One shipment was recorded in 1323 and two in 1327. This trade accounts for the small quantities of pink or yellow-coloured bricks that have been found in 14th-century contexts on sites in the vicinity of the ports, for example at Old Place in Icklesham, at Court Lodge in Bodiam, at Michelham Priory and at Norton near Bishopstone. These Flemish bricks were smaller than the modern brick, the ones at Michelham measuring only 6in (152mm) x 3in (76mm) x 1½in (38mm). In general, however, the plentiful supply of timber in the area did not encourage the inhabitants of Sussex to experiment with 'new' building materials, as was the case particularly in East Anglia, where brick building, using locally-made materials, had already become established.[2]

15th-century buildings

It was not until the middle of the 15th century that a building constructed wholly of brick appeared in Sussex: Herstmonceux Castle, built by Sir Roger Fiennes in the 1440s. Its sheer size necessitated making the bricks on the spot. The site, on the edge of the Pevensey Marshes, provided suitable raw material and it is thought that expert craftsmen were brought in from the Low Countries to supervise the brickmaking, although the main workforce would have been recruited locally. Three men from Malines, in Flanders, were living in Herstmonceux in 1436 and, although their occupation was not stated, it seems very possible that they were involved in brickmaking. The king's licence to crenellate, that is to fortify the building, was not granted until 1441 but work may have begun well before that date. Fiennes' decision to build in brick was no doubt influenced by fashion. Tattershall Castle in Lincolnshire was being built in brick at about the same time but, perhaps more significantly, from 1439 Fiennes

6. 15th-century brickwork: Herstmonceux Castle

1460s, which we know about only because the building accounts have survived. The builder, Sir John Scott, was Lord Warden of the Cinque Ports and Constable of Dover Castle and was frequently resident in Calais. He would therefore have been familiar with continental brick architecture and it seems probable that his brickmakers, like those at Herstmonceux, were recruited on the continent. They were referred to in the accounts as William and Thomas 'Brykeman', a name probably bestowed on them by the estate steward, whereas other workmen, who were recruited locally, had surnames unrelated to their trades. Sand, straw, wood and faggots were supplied by the estate but the brickmakers must have selected and dug their own brick earth, as there is no mention of this in the accounts. Frequent references to the brick-oast show that the bricks were kiln-fired. William was paid £22 3s 2d for brickmaking in the first season, then in the following year Thomas sold 137,000 of these bricks on the orders of the Lord of the Manor, possibly because they were not of the required quality. He then proceeded to make another 270,000 bricks, being paid at the rate of 22d per thousand. As for the house, it was still occupied in 1656 but its demolition appears to have begun soon after this date.[4]

was Treasurer of the Household to Henry VI, who was having a number of brick buildings erected on the royal estates. It has been suggested that the master builder at Herstmonceux was William Vesey, who was responsible for the king's works at Windsor and at Eton College .[3]

The surprising thing is that few of Fiennes' contemporaries in Sussex seem to have been inspired to follow his lead. Probably they were deterred by the expense involved: Herstmonceux Castle is said to have cost £3,800, at a time when a labourer's average wage was 2d per day. It seems probable, however, that several brick houses were built in the second half of the 15th century but have since disappeared, leaving no trace. One of these 'lost' houses is the one built at Mote Manor in Iden in the

Robert a Mill, of Boreham in Wartling, may have been trying to emulate his neighbours, the Fiennes of Herstmonceux, when he gave instructions in 1473 for his house, New Place, now transformed into the 'White Friars' hotel, to be 'made up with his own bricks'. 'Old Buckhurst' at Withyham,

18

the home of the Sackville family, which was built about 1485, was later demolished but it is known that some bricks were used in its construction. Possibly also of 15th-century date is the gatehouse, the only surviving part of the original Bolebrook Castle in nearby Hartfield.[5]

Apart from these, the only other surviving brick structures in Sussex belonging to the 15th century are a chapel and a church. The Dacre chapel was built on to the church at Herstmonceux by the same family that built the castle and with bricks of the same type. It has been variously attributed to the 1440s and the 1480s. The church at East Guldeford, near Rye, can be more precisely dated, the faculty for its construction having been granted in 1499. Here the use of brick can be explained by the total absence of stone and timber on the surrounding marshland, which had been reclaimed not long before this date. Nothing is known about the provenance of the bricks but the builder, Sir Richard Guldeford, was a local landowner who, like Sir Roger Fiennes, was an officer of the Royal Household and, like Sir John Scott, had strong links with Calais.[6]

Tudor brick and terracotta

When we enter the 16th century, the progress of brick becomes steadier and its use more widespread, albeit often only in small quantities. Former tile kilns were now used to burn bricks as well as tiles, as can be seen from documents relating to the tileries, already mentioned, at Battle and Alciston, which were now being leased to independent operators. In 1520 'the abbot's tilery [at Battle] with the

buildings and closes anciently relating to it… land in the park for digging clay and sand… and pasture for six oxen and two stallions or mares' was leased to John Trewe for a term of 10 years. The tilery was evidently in a rundown condition, as the agreement stipulated that the new tenant was to find all the tiles, clay and other material for repairs to the buildings and 'the oven called "le kylle"', the abbot finding the workmen and the necessary timber. Trewe was permitted to cut enough wood to burn six kilns of tiles per year, letting the abbot have 'as many bricks and tiles as are required for repairing the buildings of the monastery, delivered at the tilery at 3s 4d the thousand'. The tilehouse was still in existence in 1539, when the abbey and its lands were granted to Sir Anthony Browne. At the same date, the tilehouse on the abbey's estate at Alciston passed to Sir John Gage. This continued in operation until the middle of the 17th century and a lease of 1577 stated that the tenant was to be allowed to dig earth and clay for the purpose of making both bricks and tiles.[7]

There was a continuing trickle of bricks imported from the Netherlands through the port of Rye right up to the 1580s, which probably accounts for 'Flemish' bricks found at various locations in Rye itself and in the surrounding area. These imports averaged between 12,000 and 20,000 annually during the first half of the century and would only have provided sufficient bricks for building two or three chimney stacks each year. The authorities were constantly stressing the need for brick chimneys because the older-style wooden ones constituted a grave fire hazard. When a new almshouse was built in Rye in 1552, 10,000 bricks were bought locally from 'Eston's kyllne', with an additional 2,000 Flemish bricks to make the top of the chimney. These latter, at 6s per thousand, were in fact cheaper than the local bricks which cost 9s per thousand. This may have reflected a difference in size, the smaller Flemish bricks being more suitable for the ornate designs of Tudor chimney stacks. At all events, by the middle of the century, there was a brickmaker established in the district, who was capable of supplying local requirements.[8]

As bricks were by no means cheap, it is understandable that only rich men could afford to use them extensively. In the early 16th century a brick porch and projecting bay were added to the west front of Brede Place, the home of the Oxenbridge family. At the other end of the county, in about 1520, Bishop Sherburne added a brick look-out tower to his residence in the manor of Cakeham, at West Wittering south of Chichester. The continuing need for some form of defence at this period, especially near the coast, is reflected in the building of gatehouses and, in low-lying areas, of look-out towers, even if a house was not itself fortified. This was the case at Laughton Place, where a four-storey brick tower was built on to the earlier timber-framed building on a moated site east of the river Ouse in the 1530s. Bricks were also used for a building, now demolished, at the south-east corner of the moat and for a wall, with octagonal corner towers, which was presumably intended to enclose the whole area within the moat. However, Sir William Pelham, for whom the work was undertaken, died in 1538 and

building operations then seem to have come to a halt, with only about half of the wall completed. The bricks were made on the spot and were kiln-fired, as witnessed by the name 'The Brick-oste Fieldes' marked, just to the north of the site, on a map of 1641.[9]

The tower and the building at the corner of the moat, although both of the Tudor period, may not have been exactly contemporary, as the style of their brickwork was very different. For the latter, dark headers were used to create an overall diapered diamond pattern, whereas for the tower, red bricks only were used, laid in English bond. The most striking feature of the tower is the elaborately-moulded terracotta used for structural elements such as windowsills and mullions, door surrounds and corbelling and for some decorative motifs as well. Although this is the only building in Sussex in which terracotta is known to have been used in the Tudor period, the material was employed in a number of other great men's houses in the south-east, for example at Sutton Place in Surrey, at Layer Marney in Essex and at Hampton Court Palace. A specialist craftsman would have been brought in to mould and fire the terracotta, which was almost certainly made locally, as it is darker and redder than other examples, reflecting the amount of iron present in the Sussex clay. The designs used were very intricate and included the Pelham family badge, a buckle, on some of the inside windowsills and the initials WP both on structural pieces and, together with the date 1534, in ornamental plaques.[10]

Laughton Place was abandoned as a residence by the Pelhams in the 1590s in favour of a new brick house on higher ground to the north at Halland, for which some of the Laughton material, including terracotta, was re-used. The tower was left standing and has had a rather chequered history, which may be briefly summarised here. In the 1730s it was incorporated into a new brick house, the two lower floors being given a fresh facade with gothic windows and a pediment. When repairs were necessary in 1854, the Earl of Chichester ordered replacements for some of the terracotta cornices from J. & R. Norman, of Chailey Potteries but by the time the estate was sold by the Pelham family in 1927, the building was derelict and the new owner demolished the wings of the Georgian house, leaving only the tower standing. This was used as an observation post during World War 2 and finally, in 1978, it was acquired and rehabilitated by the Landmark Trust.[11]

War with France and the threat of invasion caused work to be put in hand in 1539 on the castle, known formerly as Winchelsea Castle but now more generally as Camber Castle, built earlier in the century to defend the harbour at Rye. The main structure was of stone but brick was used to line some of the walls and to build chimney breasts, galleries and passages, notably the vaulted passage which surrounds the base of the central tower. It is interesting to note that the paymaster for the building operations was William Oxenbridge, of the family whose use of brick at Brede Place has already been mentioned. The master brickmaker was Alexander King, who had up to 28 men at work under him at the height of the season, including 'earthworkers', 'strekers' (brick-moulders) and 'servers'

(labourers). King was paid 4s a week, the men digging earth and brickmaking 3s 4d a week and the 'servers' 5d a day. In addition, King and some of the other workers earned 3d a night for watching the kilns while they were fired.[12]

The building accounts show that about half a million bricks were made on the spot from brick earth dug locally. Large quantities of straw were brought in for use by the brickmakers but for what purpose is not made clear. Some of it would have provided a base on which to set the bricks out to dry and straw caps would also have been used to protect the drying bricks from rain and wind. In addition, a proportion was probably chopped and incorporated in the brick earth before moulding. A close examination of the fabric of the bricks has revealed a pattern of small holes and hollow strips which would be consistent with this, the voids being the only traces of the straw left after combustion. It is not entirely clear what method was used to burn the bricks. Reference is made in the accounts to both kilns and clamps, the two words often being used more or less inter-changeably at this period, but it is suggested that clamp-burning was in fact the method adopted and, for this, the addition of a fuel element to the basic brick earth was always desirable. The bricks vary considerably in both colour and dimensions, some small red ones measuring only 203mm x 95mm x 44mm whereas the yellowish ones which predominate are mostly larger, measuring up to 235mm x 114mm x 62mm.[13]

A brick church had been built at Twineham in mid-Sussex in the 1520s but, soon after this, ecclesiastical

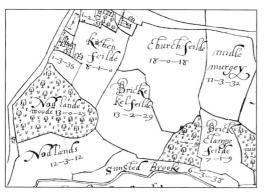

7. Map of Ewhurst, drawn in 1635, showing Bricke Kelfeilde and Brick Clampefeilde (ESRO BAT 4420)

building ceased abruptly as a result of the upheavals caused by the Reformation. After the dissolution of the monasteries, their dismantling led to quantities of building materials being made available for re-use and new building on a large scale was undertaken by magnates and others, who had been enriched by royal service and by the great redistribution of wealth which had taken place. In 1539 Sir William Fitzwilliam, Earl of Southampton and Lord High Admiral of England, began building the great mansion of Cowdray at Midhurst with stone taken from Easebourne Priory nearby but brick was used as well, as coring for the walls, to line fireplaces and for the chimney stacks. Its insulating and heat-resistant properties were by now well-understood.[14]

The Wealden ironworks

As well as military, ecclesiastical and domestic uses, brick also found industrial applications in the 16th century. The Wealden iron industry had achieved national importance by the 1540s and was to see even more

spectacular growth over the next 40 years. The charcoal-fired blast furnaces were constructed of stone but needed to be lined with clay because of the high temperatures reached during the smelting process. Initially puddled clay was used but, with the increasing availability of skilled brickmakers, the ironmasters began to employ them to make bricks for furnace linings. These needed to be dense, well-burnt and free from cracks or other blemishes, to avoid gas absorption and penetration by carbon, which would have led to the premature disintegration of the bricks. The Wadhurst Clay deposits, from which the iron ore was obtained, supplied suitable material both for bricks for furnace linings and for tiles, which were increasingly used to replace thatch on the various buildings in the vicinity of furnace and forge.[15]

The earliest evidence for the use of brick for lining purposes is to be found in the accounts for Sheffield furnace between 1546 and 1549, which included payments for 'new making and mending the furneys with bryk within'. Bricks and tiles were made at Robertsbridge in 1549, specifically for the use of the ironworks. William Ovenden was the brickmaker and the accounts record payments to him and various assistants between February and October in that year. First they dug clay and cut wood for the tile-oast then, towards the end of April, moulding must have begun as, on 8 June, Ovenden was paid for six weeks' work in the tile-oast at 4s per week, a higher rate than hitherto. Meanwhile, a mason had been brought in and was paid 'for ix days work in newe making of ii harches for the tyle kylne and new dawbing of the walls there'. From this, it appears that the kiln was already in existence and only needed repair to be used on this occasion. Brick- and tilemaking continued for another four months but no mention was made of the actual firing of the kiln. However, by October, the fuel cut at the beginning of the season must have run out, as a carrier was paid for bringing in additional supplies.[16]

In all, the expenditure on brick- and tilemaking in that one year was £14 19s ld but there was no subsequent mention of brickmaking in the accounts, which continued until 1573. On two other occasions, when small quantities of bricks were needed, they were not made on the spot but bought in. In 1555, 800 bricks were purchased for repairs to the furnace at Panningridge, which was part of the same operation, and in 1566, one load of bricks was supplied by a brickmaker called Clarke, of Ewhurst, and carried to the works at Robertsbridge. As for William Ovenden, he was paid for cutting wood in 1550 but after that his name did not recur in the accounts and it must be assumed that he had moved on, possibly to another ironworks, where his skills as a brickmaker were required.[17]

An indication that the practice of making bricks and tiles for use in the ironworks was widespread, is the number of significant field names found adjacent to the sites of furnaces and forges. A 'Brickfeilde' on Ashdown Forest, near the site of Marshall's Forge in the parish of Maresfield, was mentioned in surveys of 1564 and 1653 and a 'waste called Brickekell' was recorded near to the furnace at Ashburnham in 1647. The field names often persisted long after the closure of the ironworks. Upper and Lower Brickhouse Fields were shown adjoining Pashley Furnace, in Ticehurst, on a map of 1689 and, even into the 19th century, names such as Brickhouse Field, Brick Kiln Plat and Brick Mead were still in evidence near the sites of abandoned furnaces in Brede, Brightling, Mayfield and Frant and Tinsley Forge in Worth.[18]

There was also a flourishing glassmaking industry in the 16th century, especially in the northern part of Sussex near the Surrey border. It seemed likely that this, which required clay for crucibles, might also have made use of bricks in the construction of glasshouses. However, no definite connection has been established, although one or two Brick Kiln Fields in the parishes of Kirdford and Wisborough Green may tentatively be linked with the industry.[19]

The 'Great Rebuild'

The prosperity of the Elizabethan ironmasters was one of the factors which led to a fresh wave of house-building in the latter part of the century. In 1584 a clamp of bricks was burnt in St Leonard's Forest for use at Gosden furnace and in the house of the ironmaster, Roger Gratwick, at Cowfold and in 1587 John Robynett was granted three acres of land on Bepton Common, near Midhurst, on which to build a mansion, a furnace and a kiln for making bricks, tiles and lime.[20]

Among the country houses built, or enlarged, around this time using brick was Danny at Hurstpierpoint. Here brickwork of two different styles can be identified. The lower part of the north wing is of red brick with a darker, diapered diamond pattern. For this Gregory Fiennes, of the family which had built Herstmonceux Castle in the previous century, was probably responsible. Then, in 1582, the house was sold to George Goring, who enlarged and extended it into an E-shaped mansion, of red brick with stone-mullioned windows. The south wing was completed in 1593 but Goring died in the following year, heavily in debt, and a survey of the estate made in 1595 described the house at Danny as 'not fullye fynished builte of Bricke which coste as may appeare iiii $^{m\ li'}$ (£4,000). The exact site of brickmaking has not been determined but fields called 'The Brickott (brick oast) Croft' and 'The Sandfeild' were listed in a mortgage of 1649.[21]

Brick houses also built in the late 16th century include Cuckfield Place and Legh Manor in Cuckfield, Halland House in East Hoathly and the new house, built by the Sackville family on the site of the earlier castle, at Bolebrook in Hartfield. Other houses, although stone-faced, now regularly used brick for cellars, kitchens, chimneys, wall linings and other internal work. A brick banqueting house was built at Petworth in 1574 and subsequent alterations to the house from the 1590s onwards always required a supply of bricks. Giles Garton, a London ironmonger, purchased Woolavington manor, south of Petworth, and rebuilt the house in 1586. The contract with the mason specified that he was to furnish the stone but that Garton would supply lime, brick, sand and nails as well as other materials and tools.[22]

The bricks for most of these building operations were made on the spot by an itinerant brickmaker employed for the purpose. Often he served as the bricklayer as well. Once the task had been completed, the kiln, which may only have been a temporary structure, was dismantled, or else repaired and re-used the next time bricks were required. Even today, the pond, which formed in the abandoned claypit, may still be in evidence and, as with the ironworks, a Brick Kiln Field on a later map marks the site of the brickmaking operations.

Not to be outdone, the yeoman farmers who shared in the prosperity of the period also built new houses or extended existing ones. Here the traditional timber-framed structure still prevailed but bricks were now regularly used for fireplaces and chimneys and additionally brick was sometimes employed to replace wattle and daub in the spaces between the timber studding of existing buildings. Stone House at Steyning belies its name by having a timber upper storey with this type of brick-nogging. The old granary at Bolebrook was refurbished, using bricks from the demolished castle, laid horizontally, to fill the spaces between the timbers and a good example of bricks used in this way, but laid herringbone-fashion, is to be found in the house called Gallops, at Albourne.

4. SMALL COUNTRY BRICKYARDS

Towards the end of the 16th century, the increased use of bricks and tiles in cottages and farmhouses, as well as in the market towns, led to the establishment of permanent brickyards, as former itinerant brickmakers found it worth their while to settle in one place and other men were encouraged to enter the growing trade.

Kilns on the commons

The site chosen for many of these early brickyards was frequently a piece of waste land on the edge of one of the commons which abounded in the Weald and, to a lesser extent, along the coastal plain of West Sussex. The common, the poorest land in the locality, provided some rough grazing but generally consisted of scrub. Here, as a rule, the topsoil was thin, so the earth and clay needed by the brickmaker lay close to the surface. Also to hand was the brushwood to make faggots for firing the kiln.

The common came under the jurisdiction of the lord of the manor and evidence of the activities of brickmakers from the latter part of the 16th century onwards can be obtained from surviving manorial records. The simplest method was for a brickmaker to obtain a lease of a small piece of land, with permission to extract brick earth and build a kiln, for which he was charged an annual rent. An example of an early lease of this kind was one granted on St John's Common in Keymer where, in 1582, an un-named brickmaker was paying an annual rent of 20s for 'a tenement with a tile oste and demi acre of grounde about yt in the common at Stuffforthe where hee takes earthe to make brick and tyle'.

Alternatively, a grant of copyhold might be obtained, by which the brickmaker became the owner of the land, as was the case with the 16th-century brickyards already mentioned on Ashdown Forest and Bepton Common. If an existing copyholder decided to set up as a brickmaker, in some manors he could do so without penalty but in others it was necessary to obtain a licence to dig earth and clay, for which a fee was charged. Much depended on the customs of the manor. In general, tenants had the right to graze their stock on the common and also to cut wood fuel for domestic use and take material, such as clay, to repair their houses. But from the moment they began selling their products for profit, a charge could be made. This might take the form of a licence, for which a fixed sum was charged, or of a 'fine', which varied according to the amount of material extracted.[1]

This latter procedure was adopted in the manor of Ringmer where, in 1665 John Ramsden was fined 6s and William Garrett 2s for digging earth and clay in the Broyle to make bricks and tiles. There had been brickmakers working in Ringmer from the 1530s and resident in the parish from at least the 1580s but it was in the late 17th century that their activities expanded significantly. In 1689 three brickmakers paid fines ranging from 6d to 5s. By 1691, the number had increased to five and the entry in the Manor Court Book read as follows: The homage present that Richard Garrett dug and took earth and clay (*fundum et lutum*) in the Broyle to make bricks and tiles (*lateres et tegulas*) for sale contrary to the customs of this manor therefore he is in mercy: 12d.

Thomas Wakerell, John Stanly, John Ramsden and James Tysehurst were then presented for the same offence and fined a like amount. The peak was reached in 1702 when seven brick-makers were each fined 5s per kiln. Not all of these kilns were on the Broyle itself but all were in close proximity to the common, where the brick earth was obtained.[2]

Evidence from other manors confirms that the popularity of bricks was gradually increasing during the course of the 17th century. A licence was granted to Henry Chapman to dig earth on Hailsham Common in 1649. In East Grinstead, John Butching was fined 10s in 1670 for unlawfully digging earth and clay for bricks and tiles from the waste and this was followed in 1679 by a further presentment for digging earth and erecting a kiln. In both of these localities the adjacent market town guaranteed a steady demand for bricks but even in the remoter country areas the commons were being utilised in the same way.[3]

Expansion in the 18th century

From the beginning of the 18th century onwards, surviving manorial records become more numerous and from them it can be seen that brickyards which had been set up without permission, or which had been the subject of an annual tenancy only, were now being recognised as permanent premises, which justified the grant of copyhold tenure. On the west side of St John's Common, which lay within the jurisdiction of the manor of Clayton, a grant was made in 1711 of land on which a kiln had already been in existence for some time. In that year,

John Dunstall, a clerk in holy orders, became the owner of a brick kiln and two acres of waste land but the brickmaker was probably James Parker, who was fined for digging and carrying away earth in 1713 and, in 1730, was able to buy the yard himself. By 1741 he was the owner of two brickyards in the same area, one of which was leased to another brickmaker, George Taylor of Keymer. However, Parker had had to borrow quite heavily and in 1751 he was obliged to sell off some of his land and Taylor was able to acquire his own yard.[4]

Chailey South Common, which was part of the manor of Wanningore, also had a well-established brickyard by the beginning of the 18th century. The tenant in 1711, Richard Calchin, held one acre, on which a cottage and two brick kilns had been built and for which he paid an annual quit rent of 2s 6d. In 1754 a second brickyard was opened to the north. On this occasion a licence was granted by the lady of the manor to John Siffleet to dig earth for making bricks on the South Common for seven years, paying 16s per annum and 'not taking any earth within the space of 60 rods from the brick kiln of George Colvin (Calchin's successor) on the same common'. Siffleet died in 1759 and the probate inventory of his goods and chattels taken in April of that year lists his stock of 10,000 bricks, 1,200 tiles, 300 hollow tiles, 226 paving tiles and 34 gutter bricks unsold from the previous season, as well as moulds, tile boards, a sieve, tables, wheelbarrows, faggots and kiln ashes. He, too, had two kilns.[5]

Often the first intimation that brickmakers were at work comes from presentments at the manor court, not for clay-digging but for encroachment on the waste. Absentee lords of the manor generally left supervision in the hands of a steward and it was only with the advent of a new lord, or a new steward, that irregularities came to light. This seems to have been the case in the manor of Framfield in 1745, when a very large number of encroachments were reported. In the following year, these were listed in detail. The culprits included Edward Brooker, Nicholas Clarke and William Durrant, who had enclosed plots of land and constructed kilns on Blackboys, Palehouse and Highland Commons respectively. On Ridgewood Common, which lay partly in Framfield but mainly in the neighbouring parish of Uckfield, John Whatford had a kiln and two plots and Richard Teeling a kiln and a brickplace. This last was the only specific reference to bricks at this stage. The offenders were all fined but they must have entered into negotiations for the purchase of the land they had been using illegally as, over the next 10 years, grants of copyhold were recorded in each case and it became clear that the kilns were all brick kilns. For example, in 1756 John Whatford was granted two plots amounting to 1½ acres on Ridgewood Common together with a brick kiln and two 'workhouses', which occupied a further half acre. Nicholas Clarke, another of the offenders, had been described as 'brickmaker, of Framfield' as early as 1709, the year in which he married Elizabeth Ticehurst of Ringmer. This suggests that some of these brickyards had been in existence for a considerable length of time before action was taken against their operators.[6]

On the Dicker, the extensive common divided between the parishes of Hellingly and Chiddingly, and on Laughton Common, both of which formed part of the waste of the manor of Laughton, much the same thing happened about 10 years later. Presentments for encroachment in 1756 were followed by a series of new grants of copyhold over the next few years. One brickmaker in Laughton and three in Chiddingly benefited in this way. When it became known that land on the Dicker was available for the establishment of brickyards, applications were made for grants on the east side of the common in Hellingly and one of the new entrepreneurs, Thomas Wood, came from as far afield as Plumpton. The map drawn when the Dicker was finally enclosed in 1813 shows these

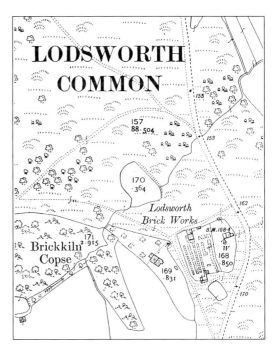

8. Brickyard on the edge of Lodsworth Common (OS Sheet XXII/6 1912)

27

numerous small enclosures dotted about the common. As long as the common remained unenclosed, the brickmakers were able to gather brushwood to fuel their kilns, but enclosure put an end to that and may have contributed to the failure of several of the smaller operators around that time.[7]

Most of the commons mentioned so far were in East Sussex but the commons of West Sussex had experienced similar development. On Horsham Common brickmakers had been active from the 16th century. Nicholas Dinnage, whose occupation was given as brickmaker in 1665, was one of two men who had brick kilns on the Common in 1709 and by 1787, three more kilns had been erected. There were brickyards on Tortington Common and on Ebernoe Common in Kirdford in the 17th century and by the 1730s there were brickmakers working on Clapham Common, Horsebridge Common in Ashurst and Broadmare Common in Henfield. Further west, Sidlesham Common had a brickyard in 1755 and two sets of kilns were in operation in 1778 on the east and west sides of Hambrook Common, in the parishes of Funtington and Westbourne respectively. The yards on Worthing Common and on Jolesfield Common in West Grinstead were also of 18th-century origin and there were many others. When North Heath Common in Pulborough was enclosed in 1815, the map showed James Cumper's brick kiln and premises, surrounded by what had previously been open ground. This brickyard, like those shown on the enclosure map of the Dicker, had clearly been in existence for some time.[8]

The Wealden-type wood-fired kiln

In the small 17th- and 18th-century brickyards, bricks were, almost without exception, kiln-burnt. The kilns were brick-built and of a type similar to the ones used in Roman times. They were straight-sided, open-topped and often built into a bank of earth. This gave a measure of heat insulation and strength to the structure which was liable to develop cracks as a result of the extremes of temperature to which it was subjected. It also made it possible to fire the kiln through two tunnels at the lowest level and have access for setting the bricks at a higher level on the opposite side. The floor of the kiln chamber was pierced either by vents, which extended across the whole width of the kiln, or else by rows of holes. These, together with spaces left between the bricks as they were set in the kiln, formed flues through which the hot gases could rise during firing. A layer of burnt bricks was laid across the top of the kiln and sometimes a temporary roof placed over all to give protection from the weather. The fuel employed was mainly brushwood, which was gathered into bundles, known as a rule as 'faggots', but in parts of West Sussex as 'bavins'. These could be pushed down the firing tunnels to reach right to the back of the kiln. The temperature was raised slowly to begin with, to drive off any moisture remaining in the bricks, and then increased gradually and maintained at about 1000ºC for 48 hours, or even longer, the whole process taking about six days.[9]

Kiln capacity was small, generally of not more than 24,000 bricks, plus the

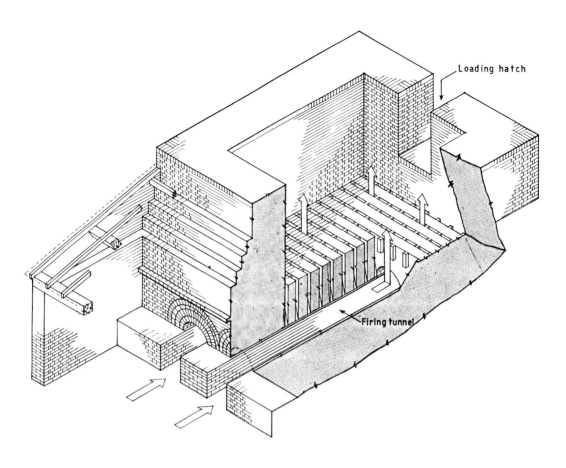

Loading hatch

Firing tunnel

9. Wealden-type intermittent updraught kiln

same quantity of tiles, and often much less than this. The kilns were intermittent, that is to say a period of time had to be allowed for cooling to take place before the burnt bricks could be drawn from the kiln and then more time allowed for the next batch to be set before firing could recommence. When demand was low, one kiln was sufficient but if greater quantities or more continuous production was required, a second kiln was constructed. This generally took the form of an extension alongside the first kiln so that one of the pair of kilns could be set whilst the other was cooling.

When kilns of this type went out of use, the bricks of which they were constructed would be removed for use elsewhere and so very little evidence of their existence now remains. The most that can be found as a rule is a pit or a pond on the edge of a shaw, with a piece of level ground where the bricks were dried in the open air and a scatter of brick and tile wasters. However, an example of the smallest type of single kiln has been preserved on Ebernoe Common in Kirdford in West Sussex and in East Sussex, on the Ashburnham estate, a double kiln, which only went out of operation in 1968, is still in

29

existence, although most of the super-structure has been removed.[10]

Bricks for country houses

The owners of big estates, who wished to alter or extend their houses, were faced with two alternatives when a fresh supply of bricks was required. Either they could purchase them from one of the yards in the neighbourhood, or employ a local brickmaker for a limited period to make the necessary bricks in a kiln built, or re-built, for the purpose in fairly close proximity to the house.

Accounts for two neighbouring estates in East Sussex reveal that a brickmaker called John Leves was employed in the 1640s first of all at Herstmonceux Castle and then at Thomas Luxford's house, now known as Carters Corner Place, in Hellingly. Leves and an assistant spent the winter of 1645 digging earth for Lord Dacre at Herstmonceux. Then, between May and July they made 29,600 bricks, at a total cost of £10 7s. No mention is made of a kiln and so possibly an existing one was used. In the following year they were at work on Luxford's estate. Here the accounts include payments for making faggots and the bricks would have been burnt in a kiln which lay to the northwest of the house. An estate map of 1671 shows the position of the kiln, which is represented as a small square building with clouds of smoke emerging from under the kiln-cover and alongside this an open-sided shed. Evidently the number of bricks made in 1647 was not quite sufficient to meet requirements as, in the following year, Luxford purchased a small quantity of bricks made at Ashburnham. This suggests that the two brickmakers were in fact based on the Ashburnham estate but, in years when their services were not required, other local landowners were at liberty to employ them.[11]

Building work seems to have taken place quite frequently at Petworth House and on each occasion a different solution was adopted to the problem of obtaining the necessary bricks. In 1607, for example, 1,000 bricks were bought in at a cost of 11s but in 1615, when a new kitchen was being built, much larger quantities were needed for the vaulted cellars, as well as the ovens and chimneys and this necessitated constructing a kiln for supplies to be made on the spot. In 1702, when bricks were again required, the steward made enquiries about their availability in the neighbourhood. He visited yards at Graffham, Fittleworth, Duncton, Lickfold and Ebernoe and reported that the last four could produce only 160,000 bricks between them in the following season and that the prices of between 13s and 15s per 1,000 did not include carriage, which would add another 4s or 5s per 1,000 to the cost. In consequence, discussions were taking place with a brickmaker in Petworth, who was prepared to use clay dug in the park and wood supplied by the estate to make 100,000 bricks the following summer at 7s per 1,000 using earth already dug and at 7s 6d per 1,000 when earth had to be dug as well. However, the old kiln was unserviceable and would have to be rebuilt.[12]

In the High Weald of East Sussex there are numerous examples of houses which were either built or substantially altered in the 17th, 18th or early 19th centuries. These include: Brickwall and

30

10. Carting bricks at Plumpton in 1897

Tufton Place in Northiam, Boarsney and Iridge Place in Salehurst, Haremere Hall in Etchingham, Whiligh in Ticehurst, Great Trodgers in Mayfield, Walsh Manor in Rotherfield and several houses in Frant. In each case, a Brick Kiln Field adjacent to the house shows that the bricks were made on the spot, probably by a local brickmaker who used materials available on the estate.

The difficulties encountered when on-site brickmaking was not possible can best be illustrated from the account of the materials used when a new mansion was being built in Stanmer Park, on the Downs near Brighton, for Henry and Thomas Pelham in the 1720s. The house was to be faced with

stone but over 1¼ million bricks were required for internal work. The nearest supply of brick earth was in Brighton and to begin with, an attempt was made to clamp-burn bricks on a site near the coast. When this proved unsatisfactory, production was switched to coal-fired kilns, which yielded bricks of the right quality but insufficient in quantity. As a result, seven different wealden brickyards – three in Ringmer and one each in Isfield, Barcombe, Chailey and Clayton – were contacted in order to make up the shortfall of about 200,000 bricks. Here the price of bricks 'taken at the kiln' ranged from 15s to 17s 6d per thousand, as compared with the 14s per thousand charged by the Brighton brickmaker, Henry Hill. But this did not take the cost of delivery into consideration. Carting bricks from Brighton cost 6s per thousand, whereas delivery from the Weald cost between 7s 6d and 12s per thousand, adding considerably to the bill.[13]

Then there were the tiles: some 160,000 plain tiles and 6,000 ridge, hip and gutter tiles. The builders probably envisaged buying these in the Weald from the outset, as there was little suitable tile clay in the Brighton area. Also transport costs were not as prohibitive as for bricks. A horse-drawn cart could carry not more than 500 bricks in each load but twice that number of tiles. This is borne out by the prices charged by Thomas Holman of Barcombe, who supplied both bricks and tiles. His delivery charges varied slightly over the four-year period from 1724 to 1727 but averaged 6s per thousand for tiles against 12s for bricks. In all, there were seven suppliers of tiles, the largest quantities coming from John Pullman of Chailey South Common and James Parker of St John's Common in Clayton. In 1726 the latter supplied 43,450 plain tiles together with 125 ridge tiles and 500 hip and corner tiles. His price was 20s 6d per thousand delivered at Stanmer, which compared quite favourably with the prices of the other suppliers but he asked for 25s in the winter, which is some indication of the state of the notorious Sussex roads.

Estate brickyards

The difficulties encountered by the builders of Stanmer House help to explain why, from the late 17th century onwards, a number of Sussex landowners chose to establish a permanent brickyard on their estates. In some cases the yard was managed directly by the estate for its own benefit. In others, land was leased to a brickmaker to set up a commercial brickyard but the estate had first call on the products, when they were required. It is probably significant that two of the earliest of these yards were on estates where the mansion house, as at Stanmer, was situated on the chalk. The house at Uppark, on the Downs south of Harting, was built in the 1690s with bricks made in the estate yard at Down Park, on the gault clay almost three miles away. The alternative solution was adopted by Sir John Shelley, whose house was at Michelgrove, north of Worthing. In 1731, he granted a licence to Thomas Colebrooke, a local brickmaker who already had a yard at Lyminster, to enclose one acre on Clapham Common and dig clay for making bricks and tiles, mainly for the purpose of supplying the estate. Colebrooke died in 1742 and his probate inventory lists the stock of bricks and tiles at both of his yards. The one on Clapham Common was subsequently leased to other brickmakers and supplied the bricks required for the rebuilding of Michelgrove House in 1769.[14]

The estate which had by far the longest association with brickmaking was the one at Ashburnham, near Battle. As already stated, there was a tile kiln here as early as 1362 and a brick kiln, located between the furnace and the forge, was built to service the ironworks in the 16th and early 17th centuries. Then in about 1670, when the family fortunes had been restored after the troubles of the Civil War, a decision was taken to rebuild Ashburnham Place in brick. An estate brickyard was established and in 1675 an injunction to 'cast enough earth for bricks' was included in a letter from William Ashburnham, in London, to his land agent, John Plummer. This yard continued in operation after the new house was complete. In 1682, bricks and tiles from the Earl of Ashburnham's kiln were carried to the blast furnace and from then onwards the brickyard, which lay just inside the park but quite close to the forge, seems to have been in fairly continuous use, supplying the needs of both the estate and the ironworks.[15]

King's Tax was paid on the Brick Fields at Ashburnham in the 1690s but after that references are scarce until 1763, when the ironworks accounts show that '700 bricks from my lord's kiln' were delivered to the furnace. From 1769 onwards, the estate accounts mention the brickyard more frequently and from 1793, the underwood accounts record all cordwood and brushwood supplied in the form of faggots to the three industrial undertakings on the estate: the ironworks, the limeworks and the brickyard. Unfortunately, the wood supplied to Ashburnham Place and to the brick kilns was generally combined in one total and so it is not possible to gauge the precise amount consumed at the brickyard. In 1780 an isolated outside sale of bricks, at 21s per thousand and tiles, at 22s, was recorded but the volume of production at this period was mainly geared to the needs of the estate. A new steward in 1814 seems to have put the operation of the brickyard on a different footing, leasing it at an annual rent of £2 2s to John Sands, who had previously been employed by the estate. He and his successor, Silas Sands, were charged for the kiln faggots supplied. This arrangement continued until 1839, when Sands was paid the balance due to him on the brickmaking account and the old yard was closed down, prior to the opening of a new one at Court Lodge ¼ mile away.[16]

The new brickyard was controlled directly by the estate, with Henry Barden employed as foreman. He was succeeded in this position by three more generations of his family: James, Harry and finally George, who retired in 1955. The history of this yard, from 1840 until its closure in 1968, was recorded in the first issue of *Sussex Industrial History* in 1970, together with a detailed account of the methods used to make and burn the bricks. Subsequently Jack Harmer, the last foreman of the yard, contributed an account of tilemaking and other uses of clay, such as drainpipe- and flowerpot-making, to a later issue. It may therefore be said that not only did brick- and tilemaking at Ashburnham cover a longer period than at any other location in Sussex but they are also the most fully documented.[17]

At the other end of the county, an estate brickyard which, for a time, was one of the biggest and most successful in the district, was the one at Westhampnett, owned by the Duke of Richmond. There had been brickmakers living in Westhampnett from at least 1730, probably working in a brickyard on the Goodwood estate, but in 1782 a new yard was opened which, from the outset, supplied customers over a wide area along the coast from Bognor to Selsey and inland from Upwaltham to

Sheffield Brickkiln at Trickland

11. *Sheffield Park estate brick kiln in Trickland Wood, sketched by George Holroyd, the future Earl of Sheffield, in 1815 (ESRO SPK/F1/3)*

Chilgrove, as well as providing for estate requirements. By the 1830s a second brickyard had been opened on the south side of Westhampnett Road but after this, activity gradually declined. The old yard closed and the second yard reverted to catering mainly for the needs of the estate. This included a large number of farms and also Goodwood Racecourse, where bricks were required for the grandstand. The yard was still operating at a profit in the early 1900s but turnover was small and it did not survive after the end of World War 1.[18]

The brickmakers from 1782 onwards were members of the Lillywhite family, which originated in Rogate but also had Hampshire connections. James Lillywhite came to Westhampnett to manage the new brickyard when it opened. He was succeeded by his nephew, also James, who was born in Buriton, Hampshire, but married in Westhampnett in 1794. At least two of his sons followed him into the business: Frederick William, who moved to Hove in 1822 and became better known for his achievements as a cricketer and John, who by 1835 had succeeded his father as manager of the yard at Westhampnett. John, who died in 1880, was followed by his son, another John, and he was in charge of brickmaking on the estate until it ceased in 1915.[19]

By the 19th century, when records

had become more comprehensive, estate brickyards were in operation at Bignor Park, Shillinglee Park in Kirdford, Wykehurst Park in Bolney, Worth Hall, Balcombe Place, Sheffield Park in Fletching and on the Battle Abbey estate, to name but a few. The Fuller family, of Rosehill in Brightling, near Battle, owned both a brickyard in Brightling, which was managed by the estate, and another yard in Waldron, near Heathfield, which was leased to tenants. This was the usual practice when a brickyard was situated in an outlying part of an estate. The Petworth estate owned a brickyard on Henley Common, in Fernhurst, for which some 19th-century tenancy agreements have survived. The tenant paid an annual rent of £5 and a royalty of 2s per thousand on all the bricks made. In addition, the estate reserved the right to purchase at a discount any bricks, tiles or drainpipes it might require. A list of prices was set out with the proviso: 'prices for drainpipes to be subject to valuation should the price of such ware be reduced at neighbouring yards. The prices of sizes 1 to 3 (1in, 1½in and 2in diameter) to be always 2s 6d per 1,000 and sizes 4 to 6 (2½in, 3in and 4in diameter) 5s per 1,000 below that of other yards'.[20]

When such brickyards were taken over by a new tenant, an inventory of the tools and unsold stock would be taken and a valuation made. A yard owned by the branch of the Ashburnham family who lived at Broomham in Guestling, near Hastings, was the subject of a detailed valuation at the end of October 1846. The buildings consisted of a tile house, a drying shed, a sand house and the brick kiln. There were five moulding tables, one wheelbarrow and two bearing-off barrows, a ladder and some poles, planks and iron bars. Implements were minimal, consisting of kiln-irons, a wire sieve and moulds of various kinds: for building, coping and paving bricks and for plain, corner, ridge and draining tiles. Unused raw materials in the yard included sand, brick earth, clay and kiln faggots. Finally came the unsold stock: quite substantial quantities of both bricks and tiles, which probably explained why the tenant was giving up his lease. The total value placed on the yard and its contents was £197 12s 3d. This provides a useful picture of the type of country brickyard which had changed very little over a period of about 300 years .[21]

5. DUAL OCCUPATIONS

Brickmaking in this country, until quite recent times, was a seasonal activity. Brick earth was dug in the autumn and left in a heap in the yard over the winter for the wind, rain and frost to temper it and make it easier to handle when brickmaking began in the spring. Moulding could only start when there was no further danger of hard frost, which might damage the 'green' bricks as they dried in the open air. Burning, in an intermittent kiln, took place at any time from midsummer until the first frosts of autumn signalled the end of the brickmaking year. The seasonal nature of the job, combined with the fact that demand for bricks was by no means constant, depending as it did on the amount of new building, or rebuilding, taking place at any given time, made it difficult for country brickmakers in particular to subsist entirely on the profits from their trade. They needed some other means to support themselves and their families when times were bad and so they often combined brickmaking with another occupation.

Farmer/brickmakers

The most common solution adopted by brickmakers, as by many other rural tradesmen, was to combine their main activity with running a small farm. These artisan/farmers either owned or rented a few acres of land on which they grew corn or raised animals, with the brickyard situated on a rough piece of ground, which was agriculturally unproductive. Brickmaking activities were fitted into the seasons when farming made the fewest demands. After clay-digging in the autumn, the slack period in the winter was spent gathering brushwood for kiln faggots and brickmaking did not begin until late spring, when sowing and lambing had taken place. The bricks were then left to dry until late in the summer when haymaking and harvest were complete and time was available to set and fire the kiln.

Some farmer/brickmakers had 100 acres of land, or more, in which case the brickyard was of secondary importance. One skilled brickburner would be employed to act as foreman of the yard and the rest of the labourers worked either on the farm or in the brickyard, as the need arose. Others had as little as five acres, which was barely enough to support the brickmaker and his family, all of whom, including quite young children, were expected to do their share of moulding bricks and tiles. The most precise information in this respect can be obtained from the 19th-century census returns, on which both occupations were frequently declared. In 1851, for example, Joseph Barrow, a brickmaker of Runtington Farm, Heathfield, was farming 100 acres and employing four men, whereas Richard Morley of Lower Beeding, with 50 acres, was employing seven men. As brickmaking was more labour-intensive than farming, this suggests that Morley derived most of his income from the brickyard, whereas Barrow was essentially a farmer, only running his brickyard as a sideline. In 1871, George Parks of Mayfield described himself as 'farmer and brickmaker' although he only had six acres, but the average small farm run in conjunction with a brickyard had between 15 and 25 acres of land.

12. Accounts of the brickyard on Newhouse Farm, Ewhurst, for the year 1853 (ESRO BAT 2928)

Typical of the smaller farmer/brickmakers was William Sargent of Hellingly, who died in April 1720. His probate inventory showed that he had 2½ acres of corn on the ground and 2 acres of oats. His stock included 5 cows, 5 horses, 34 sheep, some of them with lambs, and also 5,000 bricks, 12,000 plain tiles, 300 well bricks and a few paving bricks and hollow tiles, all presumably unsold from the previous year. The inventory of John Hills of Ashurst, who died in 1736, paints a similar picture. He had 2 acres of wheat and 3 acres of oats and his farm stock consisted of 3 cows, 2 mares and 2 colts, 2 hogs, a sow and 6 pigs. In the brickyard he had 1,050 well bricks, 1,000 paving bricks, 200 quarry bricks, 1,200 plain tiles and a few ridge and hip tiles, all ready burnt. In addition, as the inventory was taken in June, there was the current season's production: 7,000 raw (unburnt) bricks and 8,000 raw paving bricks, as well as quantities of brick earth and tile earth ready cast, 1,200 bush faggots and a load of sand.[1]

Limeburners and pottery manufacturers

Hills was even more versatile than Sargent: he also had 'four loads of chalk in the kiln'. This was not unusual, as brickmaking and limeburning often went hand in hand. In the clay and sandstone areas around Rye and Hastings, chalk was brought by sea to brickyards near the coast and in central and western Sussex, chalk from the Downs was taken considerable distances inland along the various rivers and navigations. Like the brick-kilns, the 'flare' kilns used for limeburning were wood-fired and there was generally a plentiful supply of fuel in the Weald. Customers found it convenient to be able to buy at the same time not only bricks and tiles but also sand and lime for mortar.

Abraham Cooper, a Hailsham brickmaker who died in 1603, mentioned his limekiln in his will. The brickyard at Woolbeding, run by members of the Denyer family, must also have contained a limekiln, to judge by references to chalk in the probate inventory of Robert Denyer in 1657 and to lime ashes in that of his successor in 1684. Both chalk and lime figured in the inventory of Stephen Pryer of Henfield in 1723. Several of the brickmakers on the Broyle in Ringmer and on the Dicker in Hellingly and Chiddingly also had limekilns in their yards and the OS map of 1872 shows a limekiln at the brickworks on the bank of the Rother in Beckley. Conversely, the limeburners in the Arundel area in the 19th century found it advantageous to market bricks. Charles Chamberlain of Arundel Cement Works also owned a brickyard at Tortington, and Peppers, limeburners

13. *Probate inventory of Stephen Pryer (ESRO W/INV 1619)*

of Amberley, had an interest in brickfields in the Littlehampton area.[2]

The brickyard at Piddinghoe in the Lower Ouse Valley was particularly favourably situated. Not only was chalk for limeburning and the manufacture of whiting available from a pit alongside the brickyard but the yard itself lay on clay which was suitable for making pottery as well as bricks. Brown-ware pottery, both glazed and unglazed, was produced at a number of Sussex brickyards, in some cases merely as a sideline and in others predominating over the output of bricks and tiles. It has already been seen that pottery- and tilemaking often co-existed in the medieval period, the same type of clay frequently being suitable for both products. This tradition persisted in the parishes of Graffham and Woolavington (East Lavington) over a period stretching from Roman times to the 19th century. Various sites in the district, examined in the 1970s, revealed pottery, brick and tile wasters from the Romano-British, medieval and post-medieval periods and a remarkable series of 15 probate inventories, from dates between 1617 and 1706, show that activity must have reached a high level in the 17th century. Eight of the inventories list the goods of men described as potters, two of tilers and five of brickmakers but it is clear that there was a close association between the different trades.[3]

In the parish of Ringmer, where extensive evidence for a medieval pottery industry has also been uncovered, brickmaking seems to have superseded it from the 16th century onwards but elsewhere in the area the two trades continued to flourish side by side. A yard in Wilmington containing a

14. Poling Potteries in the 1930s

brick kiln and a pot kiln, which was offered for sale in 1759, was run by members of the Crowhurst family, who also had brickmaking interests in Ringmer and the succession of potteries which sprang up on the east side of the Dicker from around 1760 onwards and continued until the middle of the 20th century, were all associated with brickyards. In the east of the county, Rye has a long tradition of pottery manufacture, which continues to the present day. In the 18th and 19th centuries the pottery was under the same management as the brickyard, as was the case in the neighbouring parish of Brede.[4]

Potteries and brickyards co-existed elsewhere, notably at East Grinstead and in the coastal region of western Sussex, at Poling near Arundel and in the parish of Westbourne but the most flourishing examples of this dual trade were on the large commons in the centre of the county at Chailey, Ditchling, Keymer, Clayton and West Grinstead. Here the small-scale potteries and brickyards of the 18th and early 19th centuries, producing domestic pottery and bricks and tiles to satisfy purely local demands, expanded in the late 19th century and manufactured substantial quantities of terracotta, a subject which will be dealt with later.[5]

Other rural trades

The tools and other items of equipment required by the brickmaker, such as moulds and barrows, were few and could be made at no great cost by the village wheelwright but capital was sometimes needed to buy a suitable plot of land and build a kiln. This might well be furnished by the local miller, who was generally one of the wealthier members of the community. In 1826 James Dives, the miller at Nutley, was reported to have enclosed land for a brickyard and dug brick earth on Ashdown Forest. John Kenward, who had an interest in brickyards in Uckfield in the 1820s and '30s, was also the owner of the town's corn mill and his son advertised in 1845 as a farmer, seedsman and brick and tilemaker. Similarly, Edward Beeney, the miller at Windmill Hill, was involved with a brickyard in Herstmonceux in the 1860s and the Beauport Brick Works, on Harrow Lane in Hastings, was owned in the 1890s by J. Cheale & Co., millers, of Ore. It seems unlikely that a miller would have soiled his hands by being actively involved in brickmaking but his commercial instincts would have ensured that the business was run profitably.[6]

Occasionally a whole group of trades was associated in one enterprise and it is hard to tell which was the main source of revenue. The following notice appeared in the *Sussex Weekly Advertiser* of 28 March 1774:

> To be sold by auction ... all that well accustomed inn consisting of a large new built Brick Messuage, 3 stables, one Blacksmith's shop, one Brick Kiln and one Lime Kiln all in exceeding good repair with about 8 acres of very good meadow land, about ¼ acre whereof is converted into a hop ground, known by the name of the Half Moon in the Parish of Heathfield.

It is not known how many people were involved but it has already been seen that the same man could well have been in charge of the brick-kiln, the limekiln and the farm and it is by no means impossible that, with a little help, he might have managed the inn and the blacksmith's shop as well. The trade of blacksmith was not linked with that of brickmaker as frequently as some others that have been mentioned but they have

been found in association in several places. In 1826 two cottages, a smith's shop and a brick kiln, near Starnash Farm in Hellingly, were offered for sale and there was a blacksmith's shop on the premises in Lower Beeding which were leased to farmer/brickmaker Richard Morley in 1848.[7]

As for the inn and the hop garden, which formed the nucleus of the Heathfield property, this again causes no surprise. Hops were grown extensively in the High Weald of East Sussex until quite recent times and brickmakers who had some spare land would plant a hop garden and dry the hops in a brick-built oast-house adjacent to the yard. This was generally circular in form and the specially-shaped bricks and tapered tiles required to build it then formed part of the brickmaker's stock-in-trade, which could be purchased by farmers in the area wishing to construct an oast to dry their own hops. In the mid-19th century, Samuel Cornford, farmer and brickmaker of Warbleton near Heathfield, owned 14½ acres of land with a house, a barn and an oast-house as well as the brickyard. The three-acre hop garden has long since disappeared but the oast remains, converted into a cottage, on the roadside north of Rushlake Green. Hops grown in this way were generally sold as a cash crop but the ones produced near the old 'Half Moon' at Heathfield in the 18th century would have been used for home-brewed beer.[8]

The liquor trade

An association between bricks and beer can be established as early as 1659, when Brownings of Steyning were both brickmakers and maltsters. By the mid-19th century, when nearly every village in the Weald had a brickyard, it was quite usual to find an inn or a beershop alongside it. Sometimes it was the innkeeper who was able to furnish some of the capital for the brickyard. For example, Benjamin Minns, of the Shelley Arms in Nutley, was the tenant of the local brickyard in 1851, although he does not appear to have done the brickmaking himself. In other cases it was the brickmaker who, realising that brickmaking was thirsty work, set himself up as a beer-retailer as well. William Weller had built a tavern adjoining his brickyard at Silverhill north of Salehurst by 1835, John Parsons, of Burwash, advertised as brickmaker and beer-retailer in the 1860s and John Franklin, the innkeeper at the 'Castle' near the station in Wadhurst, was a brickmaker as well in 1871.[9]

Many of the brickfields which were proliferating along the coast by the 19th century also had an adjacent inn or beer shop. Mr Steele, the landlord of the 'Horseshoes' at Lancing, also had an interest in a brickyard there in 1804. In 1845 John Faulkner and Francis Ide were plying the combined trades of brickmaker and beer-retailer in Shoreham and Sompting respectively and in 1871, John Gates, a brickmaker in Wick Street, Lyminster, was also the publican at the 'Globe'. In the Brighton area the association seems to have been particularly strong. In the early years of the 19th century Thomas Budgen, a builder and brickmaker, was also the tenant of the 'White Swan'. In the 1840s and '50s, William Nicholson, a brickmaker in Aldrington, was the

innkeeper of the 'Jolly Huntsman' in Old Dyke Road and the 'Brickmakers Arms' in Cross Street, Hove was run by George Henry Clayton, the eldest son of John Clayton, a brickmaker who owned taverns in Brighton and Portslade as well. Also in Portslade, in 1862, James Holes applied for a licence to sell spirits in the beer shop near his brickfield called the 'Half Brick' and this name was also given to an inn which stood near the brickfields at Navarino, to the east of Worthing.[10]

Not just innkeepers but brewers, too, took an interest in brickmaking. Henry Michell, a brewer from Horsham, bought an inn with some land attached in Three Bridges in 1838 and put the land to good use as a brickfield. For a time he managed this himself but subsequently let both the 'Plough' and the brickfield to Edward Mitchell, who advertised as 'victualler and brickmaker' in 1859. Other brewers who put some of their capital into brickmaking were the Aylwards of Rye and the Eldridges of St Leonards. Thomas Aylward advertised as a brickmaker and limeburner in the 1830s, selling his products from a yard alongside the Albion Brewery in the Rope Walk in Rye, although it seems probable that his kilns were in the adjacent parish of Playden. His successors were still in business here in 1851 but by 1855, the yard had been moved to Mint Street. There was a brewhouse associated with the Silverhill pottery and brickyard in Hastings, which was bought in about 1839 by William Eldridge, who also owned St Leonards Brewery. The success of this venture may have encouraged him to put capital into another brickyard, this time in Battle, where he went into partnership with Thomas Stubberfield in 1851.[11]

The building industry

There was a strong traditional link between brickmaking and bricklaying. In the 15th and 16th centuries, when bricks were usually made on the site of the building in which they were to be used, both operations were probably supervised by the master builder. Subsequently a number of bricklayers found it convenient to make their own bricks. Robert Calchin, of Chailey, described himself as a bricklayer in his will made in 1690 and in 1711 his son, Richard, had two brick kilns on Chailey South Common so it seems reasonable to assume that the family were skilled in both trades. Similarly, Robert Diplock of Maresfield, who gave his trade as 'bricklayer' in 1705, was described as 'brickmaker' in 1721. Others changed their designation from brickmaker to bricklayer, suggesting that, as their business expanded, they concentrated on the construction side and employed others to do the brickmaking. In 1773 Philip Elen, of Arlington, was described as a brickmaker but 12 years later as a bricklayer and John Smith, whose family had been brickmakers on Horney Common in Maresfield for three generations, called himself a bricklayer in 1862 but continued to advertise as a brickmaker.[12]

By the 19th century, in the growing urban areas, the large-scale entrepreneur was taking over from the artisan brickmaker. Jesse Dann, of Pevensey near Eastbourne, had brickfields in the neighbouring parish of Westham, where he advertised as a brickmaker

between 1867 and 1887. He was evidently a man of substance as, in October 1867, he was elected a freeman of the Borough of Pevensey. In the citation he was described as 'brick manufacturer'. However, on the list of addresses of freemen drawn up in March 1883, his occupation was given as builder. Another brickmaker who decided to venture into building was Stephen Message, the son of a Hastings brickmaker of the same name, who bought land in Polegate in the early 1880s with a view to using it for brickmaking and subsequently for development. Unfortunately he lacked sufficient capital for the enterprise. A mortgage of £400 taken out in 1885 was increased by £300 two years later. Meanwhile more land had become available in the same area, which Message decided to buy, again with the help of a mortgage. By 1889 he had a dozen houses unsold and also unpaid bills from his suppliers, one of whom, an ironmonger in Eastbourne, was threatening to foreclose.[13]

Similar difficulties, though on a larger scale, were encountered by Frederick Cruttenden, a Hastings builder who, in 1886, had unsecured liabilities of almost £9,000. His assets of £6,565 included the lease of a 40-acre brickyard, for which he paid an annual rent of £80 and, in addition, a royalty of 1s per thousand on clamp bricks, 2s on kiln bricks and 3s on tiles, drainpipes, chimneypots and other ware. From his agreement with the landowner, it appears that he expected to make at least a million bricks per year, weather permitting. His problem was that not only had he been unable to sell the houses he had built but many of the ones intended for letting remained empty, too. Cruttenden had clearly overreached himself but other builder/ brickmakers in the area managed to survive this particular crisis. The Hughes family had an interest in three brickyards in St Leonards and two more in Hollington between about 1860 and 1905 and Peter Jenkins, another builder who was based in St Leonards, stated in an advertisement in the 1890s that he could offer a choice of bricks 'of six different yards make'.[14]

Further along the coast in Bexhill and Eastbourne, the speculative builders do not appear to have produced quite such a glut of new housing. James Peerless, an Eastbourne builder, who had his own brickfield on Seaside from around 1860, obtained a number of lucrative contracts, including a church, an hotel, a brewery and some of the buildings for Eastbourne College. In this way he avoided the pitfall of having too much money tied up in houses.[15]

Many other builders decided, for various reasons, to make their own bricks. William Wenban Smith, of Worthing, who had several brickfields in the area which he was developing between 1878 and 1899, also entered into partnership with a Horsham builder called Mills to open a brickworks alongside the railway at Southwater, south of Horsham, bringing bricks into Worthing by rail. Similarly, in Horsham itself and in growing towns such as Haywards Heath, builders took over or established their own brickyards in order to have a reliable supply of materials to hand. Members of other building trades, too, entered the brickmaking business.

James Tomsett of Bognor, for example, advertised as a carpenter and brickmaker in 1839, as did George Rumary of Heathfield between 1887 and 1907. In 1895 Jesse Finch of Haywards Heath combined the trades of builder and contractor, plumber and gas-fitter and clamp brickyard proprietor.[16]

Timber merchants, especially, often saw an advantage in involvement with brickmaking. They, like the brewers, had capital to invest and this was what many of the brickmakers too often lacked. Joseph Jeffery, of Cuckfield, traded as a timber merchant and brickmaker in 1845 and James Walder, a Hastings timber merchant and builder, took over the Silverhill works in 1879 and later set up a new brickworks and pottery in Crowhurst. These men already possessed heavy waggons, to transport their timber and yards in which to store it and an additional interest in brickmaking meant that they were able to offer a complete service as builders' merchants.[17]

Other urban trades

The possession of carts is one of the reasons why some brickmakers also traded as coal merchants. The coming of the railways and the introduction of coalburning kilns in the mid-19th century meant that the horse and cart had a role to play, both in conveying bricks to the station goods yard for dispatch by train and in collecting supplies of coal and coke for the brickyard. Some brickmakers employed a carter to do this work but others acquired their own carts and extended their activities to include the sale of coal for domestic consumption. Uriah Clark, of Hellingly, was primarily a potter and brickmaker, who went into business as a coal merchant as a sideline, as did Albert Adams, who took over an established brickyard in Sidley, near Bexhill, in the 1870s. On the other hand, William Beeney was a coal merchant, who opened a brickyard alongside his coal depot at Hailsham station in the late 1850s and another, also near the station, at Polegate some years later. Frederick Tree, a Hastings coal merchant, acquired a brickyard in Hastings in the 1840s and leased another in Battle in the late '50s. He not merely sold coal but also shipped it from the Tyne.[18]

By the late 19th century, some brickmakers were advertising very extensive lists of the materials they could supply and the services they could offer. Thomas Rich, a Hailsham builder who had a brickyard at Hawklands on the outskirts of the town, also traded as undertaker, wheelwright and shoeing and general smith and George Box, of Ardingly Potteries (see advertisement) had a similar range of activities. Others advertised as house decorators, sanitary and hot water engineers, monumental masons and even as bell hangers. Men such as these, although they may be classed as brickmakers, were no longer skilled operatives themselves; they were employing others to work on their behalf.[19]

THE ARDINGLY POTTERIES AND BRICK WORKS.

GEORGE BOX,

Contractor and Timber Merchant

ARDINGLY, SUSSEX.

FLOWER PANS AND SEED PANS IN ALL SIZES.
LAND DRAIN AND SOCKET PIPES.
PLAIN AND WIND-GUARD CHIMNEY POTS, HIGH-TOP RIDGES, TERMINALS, &c.
ALL KINDS OF FENCING SUPPLIED OR FIXED IN ANY PART.
All kinds of Oak Sills and Scantling Cut by Steam to any Length and Size.
Steam Sawing done for private gentlemen as well as the trade.
Manufacturer of all kinds of Plain and Ornamental Bricks, Tiles, Drain Pipes, &c.
COACH BUILDER AND WHEELWRIGHT.
Plumber, General House Decorator and Undertaker.

15. George Box's advertisement of 1885

6. COASTAL DEVELOPMENT IN THE 18th AND 19th CENTURIES

In the early years of the 18th century, the population along the coast of Sussex was relatively low. The ports of Rye, Hastings and Seaford were in decline, as was the town of Brighton and elsewhere there were a few small fishing villages but no settlements of any size. In consequence, there was little new building taking place. In the Hastings area many houses were still timber framed, although roofs were now generally tiled. In the neighbourhood of the Downs, on the other hand, the traditional building material was locally-gathered beach and field flint, although small quantities of brick were used for bonding courses and for quoins and architraves.[1]

Georgian brick

Big changes came about when first Brighton and then the other coastal resorts began to develop. It was found to be both cheaper and quicker to build wholly in brick and, furthermore, brick was again in fashion. In towns such as Chichester and Lewes there were existing local yards to supply materials for the elegant town houses being built, or refaced, in brick but in Brighton there was no established industry and the way was open for a new type of entrepreneur to set up in business.

A band of brick earth south of the Downs provided suitable material and the Wick estate, which lay partly in Brighton and partly in the parish of Hove to the west, became the main centre of brickmaking. In 1722 the owner, Thomas Scutt, had made an agreement with the builders of Stanmer House whereby he was 'allowed 9d per thousand of all the Bricks that should be made at Brighthelmston… for the Earth the Bricks were to be made of & £5 per annum besides for the use of a Barn to keep in materials & a guinea & half per annum for the use of the ground to make and burn the Bricks upon'. In addition, Scutt was paid for the carriage of bricks and timber and for digging and carrying loads of clay to the site at Stanmer. Realising the profit to be made, he must have decided to embark on brickmaking on his own account as, in 1725 and 1726, he was also paid for bricks supplied, thus laying the foundation of a family business which grew as the town of Brighton expanded.[2]

The development of Brighton as a seaside resort began in the 1750s and by the 1770s, when building was proceeding rapidly, another Thomas Scutt was supplying bricks to the developers. From at least 1778, he was in partnership with Richard Kent, a speculative builder, but in 1790 this partnership was dissolved by mutual consent and henceforth the two men each had their own yard. This was a period when, because of the threat from across the Channel, large numbers of soldiers were encamped near Brighton. Pressure on accommodation for visitors in the resort was acute and this led to a severe shortage of building materials. Balls and assemblies, of the kind described by Jane Austen in *Pride and Prejudice*, were a feature of the 'season' and an amusing survival from one of these functions is a lady's fan, decorated with a sketch of the lay-out of Brighton Camp in 1793. This shows not only the location of the camp itself but also two groups of brick kilns north of the coast road to the west of the town.[3]

Meanwhile, the success of Brighton as a resort had led to attempts to attract visitors for sea-bathing elsewhere along the coast. Some expansion took place in Hastings, where, as in Brighton, local landowners were to the forefront in providing facilities for brickmaking. In 1766 there were two brick kilns on the estate of John Collier in Halton, on the east side of the town and Edward Milward's Priory Kiln was in operation by 1773. In Worthing, which before this time had been merely a hamlet in the parish of Broadwater, brickmaking made its appearance on the common in the 1770s, heralding the expansion which was to follow and some resort facilities were also being developed in Littlehampton.[4]

Further west, Sir Richard Hotham, a London hatter, set out to create a completely new resort at Bognor. In 1787 he bought land in the parish of South Bersted and drew up plans for the Dome and elegant terraces, intended to rival those of Brighton. Initially the bricks were acquired from yards in the neighbourhood, principally the one on the Duke of Richmond's estate at Westhampnett. This brick-yard's accounts show that receipts for bricks and tiles sold in the 1780s were never more than about £500 but in 1791 they doubled to £1,009 3s 3d and this can only have been because of the development taking place in Bognor. Subsequently Sir Richard set up his own limekiln and brickyard and even boasted that his bricks were superior to those of the Duke but after his death in 1799 work ground to a halt, the estate was broken up and further expansion did not take place until a much later date.[5]

Supplies of fuel

Whereas the Weald had abundant supplies of wood for firing kilns, the coastal plain was less well-endowed, especially in its narrowest part around Brighton. To begin with, the fuel generally used in the brick kilns here was the one traditionally employed in limeburning, namely furze. This grew naturally in the district and provided the kind of fierce heat required. The area of the Wick estate occupied by the Brighton brickyards was the part nearest to the coast, south of present-day Western Road. To the north of this lay the furze fields where fuel was gathered, a name perpetuated in the road still called Furze Hill. As demand for bricks increased, this source of fuel was clearly inadequate. By 1777, a carrier was 'bringing furze for Mr. Scutt from Rottendean' and brushwood faggots were carried from as far afield as Offham north of the Downs.[6]

The obvious alternative was coal, brought by sea and landed on the beach near the kilns, but this was expensive. As early as 1723, Henry Hill had used coal-fired kilns to make bricks in Brighton and Newhaven for the building of Stanmer House and the agreement stipulated that he should be responsible for furnishing the 'coals' himself. However, as the supplies of furze and underwood became depleted and had to be carried from ever greater distances, their cost, too, increased. By 1792 the shortage was so acute that brickmakers in Lewes and even on the Dicker were turning to coal and finding that this proved more economical to use.[7]

It is not known whether the design of the coal-burning kilns of this period

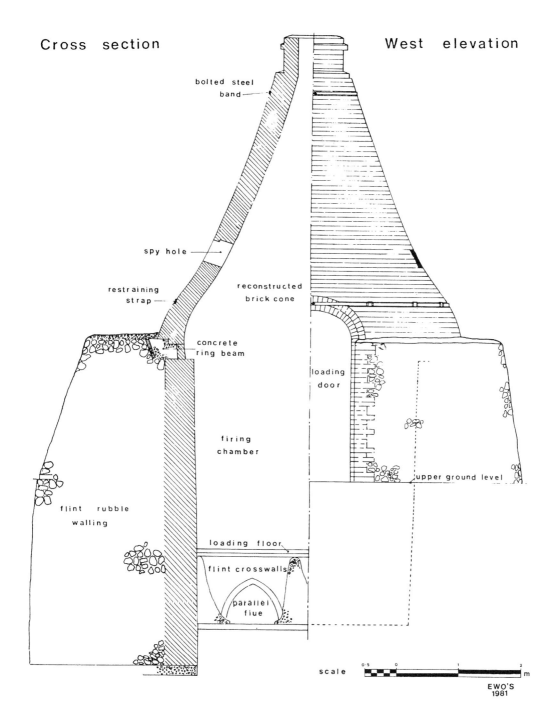

Cross section West elevation

bolted steel
band

spy hole

restraining
strap

reconstructed
brick cone

concrete
ring beam

loading
door

firing
chamber

flint rubble
walling

upper ground level

loading floor

flint crosswalls

parallel
fiue

scale

EWO'S
1981

16. Restored 19th-century tile kiln at Piddinghoe

47

differed materially from that of the woodburning ones used in the Weald. Some modification would have been required when a brickburner switched to a different type of fuel and it seems probable that this took the form of a conical extension to the usual wealden-type kiln, to help regulate the draught. A watercolour of Shoreham, painted by J.M.W. Turner in about 1830, shows a circular kiln near the coast in Portslade and photographs of kilns at East Preston and Poling, taken in the early years of the 20th century, reveal structures of a similar type. As the coastal areas used for brickmaking were all subsequently redeveloped, no traces of the kilns used at this period have been found but the recently-restored 19th-century tile kiln at Piddinghoe was probably of the same basic design, although on a smaller scale.[8]

Coal could also be used to burn bricks using an open clamp instead of a kiln. This had been tried, unsuccessfully, in Brighton in 1722 and was almost certainly the method adopted when large quantities of bricks had to be produced at short notice for the building of the Martello Towers in 1805.

Coastal defences

The Sussex coast had always been vulnerable to attack and fortifications had to be built, or repaired, whenever the threat was renewed. In 1759, during the Seven Years' War, a new battery was constructed on the seafront in Brighton and problems were encountered in obtaining 120,000 well-burnt bricks for the purpose. Brickmaking was a seasonal activity and the manufacturers did not carry over a large stock of bricks from one season to the next. In addition, several weeks had to be allowed at the beginning of each season for bricks to dry naturally in the open air before they were ready for firing and so it was usually impossible to obtain large quantities at short notice. Further batteries, or small forts, were erected at various points along the coast in 1795, by which time the local brickyards were stretched to capacity. Therefore, when Napoleon was massing his forces for invasion in 1804, a fresh solution had to be found.[9]

The decision was taken to build a string of forts, later known as Martello Towers, along the coast of Kent and Sussex. Some bricks were brought by barge from London to enable building operations to get under way but measures were taken to make the majority of the bricks – at least 500,000 for each tower – adjacent to the sites. Throughout 1805 and continuing into the following season, there was feverish activity on at least six 'brickgrounds' along the coast between Eastbourne and Winchelsea. Contractors and moulders were recruited, local landowners were obliged to make land available both for brickmaking and for the towers themselves and some 32 million bricks were produced for the towers between Rye and Seaford and the larger redoubt at Eastbourne. Some of the bricks made in Eastbourne appear to have been kiln-burnt but it seems fairly clear that, for such quantities to have been produced in the short time available, clamp-burning must have been the technique generally adopted.[10]

Clamp-burning

This was a method which had been employed by some of the Tudor

48

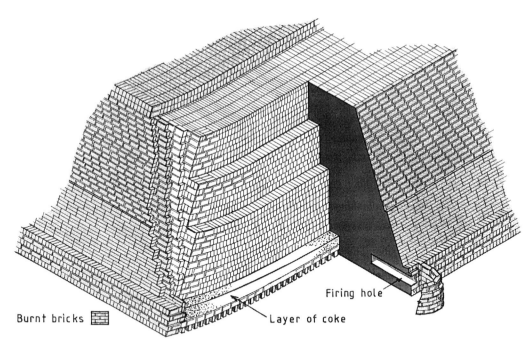

Burnt bricks

Firing hole

Layer of coke

17. Open clamp before firing

brickmakers but had not subsequently been much used in Sussex. Unlike a kiln, a clamp did not require a permanent structure. It consisted of an open stack of green (unfired) bricks built up in layers, with airspaces left between them, on top of a bed of fuel. The bricks themselves also contained a proportion of fuel which had been incorporated with the brick earth before moulding so that, once the clamp was set alight, they became self-burning. The clamp, which might contain from 50,000 to 250,000 bricks, was then encased either with turf and clay or with under-burnt bricks from a previous firing, set alight at one end and left to burn until all the fuel was consumed.

The advantage of this method was that much greater quantities of bricks could be produced and at a reduced cost. There were, however, a number of drawbacks. In adverse weather conditions, losses might be considerable. Too high a wind could raise the temperature so that the bricks became warped and over-burnt and, in the hottest part of the clamp, fused into a solid mass. Conversely, insufficient heat resulted in under-burnt bricks, which were too soft for most purposes. In consequence, even after the technique of clamp-burning had become better understood and 'clamp bricks' the main product of most of the brickmakers along the coast, 'kiln bricks' continued to be made in some yards and were often specified for the best building work.

At various times coal, ashes and coke were all employed as fuel for clamp-burning, depending on availability and cost. The most economical of these in the 19th century was 'town ash', domestic refuse which contained a high

49

proportion of cinders and other combustible material. On arrival at the brickfield, this was first sorted to remove unsuitable material such as scrap iron, then passed through a screen to separate the finer ash from the coarser cinders. The ash was added to the heap of brick earth which had been dug ready for brickmaking and the cinders were put on one side to form the bed on which the clamp was built. As the calorific value of some of this material was not very high, it was sometimes supplemented by coal and slack (coal dust). Later, when gas works were established in the coastal towns, coke became available and was widely used, the finer 'breeze' being incorporated with the earth before moulding and a bed of coke used to form the base of the clamp.

To begin with, the town corporations were only too glad to dispose of their refuse to any brickmaker who was prepared to cart it away. Then, as the numbers of brickmakers increased, competition for the available material grew and a charge was imposed. In a letter written in 1839 to the Brighton Commissioners, William Lillywhite, the cricketer, who had formerly been a brickmaker but by then had retired to become the landlord of the Royal Sovereign Inn, expressed the opinion that '11s 3d per chaldron and probably much more' could be charged for 'Ashes' as, by then, there was a demand for them from the railway company as well as the brickmakers.[11]

Mathematical tiles

It was possibly the poor quality of some of the earlier clamp-fired bricks which led to the popularity, particularly in Brighton, of mathematical tiles. In other towns, such as Lewes and Rye, these specially-shaped tiles were used as an alternative to weatherboarding or plain tile-hanging for covering the facades of timber-framed houses. The way in which they overlapped provided good weather-proofing and the fact that the finished result had the appearance of brick led to their being quite widely used in towns, where it was important to follow fashion and the fashion in the Georgian period was for brick. However, in Brighton there were few old buildings to be refaced in this way. Here the tiles were used to clad the facades of terraces of new houses as an integral part of the design. Both red and black-glazed mathematical tiles were used, the latter being particularly favoured on the seafront, where they afforded good protection from the weather.[12]

Another virtue of these tiles was their lightness, as they could be used on timber-framed bays where solid brickwork would have been too heavy for the structure. As there was no suitable material available, they were not made locally but brought from brickyards situated on the Gault or the Weald Clay north of the Downs. The black-glazed tiles were produced mainly in 'potteries' at Chailey and Ditchling and on St John's Common. Here again their lightness proved an advantage, as this reduced transport costs, tiles occupying half the space and weighing very much less than the equivalent quantity of bricks.

It is sometimes asserted that using mathematical tiles was a means of evading the Brick Tax which was in force between 1784 and 1850. However,

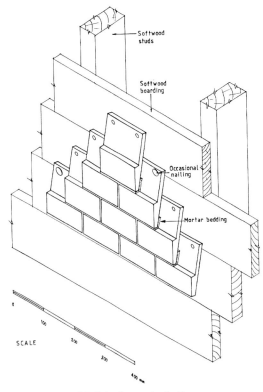

Labels on figure: Softwood studs; Softwood boarding; Occasional nailing; Mortar bedding; SCALE 0 100 200 300 400 mm

18. Mathematical tiles

examples have been found in Sussex dating from as early as the 1730s and, as tiles were subject to the tax as well as bricks until 1833, this theory has little justification. The popularity of mathematical tiles was mainly due to their suitability for the architectural style of the period and the latest building on which they were used in Brighton was built in 1848.[13]

The Brick Tax

The Brick Tax, first imposed in 1784 at the rate of 2s 6d per thousand for bricks and 3s for tiles, did not affect demand at the outset. The population was rising and with it the need for housing, which had to be satisfied. The duty was increased in 1794, and again in 1797, to help pay for the French wars.

At the same time the price of bricks, which was around 18s per thousand before the imposition of the tax, had escalated as a combined result of the increased duty and heavy demand. The peak was reached in 1805, when the duty was raised yet again to 5s 10d per thousand and the price reached about 55s. Then followed the inevitable slump. Even before the Martello Towers were completed, the threat of French invasion was removed, the soldiers quartered in Sussex were dispatched to fight in the Peninsular War and the bottom fell out of the market for bricks.[14]

Up to this point the brickmakers had been cushioned against the effects of the Brick Tax by the size of their profits but now these had to be cut to the minimum and the burden of the tax began to be felt. Complaints grew louder and tiles were exempted from duty in 1833 but the Brick Tax was not finally repealed until 1850. The amount of duty to be paid was calculated when bricks were at the 'green' stage, that is before firing. If they were subsequently damaged, or remained unsold, the loss was borne by the brickmaker, who had no redress. The experiences of two inland brickmakers will serve to illustrate these problems. In 1838, Henry Michell, who had a brickfield at Three Bridges in Worth, recorded in his diary:

The very elements seemed to have conspired against brick making this summer; large quantities were washed down in the hack and the fires were put out in the clamps before the bricks were sufficiently burned. This, of course, was a great loss as there was then a duty on bricks of 5s. 10d. per 1,000 and I paid nearly £500 duty for the summer of 1839. It was altogether most discouraging.

James Goldsmith, a Warbleton farmer who also ran a small brickyard, was prosecuted for non-payment of tax due on bricks he had made in 1849, the last year in which the tax was levied. The sum involved may appear small today: £3 18s 9d due on 12,000 small bricks and 500 large bricks (over 150 cu. ins in volume) plus a fine of £15 imposed by the magistrates at Battle, but it was enough to drive Goldsmith out of business.[15]

The resorts in the 19th century

Nearly all of the brickmakers, who had multiplied and prospered when demand for bricks was high in the period up to 1805, were now feeling the effects of the recession. Obliged to reduce their prices and in some cases burdened with heavy mortgages, a number were forced out of business and several were declared insolvent. These included William Sweetingham, a brickmaker in Lancing, who was forced to sell his brickyard to satisfy his creditors in 1810 and Thomas Budgen, a Brighton builder, who was also the tenant of one of the brickyards at Wick. He was declared bankrupt in 1811 with liabilities of £2,500.[16]

It is difficult to estimate how many brickyards were in operation at this period but some help is provided by the directories which began to be published towards the end of the 18th century, listing the names of tradesmen and the services they offered. The first brickmakers to advertise in this way in Sussex were: Samuel Gutsell, of Battle, George Sharp and [ ] Sweetenham of Brighton, William Blunden of Goring and Thomas Wicks of Worthing, whose names appeared in the *Universal British Directory* of 1798. It is significant that four out of five were in coastal locations but it is clear that by no means all of the brickmakers in business, even in the coastal towns, were as yet attuned to the idea of advertising. Numbers increased in the various directories published in the 19th century, notably Pigot's *London and Provincial Directory*, which contained entries for brickmakers from 1832 onwards and the *Post Office Directories* published from 1845. By 1832, the number of Sussex brickmakers who advertised had increased to 20 and were distributed across the county from Rye to Walberton in the south and from East Grinstead to Petworth in the north and by 1845, this number had doubled. The idea that 'it pays to advertise' had clearly caught on but there were always a number of brickmakers who were content to supply purely local requirements and therefore saw no need to spend money on advertising.

The increased number of brickmakers advertising in the 1830s and '40s nevertheless reflects the revival in the building industry which had by then taken place. Along the coast, building had slowed for a time after 1805 but had never stopped completely. In Brighton, royal patronage gave fresh impetus to the development of the resort. The population increased from 7,339 in 1801 to 24,400 in 1821 and new suburbs spread into the open fields surrounding the old town. Worthing, which had acquired a Town Charter in 1803, began to expand again in the 1820s and brickyards sprang up north of present-day Marine Parade and in the area known as Navarino along the Brighton road. In 1828 Decimus Burton began work on the new town of St Leonards, west of Hastings. Here, some brickmaking took place on the strip of flat land near the coast but, because of the sloping nature of most of the site, supplies of bricks could easily be transported from both new and existing brickyards in the districts of Bohemia and Silverhill behind the town. Elsewhere growth was fairly slow. There were signs of revival in Bognor and houses were being built in the Seahouses district of Eastbourne but in general fresh momentum had to await the arrival of the railways in the second half of the century.[17]

The location of the brickfields

Although not invariably the rule, the term 'brickyard' implied the presence of a kiln, whereas a site where clamp-burning was practised was usually referred to as a 'brickfield'. Such brickfields were often very short-lived. A property developer would acquire land, establish a brickfield close to the site where he intended to erect the first houses and then, when the supply of brick earth became exhausted, move the brickfield to another part of the site and build on the area which it had previously occupied. By the 1830s, the part of the Wick estate which lay in Brighton had been redeveloped in this way and the brickfields had moved westwards into Hove. In turn these, too, were replaced by houses and squares and the brickfields were pushed further west into Aldrington and Portslade.

The same pattern was repeated later in nearly all of the coastal towns. In Worthing, also situated close to the Downs, movement was both eastwards into the Navarino district of Broadwater and westwards into the parishes of Heene, West Tarring and Durrington. In Eastbourne, where Beachy Head blocked any development to the west, the brickfields, followed by the housing estates, moved north-east into Willingdon and the Langney area of Westham. In Littlehampton, the main brickmaking area was to the north around the hamlet of Wick and in Bognor, where large-scale development did not take place until the 20th century, the widespread availability of brick earth eventually led to brickfields springing up behind the town, in North Bersted, as well as along the coast in Felpham to the east and Pagham to the west.

However, this gradual dispersal of the brickfields, towards the perimeter of the towns did not always proceed rapidly enough for some of the residents. Whereas, in country areas, brickyards probably did not constitute a particular nuisance, as many of them were on the commons or tucked into a corner of a farm or an estate, away from the main centres of habitation, in the expanding seaside resorts, the proximity of a kiln or a clamp was sometimes the cause of conflict between the brickmakers and the more genteel inhabitants.

In September 1846 a group of Brighton residents sent the following petition to the Town Commissioners:

We the undersigned Inhabitants of Brighton beg leave to inform you that a certain kiln for the burning of bricks has been set up in the parish of Brighton on the South side of the Road leading from the London Road towards the Horse barracks in which bricks or tiles have been and are now continually burnt the smoke and effluvium of which kiln is a great annoyance and injurious to us destroys the comfort of our respective habitations and is a public nuisance; we therefore respectfully request you will adopt such measures as will cause the nuisance to be abated as soon as possible.

Similarly in St Leonards, a running battle was fought in 1856 between the residents of Warrior Square and one Charles Moreing. In April the residents complained that Moreing was preparing to burn bricks in the square itself and the Town Clerk cautioned him against causing a nuisance. Moreing's reply was to request permission to burn 'one experimental clamp' but this was refused. Nonetheless he went ahead and in June was told he must not continue. That order, too, appears to have been ignored as, in October, the local Board of Health was still discussing the matter. A little later, a similar situation arose in Eastbourne. A local worthy, whose memoirs were published in 1903, congratulated himself on having put a stop to brick-burning in the centre of the town by writing letters to the press. The environmental lobby had been born.[18]

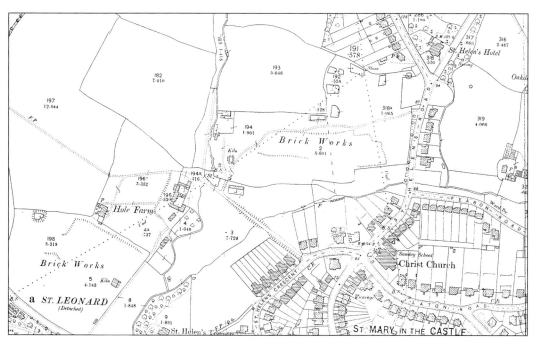

19. Brickworks on the outskirts of the expanding town of Hastings (OS Sheet LVIII/14 1899)

7. THE IMPACT OF THE RAILWAYS ON BRICKMAKING

Up to the middle of the 19th century, the increasingly widespread use of brick as a building material had relied on the proliferation of relatively small brickyards in the areas where there was a demand. When demand exceeded supply, several expedients had been adopted. Some bricks and tiles had been carried from the Weald to the coast but, as has already been shown, the limited capacity of the horse and cart and the high costs incurred precluded the movement of large quantities of material in that way.

Water transport

Transport by water was cheaper and coastwise shipments of bricks were made from Lancing, Worthing, Littlehampton and even as far afield as Hampshire, to the Brighton area, the bricks being landed either directly on the beach or, taking advantage of the shelter afforded by the Adur estuary, at Copperas Gap in Portslade. The Mr Sweetenham who advertised as a brickmaker in Brighton in 1798 was, in all probability, William Sweetingham who acquired an interest in a brickyard in South Lancing in 1805, no doubt with a view to shipping the products along the coast to Brighton. Later in the 19th century, firms such as Pepper & Sons and John Eede Butt, of Littlehampton, built up a trade in bricks for the Brighton area from yards on the River Arun and even into the 20th century the latter had a depot at Baltic Wharf in Shoreham Harbour.[1]

Some use was made of river transport but there are few records to show how extensive this was. There were a number of brickmakers in Barcombe, a thinly populated parish on the west bank of the River Ouse, from the end of the 16th to the middle of the 19th centuries and it seems reasonable to suppose that the majority of their bricks were sent by barge down the river to Lewes. In the latter part of the 18th century efforts were made to improve navigation on all of the main rivers in Sussex and in some cases the immediate effect of this was to create an extra demand for bricks for the construction of locks and bridges. On 26 July 1790 the following advertisement appeared in the *Sussex Weekly Advertiser*:

> RIVER OUSE NAVIGATION
> BRICK-MOULDERS
> WANTED IMMEDIATELY
>
> A NUMBER of BRICK-MOULDERS to mould a large quantity of Bricks this season, to whom good encouragement will be given, by applying to Mr. PINKERTON at the Bear Inn, Lewes. N.B. Moulders will be found a good job in the winter and brickmaking again next season.

As the work progressed, payments were made to the owners of the land for brick earth dug at locations such as Barcombe Mill and Freshfield Bridge and ultimately the river was made navigable as far inland as Balcombe Wharf. Bricks were not specifically mentioned in the list of tolls charged but the general rates were 1d and 1½d per ton/mile and, given the demand for bricks at this period, it is probable that yards in the vicinity of the river took some advantage of the new facilities.[2]

In Lewes, a brickyard was in operation on a site adjacent to the river in the first half of the 19th century and at Piddinghoe, in the Lower Ouse Valley, the existence of a wharf alongside the brickyard shows that the bricks and pottery made there were destined for shipment either up-river to Lewes or down to Newhaven and along the coast to Brighton. Further east there were brickyards, with adjacent wharves, on the River Brede in Westfield and on the Eastern Rother in Beckley, whence bricks could travel down to Rye. Perhaps the most strategically placed yard for both river and canal transport was the one at Harwoods Green in Stopham, on the River Arun. This brickyard was already in existence when new plans were drawn up for the Arun Navigation in 1820 and bricks could be sent by barge northwards to Pallingham Quay to link with the Wey and Arun Canal as well as downriver to Pulborough and, via Hardham Tunnel, to Arundel and beyond.[3]

However, the canals came late to Sussex and were soon to be superseded by the railways. It is ironic that probably the largest number of bricks to be transported via the Ouse Navigation were those destined for the construction of the viaduct to carry the London to Brighton railway across the Ouse valley at Balcombe. This magnificent structure of 37 arches measured 450 metres in length and required over 11 million bricks.[4]

Building the railways

As had been the case with the Martello towers over thirty years earlier, the enormous quantities of bricks required by the builders of the railways were beyond the capacity of local brickyards, although a few enterprising people did foresee the demand and established brickmaking operations in strategic positions. One of these was Henry Michell, the Horsham brewer, who bought land in Three Bridges in 1838 and in the following year, when work was in progress on the line from London to Brighton, opened a brickfield. However, being inexperienced in the business of brickmaking, he encountered all manner of problems. His foreman cheated him, adverse weather conditions interfered with brickmaking and, as he recounted in his diary, 'the Railway contractors would not buy my bricks till they were compelled to do so, or let their works stand still.' In fact he made a loss of several hundred pounds on the first season and the brickfield only began to show a profit later, when the line was in operation.[5]

From Michell's experience it is clear that the railway contractors preferred to make their own arrangements for the supply of the bricks needed for tunnels, cuttings, viaducts, bridges, stations and other buildings. Temporary brickfields were set up along the line, for example at Balcombe on the Brighton line. Here material excavated to form the tunnel was utilised for brickmaking, as well as earth dug from a series of pits along the top the tunnel. The bulk of the bricks so made were then used to line the tunnel and in the construction of the viaduct. It is possible that the brickyards already in existence on St John's Common in Keymer supplied some of the bricks for the section of the line from Cuckfield southwards, which included Valebridge viaduct, the long tunnel through the Downs at Clayton and the shorter one at Patcham, as well as the 27-arch London Road viaduct in Brighton but it is likely that the majority were made, as elsewhere, alongside the line and

20. Valebridge viaduct on the Brighton line south of Haywards Heath

moved by rail to the point where they were required.

The Brighton line, completed in 1841, was the first railway link between London and the Sussex coast. By the late 1840s the network had been extended westwards to Chichester and eastwards via Lewes to St Leonards. The South Eastern Railway line from Tonbridge to Hastings, which linked with the coastal line at St Leonards, was opened in 1852. This included tunnels at Wadhurst and Mountfield, where the excavated material again supplied the necessary brick earth. In the Hastings area in particular, the nature of the terrain necessitated the production of large quantities of bricks. Bo-peep tunnel at St Leonards, which is 1,205 metres long and Hastings tunnel (720m) are said to

have required 16 million bricks between them. To these must be added Mount Pleasant tunnel (210m) and Ore tunnel (1,282m) on the line into Hastings from Rye. Existing brickyards were utilised near the western entrance to Bo-peep tunnel and at Bunger Hill, north of the site of the later station at Ore, but the contractors again relied mainly on temporary brickfields along the line, using earth excavated from the tunnels. Even so, there were insufficient bricks and more were brought in by rail from the Lewes area and by sea from Dover.[6]

In West Sussex, on the other hand, the lines mainly ran over the relatively level ground of the Low Weald and utilised natural gaps in the Downs and so required few of the major tunnels and viaducts which characterised the lines in the east of the county. The demand for bricks was correspondingly smaller and may well have been met by the existing local yards shown on some of the railway plans, for example the one at Fishbourne, marked on the plans of the Chichester to Portsmouth line in 1844 and the one in Pulborough, shown on the Mid-Sussex Railway plans of 1856-7. However, the line from Midhurst, built in the 1870s to join the south coast line near Chichester, tunnelled through the chalk at Cocking and Singleton and several temporary brickfields were set up on the Gault Clay alongside the line north of Cocking.[7]

New lines continued to be built until the turn of the century. Some schemes, such as the Ouse Valley railway, proved abortive but not before brickmaking had begun alongside the proposed line in Lindfield and Ardingly. In 1880 work began on the line from Lewes to East Grinstead, later known as the 'Bluebell Line' and, following the usual pattern, land was acquired for a brickfield at the southern end of the line at Barcombe. Two years later, for Imberhorne Viaduct outside East Grinstead, 'typical rich red brick was fashioned by the navvies at kilns near their encampments'. The last of the many brick viaducts to be built in Sussex was the one at Crowhurst on the branch from the Hastings line to Bexhill West station, built between 1898 and 1900 but demolished in 1969.[8]

The Scotch kiln

The majority of the brickfields set up alongside the railway lines were of a purely temporary nature and it seems probable that clamp-burning was the method generally adopted. Coal was shipped from the north-east coast and from South Wales for the purpose. In 1845, for example, Robert Plumley, a Pevensey ship-owner, wrote to his agent in Stockton-on-Tees requesting supplies of coal dust and 'the slowest-burning coals' for a client who had the contract for making clamp bricks for the 'Brighton and Hastings Rail Road'. However, to obtain the bricks of engineering quality required for load-bearing structures such as bridges and viaducts, it was necessary to use kilns. The railway contractors, in many cases, brought in brickmakers from other parts of the country and it was they who introduced a new type of kiln not hitherto used in Sussex.[9]

The Scotch kiln was a simple, brick-built structure, set on level ground. It was rectangular in shape, with a loading hatch at each end, a row of low firing holes along each side and an open top. When the bricks had been set in the kiln, the hatches were sealed and a temporary cover placed over the top in much the same way as in the type of kiln in use for so long in the Weald. The main differences were that the capacity was much greater: 40-50,000 bricks as against 20-25,000 in the Wealden-type kiln and the fuel used was coal, which could be brought in via the railway network itself. As a result, the Scotch kiln grew in popularity and was still to be found in some Sussex brickyards as late as the 1960s.[10]

The migrant workers who supplied much of the labour for the railway brickfields were drawn from a very wide area, as can be seen from examination of the population census returns for 1851. This was the first occasion on which both occupation and

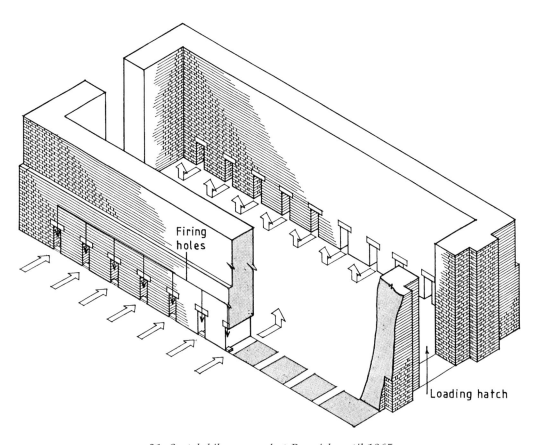

Firing holes

Loading hatch

21. Scotch kiln, as used at Berwick until 1965

place of birth were recorded. Railway-building was still taking place in Hastings and the surrounding area at this date and the census returns reveal that, although some of the brickmakers were of fairly local origin, many hailed from London and other parts of the South-East and some came from as far afield as the Midlands and the West Country. In Mountfield, for example, William Warwick, a brickmaker who had been born in Northamptonshire, was living at the Railway Brick Yard. His children, aged eight and six, had been born in Kent and Hampshire respectively, an indication of the way in which gangs of brickmakers were being

moved around the country by the railway contractors.

Many of the brickworkers, like Warwick, were living rough in huts on the sites. In Battle, George Archer, a brickmaker from Tonbridge in Kent, was living at the 'Railway Hut' and at Ore, Abraham Benham, from Clifton in Gloucestershire, gave his address as 'top of Mount Pleasant Tunnel'. In Hastings itself more than a dozen brickmakers, originating in counties ranging from Staffordshire to Somerset, were listed as living either in a hut in the brickfield or simply 'in the brickfield'. Once the work was completed, most of the brickmakers and

59

their families moved on but some remained, especially in the coastal resorts, where the arrival of the railway was followed by a new wave of development, for which large quantities of bricks were required. At the brickyard near Ore station, some attempt was made to improve the lot of the migrant workers and one of the abandoned Scotch kilns was converted into a chapel and schoolhouse.[11]

Exploiting the network

Throughout the county, brickmakers quickly became aware of the potential advantages of the railway network for the wider distribution of their products. Henry Michell, whose brickfield at Three Bridges has already been mentioned, established another yard in Horsham in 1850, expecting to do business with a local builder but found instead that his bricks were snapped up, as fast as he could make them, by outsiders, who had them carried away by rail. In 1852, when the Crystal Palace was moved to its permanent site in Sydenham, Michell supplied half a million bricks for the work. This is a little surprising, given the existence at that date of at least two brickmakers in Sydenham itself and numerous others in the surrounding area but it shows to what extent the new rail links were influencing the industry. Michell recorded in his diary that he incurred a loss over another deal with some speculative builders in Reigate but overall he made a substantial profit from the yard.[12]

This was unfortunately not the case with the Battle Abbey estate brickyard. The Webster family, who were already in dire financial straits, decided in 1853 on the bold step of re-siting the brickyard alongside the railway to the north of Battle station and equipping it with its own siding, two coal-fired Scotch kilns and new machinery including a claymill and a Beart's patent brickmaking machine. The expectation was that not only would the considerable outlay be recouped but also large profits made by sending bricks by rail to London. However, orders failed to materialise. Only one large consignment of 103,800 bricks was dispatched to a builder in Forest Hill in South London and he defaulted, leaving the brickyard with a deficit of over £1,200 at the end of 1854. This loss had to be written off and probably contributed to the decision to sell the whole estate three years later. The brickyard continued in operation until the end of the century but was never the commercial success that had been envisaged.[13]

Elsewhere, new brickyards were springing up alongside the railways, not only in places such as Horsham and East Grinstead which already had a flourishing brickmaking industry but in what had previously been isolated country districts, as well. The movement of bricks was in two directions: in the north of the county supplies were dispatched to the rapidly-expanding London market, whereas in the centre and the south they went to the resorts of Brighton, Worthing and Eastbourne, which seemed to have an insatiable demand. The advantages of proximity to the railway were stressed in the description of a cottage and workshop with a 2 acre plot of land 'close to the Brighton & South Coast Railway at Westham &

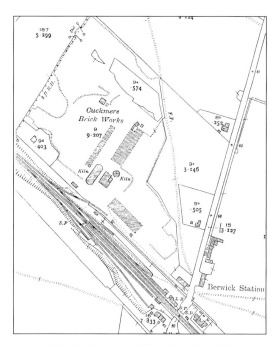

22. *Cuckmere Brickworks, Berwick*
(OS Sheet LXVIII/6 1928)

brickmaking from the 16th century. When the Keymer part of the common was enclosed in 1828, several large allotments of land were acquired by brickmakers, who set up combined brickyards and potteries, to exploit the special qualities of the clay. Proximity to Brighton was clearly an advantage and, after the opening of the railway in 1841 and the enclosure of the Clayton part of the common in 1845, business boomed. The number of people employed in the brickmaking industry increased from 48 in 1841 to 119 in 1861 and 214 in 1881. By this date there were three large potteries and eight brick fields in operation as well as the big new brickworks that had been opened at Keymer Junction in 1875. This had its own siding from the railway into the works and sent its wares both to London and the Sussex coast.[15]

The coming of the railways encouraged the growth of other new inland centres of population, such as Haywards Heath, Crawley and Crowborough, where brickyards sprang up to cater for the demand for residential development. In Haywards Heath the distribution of the brickfields followed the pattern already observed in the coastal resorts. The earliest ones, mainly owned by building contractors, occupied a fairly central position but they were soon displaced and moved to more outlying areas as the town began to take shape. Bricks for Crawley were made in yards alongside the railway at Gossops Green in Ifield to the west, and at Three Bridges in Worth to the east. Crowborough, which developed as a residential neighbourhood after the arrival of the railway in 1868, was served by a number of small brickyards

Pevensey Station', which were offered for sale in 1851. The brick earth was said to be 'of great depth and excellence' and the field was 'so contiguous to the railway that barrows can convey the tiles or bricks to the Siding'. This yard and the ones which grew up subsequently on the same line at Polegate and Berwick, all sent their products to Eastbourne, where the branch from the main south coast line had been opened in 1849, providing the impetus for new development.[14]

The growth of new towns

Meanwhile, the brickmaking industry had been largely responsible for the creation of a new town at Burgess Hill. The clay which was dug on St John's Common in the parishes of Clayton and Keymer was of particularly good quality and had been used for scattered around the district to begin with but in 1880 a new brickworks was opened on the north side of the railway line at Jarvis Brook station and as this grew in importance, its rivals declined and finally disappeared.

Re-distribution of the brickyards

The new brickworks which were growing up alongside the railway lines either had sidings leading directly into the works, as at Battle and Keymer junction, or had access to the sidings in an adjacent station goods yard. This enabled them to dispatch their products by rail and also to bring in supplies of 'town ash', coal, coke and, in some cases, sand and chalk, for use in the manufacturing process. The editions of the large-scale Ordnance Survey maps, first published in the 1870s and revised in the late 1890s, show to what extent the practice of siting new works alongside the railway was increasing. In the east of the county, in addition to the ones already mentioned, there were station brickyards at Robertsbridge and Hailsham. In the west, there was a yard at Elsted station on the line from Midhurst to Petersfield and, in the late 1890s, the Nyewood brickyard in the parish of Harting was moved to a new site alongside the railway at Rogate station. But the majority of the new brickworks were to be found along the lines of central Sussex: at Warnham and Southwater in Horsham, Partridge Green in West Grinstead, Rowfant and Crawley Down in Worth, Sharpethorne in West Hoathly and at Plumpton. All of these were 'country' locations, which offered a good supply of brick earth adjacent to the railway, an opportunity not to be missed by the Victorian entrepreneur.

Perhaps the best example of how the railway could be utilised is provided by the brickworks north of Warnham station. The Peters family, building contractors in Horsham, who had already had experience of brickmaking both in Horsham itself and at Slinfold, bought land on the west side of the line in 1888. Two sidings were built on the 'up' line, so that town refuse could be brought in for making the clamp-fired bricks and the products sent back to Horsham and beyond. In 1896 a 90-acre site was acquired on the other side of the line but three years later the business was sold and it was the new owners, the Sussex Brick Company, who put in a fresh siding on the 'down' line to bring in coal for the kilns they had erected and also take away the bricks. Between 1904 and 1927 the siding was extended and doubled, so that two rows of trucks could be marshalled each day. The trucks in the second row were loaded first, the men wheeling the crowding barrows right through the corresponding empty trucks, in the first row.[16]

Important though it was, the influence of the railways on brickmaking in Sussex in fact lasted less than 100 years. By the 1930s the peak in the use of railway transport had been passed. Steam waggons were now available to carry bricks by road direct from the works to the building site, reducing the amount of handling required and cutting out the shunting in sidings and marshalling yards which had inevitably led to a number of bricks being damaged in transit. Even firms such as the Nyewood Brick Co., with works alongside the railway, acquired their own steam waggons and the haulage firm of Penfolds transported large quantities of bricks by this method from brickfields in North Bersted (Bognor) to Brighton. Lorries had also made their appearance, even before World War 2 and after the war, the switch from the railways to road transport for the delivery of bricks became complete.[17]

Meanwhile, in the 19th century, the effect of the growth of the railway network on the existing country brickyards was not immediately apparent. The population was expanding, even in the rural areas, and the products of the traditional yards, most of which made a variety of wares including tiles and agricultural drainpipes, were still in demand. There was some rationalisation, especially in the High Weald. Parishes such as Maresfield and Ewhurst, where there had been several scattered brickyards, found their numbers reduced until only one remained but, on the whole, small-scale brickmaking continued to flourish in the country areas until at least the end of the century.

23. Warnham Brickworks in 1928 with three rows of trucks in the siding

8. VICTORIAN BRICK, TILE AND TERRACOTTA

The growth of the railway network from the 1840s onwards and the abolition of the Brick Tax in 1850 opened the way for a building boom in the second half of the 19th century. Speculative builders, who erected rows of brick terraces in the towns and brick villas in the surrounding countryside, required large quantities of material, giving rise to a big increase in the number of brickworks. The clamp and the Scotch kiln enabled larger quantities of bricks to be burnt but, as the population was expanding, there was a pool of cheap labour available for work in the brickyards and, in consequence, brickmakers in Sussex were reluctant to invest in the new labour-saving machinery which was being developed in other parts of the country.

Simple machinery: the pugmill and the pipe machine

A very early experiment may have been made at the Westhampnett brickyard where, in 1786, a payment was made to Edward Brown, 'projector of a machine for making bricks' but there was no further mention of the machine, which evidently failed to live up to expectations. Thomas Brown, a relation perhaps, was a brick-machine maker at Mark Cross, in Rotherfield, in 1851 and the Great Exhibition of that year inspired several brickmakers to install the fairly simple machines which had, by that date, become available. The experience of the Battle Abbey estate brickyard in this connection has already been recounted; the Ashburnham. estate yard bought an Ainslie's Brick and Tile Machine in 1852 but this did not prove popular and the majority of yards preferred to retain the traditional method of hand-moulding.[1]

The first mechanical device to come into general use was the pugmill for mixing clay preparatory to moulding. This consisted of a vertical shaft with several blades attached, which revolved inside a drum. Wet clay was fed in at the top, churned to the correct consistency and extruded at the base. Power was supplied by a horse, harnessed to the end of a long beam attached to the top of the shaft of the pugmill. The animal plodded steadily round in a circle and, in some abandoned brickyards, the former location of the pugmill can still be recognised from the presence of a circular beaten track on the ground. Before the development of the pugmill, loam for brickmaking and clay for tilemaking had both been tempered by hand, using a spade, or, in some of the coastal brickfields, by treading with bare feet. It is not surprising, therefore, that the introduction of the pugmill was generally welcomed. For the tilemaker, it produced a more consistent, finely-ground material, which was what he required; for the moulders of clamp bricks, which contained an admixture of ash or breeze, it incorporated the materials much more efficiently: treading a mixture of loam and cinders cannot have been a pleasant task.

The drums of the earliest pugmills were made of wooden staves, like a barrel, but these were later replaced by metal cylinders and, by the end of the 19th century, in the more modern brickyards, the horse was giving way to the steam engine. In one brickyard, at Brightling, the pugmill was driven by water-power but this method does not appear to have been adopted elsewhere.

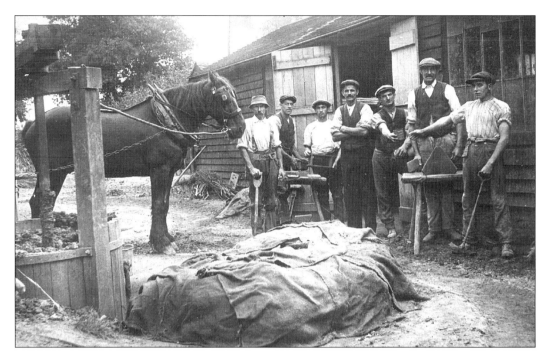

24. Typical horse-powered pugmill: the 'pugged' clay is covered with sacking to keep it moist

The earliest record of the introduction of a pugmill was again at the Goodwood estate brickyard in Westhampnett where, in 1791, Thomas Horton was paid £12 4s for work done during the year 'with the Mill Horse'. A pugmill was listed among the assets of the Brighton builder and brickmaker Thomas Budgen in 1811 and another was mentioned in a lease of the Broyle brickyard in Ringmer in 1828. On the other hand, an inventory of the yard at Guestling, near Hastings, taken in 1846, reveals no trace of any machinery: tempering there was evidently still being done by hand. After this date, however, pugmills feature regularly in inventories and valuations: there were two present at a Waldron brickyard in 1869 and by 1883 the contents of a yard at East Blatchington, near Seaford,

included pugmills which were steam-powered. In spite of this, the majority of the country brickyards and even some of the brickfields along the coast, retained their horse-driven mills well into the 20th century, probably because the horse had other uses, either on the farm or for carting fuel, clay and sand.[2]

The only other piece of machinery which was widely adopted was the drainpipe-making machine. This, like the pugmill, offered such obvious advantages that it could not be ignored. Formerly field drains had consisted of two separately-moulded parts: a flat tile, which formed the sole, with a half-round drain-tile placed on top of it. This latter, like a ridge tile for a roof, was moulded flat and then bent into shape over a wooden horse. The first machine to make its appearance was one which

25. Moulding drainpipes at Chailey in 1935

extruded pugged clay through a die, to produce a ready-shaped drain-tile but this was rapidly superseded by a pipe machine, into which different dies could be inserted to form circular drainpipes of from 1in (25.4mm) to 4in (101.6mm) in diameter. Later machines allowed for even larger pipes to be made.

The earliest evidence of a pipe machine in use is in 1846 at the brickyard on Henley Common. A price list for goods produced included, as well as drain tiles and soles, drainpipes of six different sizes. A reference to 'the price of such ware… at neighbouring yards' suggests that field-drainage schemes were being encouraged at that period and that a number of brickmakers in the district were

investing in machines to meet the demand. At the brickyard on Newhouse Farm in Ewhurst, at the other end of the county, 2in (50.8mm) and 3in (76.2mm) pipes were being made by 1853 but in many of the country brickyards, drain tiles did not give way to pipes until later. At the Ashburnham yard, for example, drainpipes were included in the list of goods sold for the first time in 1872. Quicker to invest in pipe-making machinery were some of the brickyards in or near the growing towns, where there was a demand not only for land drains but for sewer pipes as well. The latter type of ware was in production by 1858 at a brickyard at Hawkenbury (now in Kent) near Tunbridge Wells, at the Silverhill yard in Hastings and at R.

& N. Norman's works at Burgess Hill. Ten years later, a delivery note from the Rosehill estate brickyard at Brightling listed a wide variety of products from 2in (50.8mm) drainpipes to 10in (254mm) collared sanitary pipes, elbows and junctions and by the end of the century, most of the brickyards which manufactured tiles were also offering their customers a range of drainpipes.[3]

Both the pugmill and the pipe machine were fairly simple devices, which did not require a great deal of maintenance. Spare parts would be supplied and repairs carried out by a local foundry. The yard at Ashburnham bought its machinery from James Tester, of Hurst Green, who also serviced it. Tester's business was later taken over by Albert Oakley, who supplied machinery and spare parts to a number of brickyards in the Robertsbridge area. The ledgers for this firm survive, covering the years from 1878 to 1924. Dies and strainers for pipe-machines were mentioned frequently and a new grinding cylinder and bottom blade were provided for the pugmill at the Ashburnham brickyard. The ledgers also show that tile-making machines were in use in some yards in the district by the 1880s, as parts for them were sold to brickmakers in Burwash and Wadhurst and a new tile machine was supplied to a yard in Ticehurst in 1889. A foundry at West Grinstead provided a similar service for brickmakers in that locality, Everys of Lewes reconditioned some second-hand machinery which was installed in the Hamsey brickyard in 1889 and by 1899 Lintotts, of Horsham Engineering Works, were advertising as brick and tile machinery makers. Their speciality was a belt-

driven pugmill, which they continued to manufacture until the foundry closed in the mid-1950s.[4]

The first large-scale brickworks

So far the changes noted in brickmaking technology have been small-scale. Increased volume of production had resulted from the pro-liferation of quite small brickyards: often several brickmakers would congregate in one area, as on the commons at Burgess Hill and Horsham and at Hawkswood, on the boundary between Hailsham and Hellingly. Here there were five different brickmakers operating in the 1880s and 1890s, each yard having a single updraught kiln of limited capacity for firing good-quality facing bricks and tiles whilst the bulk of the bricks were burnt in open clamps. Hand-moulding and clamp-burning were also practised in the brickfields which sprang up in Plumpton from the 1870s to supply the Brighton market. One brickmaker advertised in 1874, four in 1882 and five in 1899, including the firm of E. & R. Norman, of Chailey and the Keymer Brick & Tile Co., whose main works was at Burgess Hill. In both

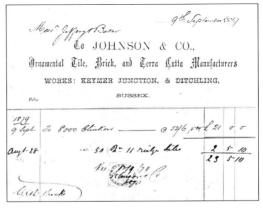

26. Bill for goods supplied by Johnson & Co.

of these cases, the brickfields at Plumpton made clamp-fired common bricks to supplement the high-quality facing bricks produced in the kilns at their other yards.[5]

However, changes were already taking place and it was the new works opened by Henry Johnson at Keymer junction in 1875 which led the way. He had also taken over the running of the existing brickyard and pottery at Ditchling Common two years earlier and both works were equipped with steam-powered machinery, steam-heated drying sheds and kilns of new designs and a capacity previously unheard of in Sussex. Henry Wolf, in one of a series of articles on Sussex industries, published in the early 1880s, stated:

> Messrs. Johnson have twelve large kilns at work, in addition to one of exceptionally gigantic dimensions, which, if completely filled, would hold about 450,000 bricks. This kiln consists of twenty-three chambers ranged in a row, broken by an angle in the middle, so as to partially enclose the large steam drying-floor. The kiln, with all its length, has only one shaft, which draws up the smoke out of all the chambers. The work of filling, firing and emptying is constantly going on in its various stages, and in separate chambers. The convenience of this arrangement is apparent.

This multi-chambered, continuous kiln was a variant of one designed by Friedrich Hoffmann and patented in 1858, in which the chambers were arranged in a circle round a central chimney. The linear arrangement adopted at Keymer seems to have been designed to make use of some of the surplus heat from the kiln to dry the 'green' bricks in the adjacent shed. Wolf continued:

Of the other kilns, three very large ones are built on a peculiar design, the invention of one of the partners in the firm. They are double-domed, self-consuming updraft kilns, capable of holding 200,000 bricks and tiles each. Each of these kilns has sixteen fire-holes. The heat produced in them, when the chimney-cap or damper is lowered, and the air-holes are stopped, is intense, and the firing is done very thoroughly.

It is less easy to visualise this type of kiln, which was evidently circular and of the intermittent variety, having to be set, fired and then allowed to cool down, before the bricks could be 'drawn' and the whole process begun again. It was probably intended for firing the more specialised products and the design may have been based on the bottle-shaped kilns used in the Stoke-on-Trent potteries. However, it seems that the Keymer version was not a complete success as these kilns were later replaced by circular downdraught ones of much smaller capacity.[6]

At all events, we have here a description of probably the first brickworks in Sussex capable of working all the year round. Sheds for the moulders to work in, covered and heated drying floors and modern coal-fired kilns made it possible for work to continue during the winter, whereas in the seasonal yards, after the last clamp of bricks had been fired and drawn in the autumn, the majority of the men were laid off, only the foreman being retained together with a few other men to dig clay in preparation for the following season. Wolf stated that the Keymer and Ditchling works together provided employment for about 300 workmen and this marked the arrival in

Sussex of brickmaking on a truly industrial scale.

Terracotta

Another feature of the brickworks at Ditchling and Keymer Junction was the production of specially-moulded bricks and terracotta to cater for the demand for ornamental bricks and tiles, which were becoming increasingly popular at this time. Terracotta was not new in Sussex. It had been used in the building of Laughton Place in the early part of the 16th century but then went out of fashion. It reappeared at the very end of the 18th century, not as a building material, but in the form of ornamental panels incorporated in church memorial plaques and tombstones. These were the speciality of Jonathan Harmer, a stonemason whose workshop was in Heathfield. The local clay, which burnt to a bright red, was his main material but some of his products were cream-coloured. Harmer had a number of designs, which he used repeatedly, including a cherub's head, a basket of fruit and flowers and an urn with rams-head handles, as well as rosettes of various kinds. He seems to have had a monopoly of this trade, which died out after his death in 1849, although members of the Harmer family continued as brickmakers in the Heathfield area for the next two or three generations.[7]

The pottery-making tradition was strong in Sussex and had long co-existed with brickmaking at a number of locations. One of the best-known firms was that of William and Richard Norman at Chailey Potteries. Their bill-head of 1828 described them as 'Manufacturers of all sorts of Bricks, Tiles and Brown Ware Pottery' and from this it was a short step to the production of more elaborate terracotta ornaments. As already noted, when restoration work was being done in 1854 at Laughton Place, replacements for some of the 16th-century terracotta cornices were supplied by the works at Chailey. But it was from the 1870s onwards that the high Victorian style of building encouraged a number of manufacturers in Sussex to turn to the production not only of chimney pots, crested ridge tiles and roof finials but often of the more elaborate moulded terracotta ornaments as well.[8]

The old Ditchling Pottery, now known as the Ditchling Terra Cotta Works, was the foremost producer of this kind of ware. A speciality was 'grotesque' finials, such as dragons and wyverns. Henry Wolf, in his contemporary account, describes the process involved:

The Terra Cotta Works are by their very nature more of an art-factory than the purely industrial brick kilns. The product requiring more perfect finish, every operation has to be performed with correspondingly greater care. The clay is thoroughly soaked and afterwards ground under rollers… . It is next shaped in moulds taken from models designed by artists kept on the premises. The model is formed of Plaster-of-Paris. From this is taken a mould of the same material, and cut up into fragments according as its shape may demand. Some moulds comprise a very large number of pieces which have to be put together with extreme nicety, and removed one by one… . When taken out of the mould the shaped pieces are left to dry for three or four weeks or more. They are then polished with a

69

piece of leather, to give them a "face". Afterwards they are placed in the kiln, carefully surrounded by seggar bricks, to keep them secure from any pressure or displacement. The heating has to be done very gradually.

Wolf goes on to list buildings in which terracotta made in Ditchling had been used. Some, naturally enough, were in Brighton but others ranged as far afield as Manchester and Dublin.[9]

Other established potteries in the district, such as those of John Gravett, W. & F. Meeds and R. & N. Norman at Burgess Hill and E. & R. Norman at Chailey, as well as ones further afield in Poling and East Grinstead, on the Dicker and in Brede, Hastings and Rye, extended the range of their wares to include some ornamental terracotta. New firms were added to the list, including the Brick, Tile, Drainpipe & Pottery Works at Bosham near Chichester, the Crowborough Brick & Terra Cotta Co. and works at Lower Beeding, Partridge Green and Ardingly. In 1883 Benjamin Ware, an Uckfield brickmaker, moved to a larger site and named his new enterprise the 'Sussex Pottery, Brick, Pipe & Tile Works'. A catalogue of his products illustrates several types of crested ridge tile, 12 different roof finials, including two examples of the wyvern pattern, some relief-patterned mural tiles, which were 9in (228mm) square and 6in (152mm) deep and intended for decoration on the external walls of houses, seven different designs of chimney pot and two free-standing urns. Other factories had a more limited range of wares, mainly confined to chimney pots, crested ridge tiles and the simpler type of finial. Like many of the other potteries, Wares also

27. Wyvern-pattern finial and crested ridge tiles on the house built for Benjamin Ware in Uckfield

produced flower pots and seed pans. These were in demand for the gardens and conservatories of Victorian villas and also in the greenhouses of the market gardens along the coastal plain of Sussex from Worthing westwards, which supplied vegetables, tomatoes and flowers for the London markets.[10]

Other new products

Fashion in Victorian times demanded a much greater variety of building products and an extended range of colours. The peg tile, with two square holes punched in by hand, was supplemented by the nib tile, with raised nibs and one or two round holes made by a hinged metal attachment at one end of the mould. New shapes of plain tile were also introduced, some for use on roofs but mainly for tile-hanging. Special moulds were designed with rounded or pointed ends to produce tiles which created scalloped and other ornamental patterns. The natural red colour of the tile was varied by the addition of manganese to the pugged clay, to achieve a darker brown shade. The different coloured tiles could then be mingled or alternated to produce various striped and mottled effects.

Similarly, bricks of different colours, were used, often in the same building. Grey headers had always been available as a natural product of wood-fired kilns but it was now possible to produce dark blue bricks in some of the newer coal-fired kilns and yellow gault bricks, some made paler by the addition of powdered chalk, were also available. As a result, many houses and also railway stations, churches and civic buildings, were built in the polychrome style favoured at this period.

Another feature of Victorian brickwork was the use of smooth-textured bricks with narrow mortar joints. Closer joints had been made possible from the late 18th century onwards by the introduction of the 'frog', a depression made in the brick by fixing a 'kick' to the top of the stock-board on the moulding table. The hollow so formed was filled with mortar, enabling less mortar to be used between courses of bricks. Some of the brickmaking machinery introduced in the latter part of the 19th century incor-porated a press, which produced the frog mechanically. Machine-made bricks, both extruded and pressed, had smoother surfaces and sharper arrises than the hand-moulded ones and for this reason became increasingly favoured by architects and builders.

It is difficult to ascertain how widely brick-making machines had been adopted by the end of the century. A certain number of brickyard inventories and valuations have survived and these suggest that, in the main, brickworks were still seasonal, employing hand-moulders, and using a minimum of machinery. However, Peter Jenkins, a Hastings builder who had an interest in several brickyards in the area, advertised both pressed and wire-cut stocks in 1899 and from the evidence provided by the buildings of the period, it appears that wire-cut bricks were being used quite extensively.[11]

The production of extruded, wire-cut bricks had been made possible by the introduction of grinding machinery to supplement the work of the simple pugmill. The brick earth was first crushed under rollers, then mixed with a small quantity of water in a grinding pan, compressed and forced through a die. Enough of this extruded material to form a brick was then cut off by means of a taut wire. Machinery of this kind must have been in use at Beauport Brickworks in Hastings by 1898, as in that year, the manager was brought before the local magistrates 'for having failed to fence the very dangerous cogwheels of a crusher. He pleaded guilty but... alleged in mitigation that his attention had never been called to the matter by any inspector'. The managers of the Keymer and the Crowborough brickworks also fell foul of the regulations governing the fencing of machinery, resulting in prose-cutions at around the same time.[12]

The peak in the number of brickyards

By the end of the 19th century, information of various kinds was being collected and published which allows

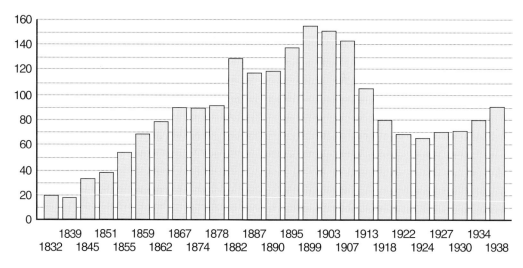

28. *Numbers of brickmakers who advertised in trades directories between 1832 and 1938*

estimates to be made both of the number of brickworks in the county and the number of people engaged in the industry. The decennial census returns, which included occupations from 1841 onwards, reveal the identity, and to some extent the numbers, of brickmakers in a given locality, although many workers in rural brickyards were almost certainly entered in the category of 'agricultural labourer'. The general statistics, published in the form of population tables, show that between 1841 and 1851 the number of workers in the brickmaking industry in Sussex nearly doubled, from 347 to 633. In 1861 there were 868 and after that the numbers rose more slowly, reaching 966 by 1891.

A study of trades directories shows that the increase in firms and individual brickmakers who advertised, already noted in the period up to 1845, was even more marked from 1851 onwards. Not only the brickmakers in the larger centres of population but also the proprietors of small country brickyards

now had their names included. The numbers continued to increase until the 1870s (see graph), when they levelled out for a time. Evidently growth had proceeded too rapidly in some areas, a fact borne out by a local street directory for Hastings published in 1876, which recorded houses standing empty on several new developments. From 1882 onwards, numbers rose again sharply and the peak was reached in 1899, when 155 brickmakers advertised in Kelly's *Directory for Sussex*. Of these, 92 were in East Sussex, where the population was expanding and the towns growing more rapidly than in the west.[13]

The revised large-scale Ordnance Survey maps, published in the late 1890s, show that by this date there were some 175 brickworks and brickfields scattered across the county, a total which was never to be exceeded. This figure is only 20 more than the number of brickmakers advertising in 1899 and the discrepancy may easily be accounted for by the fact that building contractors in the towns often had an interest in more than one brickfield and the small estate yards, which made bricks for their own requirements only, saw no reason to advertise. Comparison of these maps with the ones brought out earlier, in the 1870s, shows both the increase in the number of sites and the way in which claypits had been extended and buildings erected. The larger brickworks now had rows of sheds and several kilns whereas on most of the brickfields, only the claypit and a pond were marked, showing that operations there were still conducted in the open air and the bricks clamp-fired.

After the passing of the Quarries Act in 1894, brickworks with pits over 20ft (6.1m) deep came under the aegis of HM Inspector of Mines, who produced annual reports which throw some light on the state of the industry in Sussex. In 1897 there were only six brickworks on his list. In three of these, at Keymer, Hove (Aldrington) and Portslade, it was clearly the claypit which had reached the depth required to qualify for inclusion but in the other three: Beauport (Hastings), Filsham (St Leonards) and Washington, the deep pit was probably an associated one in which stone or sand was quarried, the brick earth still being taken from shallow pits of a depth of no more than 6ft (1.8m). Crowborough brickworks was added to the list in 1898, Hackenden brickworks at East Grinstead in the following year and by 1900, the total had reached 11, with the addition of Grange Road (Crawley Down), Rowfant (Worth) and Warnham. A new trend towards larger but fewer brickworks had been established.[14]

PITSHAM AND HENLEY BRICK YARDS.

OF A GOOD RED COLOUR.

PRESSED & DRESSED FACING BRICKS.

CLAMPS & KILNS.

PAVING BRICKS OF EX- CEPTIONAL QUALITY.

PLAIN & FANCY TILES.

RIDGES OF PATTERNS.

GARDEN EDGINGS.

DRAINING PIPES.

RUBBING BRICKS equal to FAREHAM WARE.

Apply for further Particulars to the Foreman at each Yard, or to

TALLANT BROTHERS,

BRICKMAKERS,

MIDHURST, SUSSEX,

WHO ALSO KEEP IN STOCK A GOOD SUPPLY OF THE BEST

PORTLAND CEMENT, KEEN'S CEMENT, PLASTER, GLAZED SOCKET PIPES, AND SANITARY WARE, STONEWARE SINKS, &c.

(3)

29. Tallant Brothers' advertisement of 1887

9. BRICKMAKING: A FAMILY BUSINESS

Few of the names of the early itinerant brickmakers are known but, as permanent brickyards were established from the latter part of the 16th century onwards, names begin to appear in the records. For example, Abraham Cooper, a brickmaker who was born in Framfield, had settled in Hailsham by 1579 and died there 23 years later. In 1584 another Framfield man, Austin Browning, moved to Barcombe, where he established a brickyard. In his will, made in 1603, he mentioned his son, John, who was still a brickmaker in Barcombe in 1620.[1]

The pioneers

Four generations of the Garrett family are known to have been brickmakers in Ringmer, beginning with John, who was born in about 1567 and was a brickmaker in 1623, when he gave evidence to an enquiry about the customs of the Broyle. He was a man of some substance, owning property both in Ringmer and in the Cliffe, near Lewes. He died in 1640 and the next generation was represented by William Garrett, who was fined for clay digging in 1664 and died five years later. William's son Richard was presented at the manor court for clay-digging in 1689 and after that his name appeared regularly until 1712. His son Thomas inherited a cottage and brick kiln at Rushey Green on his father's death in 1715 and must have carried on the trade, as he was presented for clay-digging in the same year, the last occasion on which such fines were recorded.[2]

Similarly, four generations of Chapmans were brickmaking in Arlington and on Hailsham Common in the 17th century. William Chapman, who was born in Rotherfield, was 50 years old before he finally settled in Arlington in 1605. In 1636, another William was married by licence and in 1649 Henry Chapman obtained permission to dig earth for brickmaking on the common. When he died in 1673, he was succeeded by his only son, another William. Five generations of

30. Part of a deposition made in 1598 by Austin Browning, who used a brick mould as his mark (WSRO EpII/5/6 f206)

Martens were brickmakers on St John's Common in Keymer between 1615 and 1736 and after this date, although no longer running the business themselves, they retained the ownership of the yard, which was leased to George Taylor, a member of another family, who were brickmakers in this area for several generations.[3]

The Denyers of Woolbeding near Midhurst also owned their own yard on the edge of Bepton Common. The contents of the house and brickyard were recorded in the probate inventory of Robert Denyer, who died in 1657 and again on the death of another Robert in 1684. William, who stood surety for Thomas, probably his son, when the latter was married by licence in 1699, was the owner of the freehold of the 'Brick Kiln House estate' in 1724 but must have been succeeded soon after this by Thomas as, when the latter died in 1730, the contents of the brickyard were included in his inventory. A fifth generation is represented by another Thomas, who was a brickburner in Woolbeding in 1743. Meanwhile the family had multiplied and moved further afield in search of employment: a brickmaker called Francis Denyer died in Kirdford in 1729, William Denyer was a brickmaker in Westhampnett in 1731 and Robert Denyer was a brickburner in Blendworth, just over the Hampshire border, in 1755. Two of the female members of the family married other brickmakers: Jane, a widow, married Richard Pearson in 1709, then in 1743 Ann Denyer married another Richard Pearson, who may have been a cousin. The Pearsons worked to begin with in the Woolbeding yard but by 1751 had established their own business on the other side of the common in Bepton, where they remained until the 1880s.[4]

Two more linked families were the Philps and the Champions, who worked as brickmakers and tilers in the Petworth area from the late 16th to the early 18th centuries. The name Philp first appears in a brickmaking context in building accounts for Petworth House in 1595. Then in 1602, John Felpe, a brickmaker from Woolavington, used his cart to deliver glass from the glasshouse in the neighbouring parish of Graffham to Arundel. This may have been the same man as the John Philp, a brickmaker who died in Poling in 1631, as the experts called in to value his goods for his probate inventory were none other than Roger Philp the younger and Robert Champion, brickmakers from Graffham. Roger Philp had performed the same service for Richard Champion, another of the Graffham brickmakers, in the previous year and when Roger Philp, a tiler, died in Graffham in 1686, one of the appraisers of his goods and chattels was Richard Philp the elder who, although he described himself as a yeoman, nevertheless used a representation of a valley tile as his mark. Altogether there are nine probate inventories extant, six for the Philps of Graffham and Poling, and three for the Champions of Graffham and Woolavington, covering most of the 17th century. Several of them are of quite high value, showing that brickmaking was flourishing at this time. Two further brickmakers, by the name of Philp were mentioned in the Petworth House accounts in 1691 and 1692 and in 1702, a Philp who was living in Petworth was approached withRout doxes in the Barne

It ap axrett of Hoy	01	10	00
In the worke house aparrell of raw tyles & brikes & & tooles there	01	00	00
It 3 vessells & 3 baggs	00	05	00
It 2 cords & halfe of woods	00	15	00

Live goods

Item one little horse & 2 small bullockes	04	10	00
It mony upon Bond	35	00	00
It ready mony in the house	19	10	00
It ap arrett of leafe land value	105	00	00
It in dangerous debts	00 1	00	00
It lumber within & without doxes	000	15	00

RRishard Philp Sum totall 187 00 10
his
marke

31. *Part of the probate inventory of Roger Philp, taken in January 1685/6 (WSRO EpI/29/93/52)*

with a view to making bricks for yet more building work at the house. Finally, over a century later, William Philp was taxed between 1805 and 1813 on the house and brick kilns in Woolbeding, which had formerly belonged to the Denyer family.[5]

Family-run brickyards in the 18th and 19th centuries

Few brickmakers seem to have served regular apprenticeships, probably because most of them entered the family business at an early age and learnt their trade in that way. Of the rare apprenticeship indentures which have been preserved, one, strangely, appears to have been a family agreement: in 1746 Robert, the son of Samuel Coney, was apprenticed to Stephen Coney of Wadhurst, brickmaker. Another is that of Thomas, the son of William Weller, a

brickmaker in Westfield, who was apprenticed in 1795 to John Eldridge, a master potter and brick-burner at Brede. The Wellers were a large family with interests in two brickyards in Westfield, a yard on Fairlight Down in the parish of Guestling and another in Ore. In addition, from 1806, a Mr Weller was the lessee of the Priory kiln in Hastings. Thomas's elder brother John inherited the Westfield brickyard (which later came into the hands of the Carrick family) and Thomas himself founded a line of potters which ran the Brede pottery and its associated brickyard until its closure around 1900. Another William Weller, probably a brother, moved to Salehurst in 1816, when he bought land at Silverhill north of Robertsbridge, on which there was an established brickyard. He emigrated to America in 1835, leaving his son, also

William, in charge of the yard and by 1841, when the economy was recovering after the agricultural depression and riots of the 1830s, this William Weller was the tenant of a second brickyard further north, at Hurst Green. The Silverhill yard closed in 1844, after which nothing more is heard of this branch of the family.[6]

The Alcorns, originally of Isfield, provide another example of a large family of brickmakers, some of whose members were obliged to look further afield for employment. The first mention of a brickmaking connection comes with the marriage of John Alcorn of Isfield, brickmaker, to Mary Davis in 1724. Twenty years later he was able to build a new house adjoining the brickyard and a brick panel in the north wall of the building, now called Greens Farm, bears the inscription:

> IOHN
> MARY ALC
> HORN BR
> ICK MAC
> KER 1744

John's brother George was also a brickmaker. He was working on Laughton Little Common in the 1750s and in his will of 1770 he left his property there to his brother's sons, John and Thomas. John Alcorn the elder died in 1775 and from his will it becomes clear that he had four sons, all of them brickmakers. George, John and Abraham were living in Isfield but Thomas had moved to Chailey, where he had taken over the brickyard of John Siffleet, who had died in 1759. It is possible that there was a family connection, as John Alcorn the elder had been one of the appraisers of Siffleet's probate inventory. The Isfield brickyard was sold to Thomas Best in 1795 and the Laughton yard, although still owned by an Alcorn, had gone out of use by 1841 but the Chailey business prospered. Thomas Alcorn died in 1815 and was succeeded by his son John, who advertised regularly from 1828 onwards. In 1835 he was named as executor of the will of Thomas Best, who had sold the Isfield yard in 1801 and moved to Hamsey. The close links which existed between the brickmaking families in this area are further evidenced by the fact that Best's daughter Mary Ann was married to Thomas Diplock, a brickmaker who worked for Alcorn at Chailey. On the census returns of 1851, John Alcorn was stated to be 75 years old, still working as a master brickmaker and employing three hands but by 1859 he had been succeeded by his nephew William, the last brickmaker in the family, who advertised until 1887.[7]

From the middle of the 18th century onwards, an increasing number of brickyards were established and most of them were family-run. Some belonged to quite substantial yeoman farmers, such as the Guys of Chiddingly. Richard Guy, first mentioned as a brickmaker in 1754, had a yard on Limekiln Farm, on the boundary between Chiddingly and Chalvington and bought another, at Millhouse Farm on the west side of the Dicker, in 1789. By this time he was working in partnership with his son Walter who, in 1800, acquired a third brickyard to the north of the others. In his will, made in 1802, Richard Guy left his share of the brickmaking business to two more of his sons, Jesse and David, but Walter Guy seems to have retained the management of it. During the slump of the 1820s he was forced to sell all three yards, but leased two of them back. 'Guy & Co.' were still the tenants of the Limekiln Farm and Millhouse Farm brickyards in 1844 but, by the late 1850s, these were under separate management, John and Thomas Guy both advertising as brickmakers on the Dicker. John's widow appears to have kept the yard at Millhouse Farm going until the mid-1880s and Thomas was succeeded at the other by his son Gaius, who continued in business until about the same date. However, these small country brickyards had by this time become uneconomic and, by 1887, John Guy's son Stephen had moved to a yard at Hawkswood on the outskirts of Hailsham, where he could supply bricks to local developers and send them to Eastbourne by rail. A final generation was represented by William Guy, who advertised as a brickmaker in the same area until the 1920s.[8]

On the east side of the Dicker, the Goldsmith family, instead of concentrating their resources into one family business as the Guys had done, tended to operate independently. In fact there were so many Goldsmiths involved in brickmaking that it is difficult to determine their relationships. In 1800, James, George, Robert and Benjamin each owned a brickyard but all had had to borrow to finance their purchases and first James, in 1811, and then Robert, were unable to pay the interest and were obliged to forfeit their property. George sold his original brickyard but continued in business as the tenant of the one vacated by James. He was succeeded by his son John but by the 1850s he, too, was in financial difficulties. The longest lived of the Goldsmith brickyards was the one

at Upper Dicker, which was in the hands of Benjamin and his descendants from 1799 until about 1900. Another family of Goldsmiths, who may have come of the same stock, had brickyards in Wartling and Warbleton and the name of Goldsmith is also to be found in connection with yards in Fletching, Uckfield, the Eastbourne area and Bexhill.[9]

Many other families carried on the brickmaking trade, though not always in the same yard, for five or six generations. The Cornfords, who had owned a small farm in Warbleton from the early 18th century, took up brickmaking at some time before 1796 and, although forced to sell their property in 1880, remained as tenants of the brickyard until World War 1. By the mid-19th century, however, the family had grown to such an extent that some of its members had to seek work elsewhere and found it at brickyards in Herstmonceux and Hailsham. The Stevenson family, who ran the brickyard on Piltdown Common in Fletching for over a hundred years, were in all probability related to the Stevensons who were brickmakers at Nutley, in the neighbouring parish of Maresfield, over an even longer period of time. The Funnells were associated in the 18th century with two of the brickyards in Chiddingly later taken over by the Guys. In the 19th century the name reappeared in Westham, where James Funnell, the senior brickmaker at Red Dyke in 1871, was followed by his son George and grandson Harry. Other members of this family also worked briefly in Hailsham, Berwick and East Blatchington.[10]

The non-conformist connection

In the 18th and 19th centuries,

artisans and tradesmen often figured prominently among the elders of the numerous dissenting congregations which grew up across the county. In this the brickmakers were no exception. Indeed, the fact that so many of the early brickyards were situated on commons, away from the main centres of population and the influence of the parish church, may account for the strong link which existed between brickmaking and religious non-conformity.

John Billinghurst, who was born in 1714 and died in 1791, was a brickmaker in Ditchling, where he was also a prominent member of the General Baptist, later known as the Unitarian or Free Christian, Church. His brickyard on Ditchling Common was over two miles north of the village and his house became the focus of the life of the local Baptist community. He appears to have had either family or business connections with a number of other brickmakers in similar locations, many of whom were also Baptists. Edward Billinghurst, a brickmaker at Wisborough Green, died in 1749, another member of the family had an interest in a brickyard on St John's Common in Clayton in the 1750s and in 1762 John himself acquired one of the yards on Chailey South Common. In this connection it is interesting to note that John Siffleet, who ran the other Chailey brickyard in the 1750s, was also a member of the Ditchling Baptist Meeting. Billinghurst, however, remained at Ditchling and leased his Chailey yard to Richard Norman, another General Baptist, who was given the chance to purchase the property under the terms of Billinghurst's will.[11]

Meanwhile another branch of the family had become established at a brickyard on Jolesfield Common in West Grinstead. Noah and Thomas Billinghurst were both working there by 1784 and in 1791 Thomas, who by this time was a deacon of the General Baptist Church in Horsham, was granted the copyhold of the brick kilns and land but in 1794 he followed the example of a number of other Baptists and emigrated to America. The brickyard was left in the hands of William Evershed, a brickmaker and potter who was also a member of the Horsham meeting. The next owner, in 1801, was Philip Kensett, another General Baptist, who married William Evershed's widow and his descendants continued brickmaking, at Jolesfield and later at Partridge Green, well into the 20th century. Kensett's brother, William, was a brick- and tilemaker at Slaugham until at least 1819 and it was this branch of the family that maintained the non-conformist tradition.[12]

After John Billinghurst's death, the brickyard on Ditchling Common was taken over by two more General Baptists, John Caffin and Francis Foster, but their partnership was dissolved in 1815. In 1820 the new owner was William Gravett, a potter from Westmeston, a member of a different group of Dissenters, who had been the pastor at Ote Hall Chapel in Wivelsfield since 1817. By 1851 he was also the minister of another Independent congregation at Yokehurst Chapel in East Chiltington. In the late 1850s he retired from brickmaking altogether, to devote his time to preaching until his death in 1872. His son John moved in 1854 to St John's Common, Keymer, where he took over the tenancy of an established pottery and brickyard and from 1872 to 1900 he was Secretary at Ote Hall Chapel.[13]

Some of the brickmakers on the Dicker, too, were active members of non-conformist sects. In 1811 a licence was granted 'for an assembly for religious worship of Protestant Dissenters in the dwelling house of George Goldsmith situate near the Dicker in the parish of Hellingly'. In 1839 the new Zoar Chapel was opened and a book recording proceedings and the names of members was begun in the same year, entry No 10 being the dismissal of S. (probably Stephen) Goldsmith for bad attendance. However, other members of the family remained loyal and George Goldsmith was interred in the burial ground there in 1849. His brickyard, which was adjacent to the chapel, had been taken over in 1845 by Uriah Clark, who was received into membership of the Zoar Chapel congregation and baptised in 1849, thus continuing the tradition. On the western side of the Dicker, in Chiddingly, the Guys belonged to a group of Dissenters of a different persuasion: the Independent Calvinists. A barn was registered as a place of worship in 1813 and in the following year a site was acquired for the construction of a chapel on the north side of the Lewes road at Lower Dicker. The names of several of the Guys figure among the founding members and also in the building accounts: Walter was paid £62 13s for bricks and tiles and Jesse received £8 due for carriage of materials.[14]

Richard Norman, a Baptist already mentioned as the successor to John Billinghurst at Chailey, was married at Ditchling in 1777 and founded what became the most widespread and successful of all the Sussex brickmaking dynasties. On his death in 1818, management of the Chailey brickyard and pottery passed to his sons William and Richard. They, in turn, handed on their shares of the business to their respective sons John and Richard. By 1882 a fourth generation, John's son, Ephraim, and his cousin, another Richard, were in charge and henceforth the firm was known as E. & R. Norman. The business survived both world wars under the control first of Ephraim's son and then of his grandson, Wallace, the last member of the family to be involved before the works was sold in 1959 to Redland Brick.[15]

In 1813 William Norman, the son of the first Richard, who was in partnership with his brother at Chailey, acquired an interest in another brickyard on St John's Common, Keymer. He moved to Clayton to supervise this expanding business and after the enclosure of the Keymer part of the common in 1828, he established a new brickyard and pottery on London Road. On his death in 1849, management passed to two of his sons by his second marriage, Richard and Nathan. This firm then traded under the name of R. & N. Norman until the works closed in the 1930s. Meanwhile, in the 1850s, another of William's sons, Thomas, moved to Lower Beeding, near Horsham, where he took over an existing brickyard at Holmbush and enlarged the range of wares to include pottery. He was later joined there by his brother Jesse and, by 1874, they had opened a second works at Southwater. However, when Thomas died about 10 years later, the Southwater works was sold. Jesse and Henry Norman were still

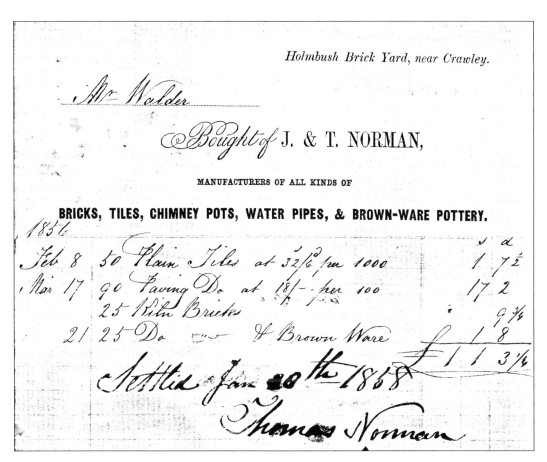

32. Bill for goods supplied by J. & T. Norman

at Holmbush in 1887 but by 1890 that works, too, was in other hands. Two other brickmakers may also have belonged to this family: John Norman, the tenant of a brickyard at Horsted Keynes in 1839 and William John Norman, who advertised at Partridge Green in the 1890s.

The migrants

Most of the families so far mentioned either owned their own brickyards or held long leases but there were many more who subsisted on short-term tenancies and for these, links are much more difficult to establish, as they were frequently on the move. Short leases were particularly common in the coastal resorts. Here one of the few families which can be traced for even three generations were the Claytons. John and his son James worked in the Brighton and Hove areas from about 1820 to 1860, then James Frederick moved along the coast, first to Southwick in the 1870s and finally to Portslade, where he remained until 1887.[17]

Further east, the Martins began as hired labourers in various brickyards in Bexhill, Hastings and Eastbourne. John Martin, who was born in Battle, was working as a brick and tile maker at

Bexhill Pipe Kiln in 1851. Five years later he moved with his family to Silverhill in Hastings. At least two of his sons followed him into brickmaking: Frederic, at the age of eight, began work with his father in a brickyard on the boundary between Hastings and Hollington and later worked with his brother James at Beauport Brickworks in the same area. Frederic then moved to Wallis's brickyard in Eastbourne, where another brother, Joseph, was employed in the building industry. By 1900 the latter, who by now had a very successful business, embarked on a new development in Hellingly, on the outskirts of Hailsham, and installed Frederic as the manager of Rucklands Brickyard, which was to supply materials for his building operations. Frederic continued to work in the yard until he was in his eighties and in 1936, received an award for 76 years service to the industry. Meanwhile, management of the brickworks had been taken over by his son Gordon, a builder, who ran it until it closed at the outbreak of World War 2.[18]

The Gealls were also builders and moved from place to place, making their own bricks wherever there was a demand for new houses. Ebenezer Geall first advertised in Burgess Hill in 1878. In the 1890s and early 1900s he and his son Henry had brick fields not only in Burgess Hill and Plumpton, supplying the Brighton market, but in South Bersted as well, furnishing bricks for the expanding resort of Bognor. From 1913 onwards, activity was centred in the Bognor area, where Henry was joined by his brother-in-law, Thomas Hawes. Hawes' son Alfred opened his own brickfield in North Bersted in 1928 and

the last of the Gealls, Harold, had a yard on Nyetimber Lane in Pagham, from just before World War 2 until about 1960.[19]

No job for a lady?

It may be thought that brickmaking was an exclusively masculine preserve but this was not always the case. The women of the family were frequently pressed into service in the yard when labour was in short supply. More importantly, a number of family businesses would not have continued for as long as they did if, at one point, a widow had not taken up the reins until such time as one of her sons was old enough to assume control. For example, Mrs Catherine Blunden ran the Poling Pottery for about 15 years in the 1860s and '70s. Her late husband, Stephen, probably came of the same family as James, William and George Blunden, who were brickmakers in Durrington, Goring and Tortington respectively from the 1760s onwards. Stephen advertised as a brickmaker in Poling in 1855 and 1859 but must have died soon after this and his son, Osmond, did not take charge of the business until about 1880.[20]

Two branches of the Gravett family had rather different experiences in this respect. Samuel Gravett of Eastbourne (no connection has been established with the Gravetts of Ditchling and Burgess Hill) was first mentioned as a brickmaker at Seahouses in 1796. In 1841 his son Samuel was the tenant of a brickyard owned by H.B. Gorringe. The Gorringes, as copyholders, were obliged to obtain licences to dig brick earth, which they did in 1849 and again in 1867 but members of the Gravett family ran the yard throughout this period. The last was Mrs E. Gravett who advertised in 1867 but shortly after this the yard went out of business. On the other hand, Mrs Gravett of Hailsham (the relationship, if any, to the Eastbourne family is unclear) whose husband William had opened a brickyard at Harebeating in about 1860, kept the business going for some 10 years after his death, until her son William took over in 1903.[21]

A crucial role in the development of one family business was played by Mrs Nightingale of Horsham. Nightingale and Butcher advertised as brickmakers on the Common in 1832 and Moses Nightingale was working there in 1844. T. Nightingale followed in the 1850s but then Mrs M. Nightingale, who was either his widow or his mother, ran the business for several years. In the mid-1860s she was able to hand over to the partnership of J.D. & J. Nightingale but by 1882 they had decided to go their separate ways, Daniel working on the original site in Hurst Road, whilst James opened a new yard in Depot Road. Peter Nightingale followed on at the Depot Brickworks from about 1903 until his death in the late 1930s, when he was succeeded by Leonard, the last representative of the family. Several brickmakers called Nightingale, who worked in the Crawley area in the 19th century, may have been related.[22]

Altogether about 20 ladies advertised as brickmakers in trades' directories issued between 1859 and 1922. Most of them made only brief appearances, holding the fort until their late husbands' affairs were settled and the business could be sold. This was evidently the case at Redford in Woolbeding, where Mrs Osgood advertised in 1855 and Mrs Gale in 1887. Others were at the helm for longer periods. Mrs Jane Page, whose husband Thomas had been the brickmaker at Sayers Common in Hurstpierpoint from the 1850s, ran the yard from the 1890s until about 1910, when Edwin Page took charge. Two of the ladies who advertised may even have set up their own businesses. Mrs Charlotte Washington, who was probably the widow of either Thomas Washington, or of his son George William, both of whom were brick merchants in Aldrington in 1883, ran her own brickyard north of the Old Shoreham Road between 1895 and 1903. At the same period, Mrs Sarah Sparks was advertising as a brickmaker in Yapton. The Sparks family owned an engineering works and it may be that the brickfield was only a sideline but it continued in operation until the 1930s.[23]

The last of the family firms

According to billheads and advertisements, the firm of Benjamin Ware & Sons was established in 1770 but this claim has not so far been substantiated. However, it has been possible to trace in some detail the history of the family which, from humble beginnings, built up a business which was one of the few to survive into the second half of the 20th century. Thomas Ware, the first member of the family definitely known to have been a brickmaker, was born in Buxted in 1797. He married in Uckfield in 1821 and his eldest son Benjamin was born in the following year. In 1826 Thomas was living in Framfield and working at a brickyard just over the parish boundary in Uckfield as, in that year, he reported the theft of some of his geese from a pond on the common at Ridgewood. He was employed by John Kenward, the owner of the brickyard on Ridgewood Common, as appeared from the accounts of the Buxted overseers, to whom Ware was obliged to apply for poor relief in 1832. By now he had six children and clearly could not make ends meet, so he received an allowance of 3s 9d per week plus £2 to cover the rent of his cottage for that year. This was a time of economic depression, when demand for bricks was slack and the problem may have been aggravated by the fact that his employer was in process of transferring his brickmaking business from Ridgewood to a new site he had acquired in 1831 at Bates Hole, nearer to the growing town of Uckfield.[24]

Once the new yard was in production, however, things began to look up. Ware was able to increase his earnings and by 1838 had bought a cottage in Uckfield, although he was still living in Framfield, in a house owned by another member of the Kenward family. Thomas Ware died in 1844, by which time his son Benjamin was presumably also working in the brickyard, although he was merely described in the court roll as a labourer, when admitted to his father's property in the following year. Benjamin Ware's energy and business acumen immediately became apparent. He raised a mortgage on the cottage on the Lewes road to enable him to build an alehouse alongside it and he worked as both brickmaker and liquor retailer for a number of years. In 1845 Kenward sold the brickyard at Bates Hole, which became the property of the Buxted Park

estate but his son continued to run the business for a while, with Benjamin Ware in his father's old job as foreman of the yard. By 1859 Ware and a partner were the lessees of the yard and he advertised in that year as 'publican of Four Poplars Inn (later called New Inn) and brick, tile and drainpipe maker'.[25]

Ware's partner in the brickyard at Bates Hole (by this time known as Union Point Brickyard) was probably Henry Tyhurst, a builder in Uckfield, but from 1866 onwards they advertised separately as brickmakers. Tyhurst retained the lease of the old yard and Ware opened a new one on two fields he had rented on the north side of what was later called New Road in Ridgewood. His younger brother Samuel had been working with him from the mid-1850s, to judge by a tile which he had made and inscribed 'Sam[l] Ware for his brother Benjamin 1856'. In 1865, Samuel's wife inherited some property in Framfield and on the strength of this he was able to raise a mortgage in 1868 to buy a site adjacent to his brother's new brickyard. Here another alehouse was built, which later became known as the Brickmakers Arms and two of Ware's associates, James and George Best, were installed as managers of the alehouse and brickyard respectively, leaving Benjamin to look after the New Inn and oversee his growing empire.[26]

In 1871 he bought the property previously owned by his brother Samuel and in the late 1870s advertised as a brickmaker not only in Uckfield but also in Hamsey. This latter venture, however, was short-lived and in 1883 Ware decided to concentrate on expansion in Uckfield. The site on the

33. Brickyard workers with their tools and products: Union Point, Uckfield, c1900

north side of New Road was too cramped for what he envisaged and so he sold some of his land, raised an additional mortgage from an associate in the liquor trade and purchased a new site on the opposite side of the road. Here expansion continued throughout the 1880s and 1890s, new lines in terracotta were developed, new kilns built and houses erected on both sides of New Road for the growing number of workmen. More land was leased from the owners of nearby Shipreed Farm and the area available for clay digging extended, as appears on the 2nd edition Ordnance Survey map of 1899, where the grandly-titled Sussex Pottery Brick & Tile Works is seen to occupy about 26 acres at the junction of New Road and Eastbourne Road.[27]

By this time Benjamin Ware had become a prominent figure in local life and a member of the Uckfield Urban District Council. His firm was tendering for the supply of bricks and also for the removal of domestic refuse, which in those days consisted largely of ashes from coal fires and would have been used at his works in the manufacture of clamp bricks. Benjamin's sons, Amos and William Joseph, had by now taken over the running of the business. In 1894 an agreement was drawn up whereby they paid their father £100 a year for the lease of the premises, the business at that date being valued at £1,850. The lease was renewed for a further 21 years in 1903, the rent being raised to £130 and the premises described as: land and brickyard in Uckfield and Framfield, 9 cottages, 1 square open brick kiln, 2 round flower-pot kilns, brick and tile heated warehouse and shop and loft over, open drying sheds, pot-making shed and 4-horse stable. Benjamin Ware himself had finally retired from the business in 1901 and when he died in 1910, his funeral was attended by 62 employees of the works, a far cry from the four men and two boys he had employed in 1861.[28]

Meanwhile, in 1902, a mortgage of £2,300 was raised on the premises. As no further expansion was taking place, it seems probable that this money was to be spent in connection with another venture with which Amos Ware had become involved at about this time. The Keymer Brick & Tile Co. at Burgess Hill had got into financial difficulties and Ware was called on to render assistance. He became the Managing Director and moved to Burgess Hill, leaving his brother to manage the family firm, which was going from strength to strength. In 1905, the rival firm of Tyhurst & Son surrendered the lease of the brickyard at Union Point and Wares were able to take it up again, in addition to their main premises. In 1908 the firm was incorporated as Benjamin Ware & Sons Ltd. [29]

After the death of Amos Ware at the age of 50 in 1913, the association with the Keymer Brick & Tile Co. ended. His son Walter joined the family business and he, in due course, was joined by his son Robert. The firm survived both World Wars, supplying bricks and tiles over quite a wide area. The ornamental terracotta lines were discontinued but clay flower-pots remained an important part of the output of the works. By the 1960s, however, clay reserves were diminishing, the right type of skilled labour was difficult to obtain, clay flowerpots were being superseded by the plastic variety and the Smoke Abatement Act would have meant changing from coal to liquid gas or oil for firing the kilns. Walter Ware was unwilling to make the necessary changes and by the time of his death in 1970, the decision to wind up the business had already been taken.[30]

10. FLUCTUATING FORTUNES (1900-1940)

At the beginning of the 20th century, the demand for bricks was once again affected by the cyclical nature of the building industry. The boom of the 1890s was followed by the inevitable cut-backs in the early 1900s and in Sussex the reduction in demand was exacerbated by the fact that, for the first time ever, local brickmakers were facing competition from outside the county. Firms with direct rail links to London had for some time been supplying bricks to the metropolis. However, in the last two decades of the 19th century, the development of the Fletton brick industry on the Oxford Clay deposits in the Peterborough and Bedford areas had resulted in the establishment of large-scale brickworks there, with greatly reduced costs. This, in turn, led to overproduction and ultimately to a catastrophic drop in prices. Flettons, which had been selling at 22s per 1,000 in the 1890s, were being offered at 8s 6d per 1,000 by 1908. There was no way in which these prices could be matched by even the most efficient of the Wealden brickmakers and so they lost nearly all of their share of the London market, except for specialised products. Furthermore, some Flettons were even finding their way by rail into Sussex.[1]

Modernisation: the Sussex Brick & Estates Company

Many of the new firms which had entered the brickmaking business in Sussex during the boom period of the 1890s were unable to survive and a number of older-established companies were in trouble as well. This was probably the cause of the crisis at the Keymer Brick & Tile Co. and was certainly the reason for changes which took place at Warnham brickworks in the early years of the century. Peter Peters, of the firm of Horsham builders which had been responsible for the initial development of the business, sold out in 1899 and the new owner, a London builder, formed a company, the Sussex Brick Co. Ltd, and installed new plant and buildings, intending to exploit the lower measures of the Weald Clay to make pressed bricks using the 'stiff plastic' process. Two new coal-fired continuous kilns of the Hoffmann type were built, the coal being brought in by rail from Nottingham. Behind the kilns was a line of presses, fed with clay

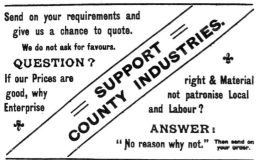

34. *Advertisement of 1910 showing the effects of competition from outside the county*

87

from a parallel line of grinding mills. The clay, at this stage, was still dug manually and delivered to the grinders in trolleys, propelled by an overhead continuous chain drive. However, the company soon ran into trouble. Initial problems, which led to uneven output and rising costs, were compounded by the recession in the industry and in 1903 a new manager was appointed, fresh capital was injected and the Sussex Brick & Estates Co. Ltd formed.[2]

The new company brought a third continuous kiln into use and increased the output of pressed bricks to 12 million annually. In addition, 8 million bricks a year were being turned out by the two seasonal yards which were still in operation, using the top six feet of clay which was unsuitable for the production of pressed bricks. All of this was running counter to the general trend in the county, which was one of decline, and may have been attributable, in part, to the company's superior marketing technique as well as some imaginative use of public relations to advertise its wares. In 1912 a steam excavator was brought into use in the claypit at Warnham and was made the occasion for celebrations, which were reported in the *Sussex Daily News* on 8th February.[3]

A WARNHAM INDUSTRY

A leading Sussex industry is that of brickmaking, for on large and small scales, it is to be met with wherever one cares to travel. At Warnham, modern methods can be seen at work to the fullest extent. There the Sussex Brick and Estates Company Ltd., who have also another works at Southwater, show the latest thing in brickmaking, for speed of output, combined, of course, with quality. The latest venture of this progressive Company is in the direction of a more rapid and more economical method of excavating the clay, and yesterday afternoon, a party was taken over the place, and shewn exactly how this is done. First, the party was entertained to dinner at the Station Hotel, Horsham. Mr. Harry Waddy, the Chairman of the Company, presided, and was supported by Mr J. Stewart Whitehouse, the Managing Director, with other Directors and a representative company of interested persons. Subsequently, Mr. C.J. Stott gave the toast of "Success to the Sussex Brick and Estates Company, and continued prosperity," saying he could confidently anticipate its realization. The Company had gone through many vicissitudes and many trials, but the courage of the Directors had brought them safely through, and now they were in a very strong position.

Plenty of work for men displaced

Mr. Harry Waddy responded in happy terms, and incidentally remarked that while the new machine would displace about 12 men, it was a great gratification to all members of the Board to know that the services of the men would not be dispensed with, but that they would be found plenty of work in other branches of the Company. By special train the company were then taken to Warnham, where Mr. Waddy pulled the starting lever of the steam digger, and all were able to have a good view of its work and possibilities. The plant consists of a steam navvy, automatic hopper, and clay conveyor, and can dig and discharge into wagons about 1½ tons of hard clay in half a minute, the speed and facility of working being a revelation. A driver and a fireman upon the machine, and two or three men around it, are all that are necessary for the output of 400 tons of clay, required by the Company to make

35. The official inauguration of the Ruston steam navvy at Warnham in 1912

their output of 100,000 bricks per day. The enormous demand for their common pressed bricks has rendered imperative the expenditure of £1,250, which has been incurred on the installation of this plant. After an inspection of the works, the company were taken by train to Southwater, to view the works there, and subsequently back to Horsham, where tea was served.

The running of the works at Southwater, formerly known as the Southwater Brick & Tile Co. but now renamed the Southwater Brick, Tile, Terra Cotta, Pipe & Clay Co. Ltd, had recently been taken over by the SBEC and both this and the works at Warnham figured in an illustrated article about the Company in a

magazine called the *Pictorial Trade Record*. This not only listed the different types of brick produced but also showed how widely they were distributed. Southwater engineering bricks were being used for the construction of sewers and waterworks and also for railway building, on the extension of the line from Redhill to Balcombe. The Public Library in Hove and municipal buildings in Worthing, Bognor and Brighton had been built of SBEC bricks, as had a telephone exchange at Faversham, in Kent. Recent orders included bricks for several railway stations including Victoria and Portsmouth, the East Sussex Asylum at Hellingly, harbour works at Shoreham and Christ's Hospital school. In all of this the railway played an important part and one of the photographs accompanying the article showed a long line of London Brighton & South Coast Railway waggons in the siding at Warnham, alongside the row of Hoffmann kilns with their three tall chimneys.[4]

World War 1 and its aftermath

However, the number of Sussex brickmakers advertising in Kelly's Directory, which had reached a peak of 155 in 1899, had declined by 1913 to 105 and the war years which followed saw the demise of many more. Most brickworks closed for the duration of the war, although some stayed open, employing a skeleton staff in various kinds of war work. For example, the family-run brickyard at Three Cups in Warbleton stopped production and the few workmen who had not joined the army were transferred to forestry work, cutting timber and hauling it to the sawbenches of contractors, for conversion into pit-props and railway sleepers. The brickworks at Crowborough station was used as an army storage depot and at Warnham, where the works was taken over in 1915 by the Ministry of Munitions, the kilns were adapted for the storage of high explosives.[5]

After the war, although many of the smaller brickyards never re-opened, demand for bricks grew fairly rapidly and the bigger companies were soon back in full production. The number of workers in the industry in Sussex, which had dropped from 1,040 in 1911 to 469 in 1921, reached 1,841 by 1931. Along the coast, where new housing developments, such as the one at Peacehaven, were getting under way, old-style seasonal brick fields sprang up to supply the building materials. These were labour-intensive but required no permanent buildings and very little machinery. They were generally only a short distance from the building sites, which cut down on transport costs and, as long as labour remained cheap, this was the method of brickmaking preferred by the speculative builder, who was happy to use clamp-burnt bricks and did not require the high-quality facings and other specialised products of the better-equipped brickworks. Seasonal brickfields also continued in operation on a number of sites alongside the railways, which remained the most economic method of transporting bricks until after World War 2.

Work in the seasonal brickfields

An insight into the way in which these brickfields functioned has been obtained from the reminiscences of three former brickmakers: H.J. Paris, whose father was the manager of Hillman's at Partridge Green for 30 years, Harold 'Darky' Simmons, who worked at Cox's at Plumpton and Ben Foreman, who worked, first with his father and then independently as a moulder, in six different brickfields between Barnham and Rustington in the years between the wars. The first two remained at the same brickfield throughout but the Foremans had to seek re-engagement annually, taking a 'berth' for the season from March to September and negotiating rates of pay which ranged from 18s per 1,000 bricks in the early 1920s to only 9s 6d per 1,000

36. Workers in the brickfield at Peacehaven c1920

during the depression of the late '20s and early '30s. All of their accounts agreed in broad outline, differing only in some of the specialised vocabulary they used to describe the various processes.[6]

In essence methods had remained unchanged since the early 19th century. Clay was still dug manually, using a thin spade called a graft. It was stacked in a mound, or curf, from two to three metres high and about 10 metres in circumference, covered with ash or coke breeze and left to weather. In spring the curf was broken open with a long-handled tool, variously referred to as a tomahawk or hommicker, and carted in navvy barrows to the pugmill. Mr Foreman had some early recollections of mixing the clay by hand, using a turning iron but by this date most brickfields were equipped with pugmills, either horse-powered or belt-driven, using steam or diesel engines.

One mill could extrude enough pugged clay to supply three moulding tables (berths or benches), which were set up near to it in the open air.

Moulding followed the time-honoured pattern, the moulder generally having one or more assistants, who were each paid a share of his piece-work rates. The 'hommicker' (or 'pugger-up') maintained the supply of pugged clay at the right-hand end of the table, which also had a heap of sand on the left and a tub of water at the back. The 'flatter-in' used a two-handled knife with a curved blade, called a cuckle, to cut off a warp of clay from the heap and, in three movements, knocked it roughly into shape. The moulder then slapped it into the mould, which fitted over the stock fixed to the table, and removed the surplus clay with a strike. This consisted of either a flat piece of wood with rounded ends or a wire stretched between the two ends of a

37. Setting bricks on the hacks to dry in the open air: Three Cups Brickyard, Warbleton, in the 1930s

laid on boards. For the first row, 30 bricks were grounded out at a time and a pallet board used to make a nick in the last one to facilitate counting. The bricks were set out on edge, with air spaces between them and when one row was complete, a second was laid over the joints of the first. When this was in position the hack was said to be 'twice high'. A completed hack would be from six- to ten-high and contain some 1,500 bricks. Wooden caps were used to protect the tops of the hacks against rain, and wooden 'lew' boards or hurdles to shield the sides from both wind and rain. When it rained hard, the moulders, would be forced to stop work, 'cap-up' and 'lew-up' and wait until it stopped. As soon as the bricks were sufficiently dry, they were skintled, that is: the hack was rebuilt with the bricks set herring-bone fashion to allow air to circulate. This job was generally done, not by the moulders but by the crowders, who took over operations at this point.

When the bricks were ready for firing, the crowders transferred them to the clamp on crowding barrows, which had a vertical platform at the front end and held up to 60 bricks. When loaded, the barrows were tipped forwards and carefully balanced so that they could be wheeled at quite high speed along the metal plates which had been laid down between the hacks and the clamp. The 'setting' of the clamp was the responsibility of the brick-burner, who was generally the foreman of the yard. At Partridge Green and Plumpton, the fuel used was still town ash, brought in by rail from London and by cart from Brighton respectively but in the Littlehampton area, this had been

bent piece of wood, resembling a bow. The mould was then lifted off the stock and the brick knocked out and transferred, on a wooden pallet, to a bearing-off barrow (also referred to as an 'off-hand' or hack barrow), which held between 30 and 36 bricks, in two rows. This was the job of the 'page', a boy who learnt the trade by watching the others at work. Bearing-off, or wheeling a load of green bricks to the drying area and setting them out on the hacks, was generally done by the moulder's mate, who might exchange jobs with the moulder for the second and fourth quarters of the working day. This lasted from daybreak until 5.30 pm, with three breaks for breakfast, lunch and tea.

The hacks, where the bricks were dried in double rows in the open, were

38. Clamp at E. & R. Norman's brickfield in Plumpton in 1897

replaced by coke from the gas works. 'Burn-overs', rejected bricks from previous firings, were used both for the base of the clamp and for casing its ends and sides, which were then sealed with wet clay. In the event of high winds, 'lews' were placed against the side of the clamp to give protection during burning, as too high a temperature could lead to over-burning and fusing of the bricks. A clamp took from three to four weeks to burn, depending on its size. It then had to cool down before being 'drawn' by the crowders, who sorted the bricks into different qualities. The size of the clamp varied from around 100,000 bricks at Partridge Green to 250,000 at Plumpton. Both of these brickfields produced about half a million bricks per year.

Improved techniques and new machines

In total contrast to this primitive style of brickmaking, great strides were being made towards increasing output and efficiency in the more up-to-date brickworks, where the use of heated drying-sheds and continuous kilns had for some time made all-the-year-round work possible. Hoffmann-type kilns were in use before World War 1 in a number of works including those already mentioned at Keymer, Warnham and Southwater and also at Linchmere (Hammer Brickworks), Crowborough, Hamsey, Berwick (Cuckmere Brick Co.) and Bexhill (Jackson & Adeney, later The Lunsford Co.). Some works, which manufactured

39. Downdraught kilns at Wares' works in Uckfield

both bricks and tiles, still used simple updraught kilns for the former but for the latter installed intermittent circular downdraught kilns which could be carefully controlled to reach the optimum temperature and admit the correct amount of oxygen during burning and so produce consistent, high-quality ware. These beehive-shaped kilns were particularly favoured by brickworks, such as Chailey Potteries and Wares' at Uckfield, where earthenware was also produced but they were in use at the Cuckmere works at Berwick station and at Rowfant, in Worth, as well. All of these types of kiln were coal-fired, as were the boilers which heated steam for the pipes in the drying sheds and the stationary steam engines used to power the grinding mills and other machinery.[7]

The years between the wars saw attempts being made to improve efficiency not only in methods of brick-burning but in all the other stages of the brickmaking process: clay-extraction, preparation, moulding and drying. Clay-digging by hand from fairly shallow pits continued to be practised, especially in the seasonal brickfields, but the larger works were looking for ways to speed up the process and increase the size of their stockpiles of weathered clay. Following the introduction of the steam excavator at Warnham, other works had followed suit, also installing tramways, along which tubs of clay could be hauled from claypits which were now being dug to a much greater depth. By the late 1930s Warnham had a light railway, on which trucks were pulled by a diesel locomotive, in one part of the works, and a wire-rope haulage system in another part. At the Sussex Brick Company's other works at Southwater, a continuous overhead chain was employed.[8]

Clay-preparation had already been mechanised to some extent with the

94

introduction of simple pugmills but these were gradually being superseded by different kinds of grinding and mixing machinery, such as mills consisting of two horizontal rollers moving at different speeds, double-shafted mixers and grinding pans, in which two large vertical rollers both rotated and revolved. The choice of method depended to some extent on the nature of the raw material but also on the type of end product. For the stiff-plastic process being used to produce engineering bricks at Southwater and common pressed bricks at Warnham, dry-grinding between rollers to break the clay down was followed by mixing in double-shafted machines, at which point sufficient water was added to achieve the desired consistency. For the traditional Sussex stock bricks, on the other hand, what was now known as the 'soft-mud' process was being used. The weathered clay, with its admixture of fuel, was ground and mixed with water simultaneously in grinding pans, then put under pressure and extruded, as in the older type of pugmill.[9]

Even at an advanced brickworks such as Warnham, moulding of the 'Wealden' red facing bricks was still done by hand up to 1940. For stocks, however, a semi-automatic moulding process was employed. The rather cumbersome machinery which had formerly been used was replaced in 1934 by a triple-mould Berry machine, which automatically sanded the moulds and filled them with pugged clay but an operative was required to strike off the surplus clay and place the green bricks on a revolving table, whence they were transferred to the racks of drier cars. Common pressed bricks at Warnham

and engineering bricks at Southwater were, as the name implies, moulded in 'press boxes', into which the semi-dry ground clay was forced through a die and then subjected to a long press of about 80 tons, followed by a short press of 60 tons, surplus material being forced out through the bottom of the box. Other works, such as that of the Lunsford Company at Bexhill, were using the wire-cut method of producing bricks, which did away with moulds altogether. This was a development of the process first introduced in the 19th century but now made fully automatic. A column of prepared clay was forced through a die with the profile of a brick 'on edge'. This was first cut into sections about three or four feet long and then forced through a set of parallel wires, to emerge as bricks, ready for drying.[10]

Drying sheds were by now in general use in all but the seasonal brickyards. In some sheds, steam-heated pipes were laid just above the ground and slatted boards placed over them, on which the bricks were set manually, as in traditional 'hacks'. This method protected the green bricks from the vagaries of the climate and also permitted work to continue all the year round but it did not greatly reduce drying time, as bricks might have to remain in the sheds for as long as five weeks. To speed up the operation, special insulated drying chambers were introduced, through which trolleys laden with bricks passed on rails. Hot air, generated by a steam heater, was introduced into the opposite end of the chamber, or tunnel, to the one at which the trolleys entered. As it travelled down the tunnel, the stream of air picked up more moisture from the

40. *Continuous kiln and narrow-gauge railway at Crowborough Brickworks*

drying bricks, over which it passed. In this way, the bricks which entered the drier were met by a current of warm, moist air, which became gradually hotter and drier as they progressed through it. This counteracted any tendency for the bricks to shrink unevenly and crack, which would occur if they dried hard on the outside before moisture from the centre had a chance to evaporate.[11]

A number of companies installed narrow-gauge railways either, as already mentioned, to haul clay and sand from the pits into the works or, as at Crowborough, to transport bricks within the works, collecting trolleys from the drier for transfer to the hatches of the multi-chamber continuous kilns and returning the empty trolleys to the moulding shed for re-use. On some tramways, trucks were hand-propelled but in general diesel locomotives were employed on the floor of the claypit and in the main works, with a cable-operated inclined plane to raise the trucks from the pit. At Keymer, there were two separate narrow-gauge systems in operation in different parts of the pit but mostly the tracks were 2ft gauge, only Warnham and Midhurst using a wider 2ft 6in gauge and the Sussex Pottery, Brick & Tile Works at Uckfield a narrower one of 1ft 8in. In all, 13 brickworks in Sussex are known to have used locomotive-operated light railways, although some of these were not installed until after World War 2.[12]

Re-structuring the industry

All of these improvements required much greater capital expenditure than

96

had been the case with the seasonal brickfields or even the traditional brickyards, with their up-draught kilns and simple machinery. As a result, several mergers of existing enterprises took place in the 1920s and new companies were formed to attract the necessary investment. Advertisements in directories show that the number of family-run firms and even partnerships had been greatly reduced and their places taken by companies. Some of these sought to appeal to customers by adopting names such as the Lion Brickworks (Nyetimber, Bognor) and the Trojan Manufacturing Co. Ltd (Selsey), both of which made their appearance in the mid-1920s when the pace of development was increasing, especially along the coast of West Sussex. Other companies adopted the name of the locality in which they were operating: the Job Brick Co. in Job's Lane, Hurstpierpoint and the Rose Green Brick Co. at Bognor first advertised in 1927 and were followed in 1930 by the Denton Brick Co. at Newhaven, the Felpham Brick & Estates Co., the Ferry Brick & Tile Co. at Selsey, the Goring Brick Co., Nutbourne Brickworks, Ore (Hastings) Brickfields and the Wilmington Brick Co. [13]

The life of some of these new companies was only brief, as world recession in the late 1920s was making itself felt in the brickmaking industry. The population in Sussex, and hence the need for new housing, continued to grow but the prices charged by local brickmakers were being undercut, not only by the giant London Brick Company with its cheaply-produced Flettons but also by Belgian brickmakers, who were dumping their surplus products on the British market. Trade in Europe was bad and ships, which would otherwise have lain idle, were prepared to carry bricks across the Channel at low tariffs; the principal centre for these imports was Shoreham harbour. However, in 1931, Britain came off the Gold Standard and this had the immediate effect of making the trade less attractive to continental competitors. [14]

During the 1930s, as the economic position improved, existing companies were able to step up production once more. The Keymer Brick & Tile Company, which had become part of the Maidenhead Brick & Tile Company in the late 1920s, continued to operate under its own name in Sussex and, as well as its other works at Ditchling, now controlled the former Southdown Tileries at Polegate as well. At Warnham, the Sussex Brick Company, which had reverted to its former name in 1927, decided to increase output, reduce costs and improve quality and, to that end, a fifth continuous kiln was built and one of the older ones re-built and enlarged. In the section of the works where stock bricks were produced, a new, more efficient drier was installed as well as new moulding machinery. Additional land was acquired nearby at Graylands and a merger was negotiated with the Dorking Brick Company in Surrey, making the new Sussex & Dorking United Brick Companies into formidable rivals for their competitors in the South East. Yet in spite of this, three other firms of brickmakers, Agates, Dinnages and Nightingales, were still at work in Horsham itself and in Crawley and the area to the south and west, a number of new brickworks appeared in the late 1930s. Elsewhere, particularly in places such as Pulborough and Thakeham and in the coastal area of West Sussex, brickworks were also springing up; altogether there were 15 new firms, out of a total of 91 advertising in the 1938 edition of *Kelly's Directory*.[15]

Silica products

A variety of new products made their appearance in the years between the wars. Concrete bricks and tiles were manufactured by several firms, including the Chichester Tile & Concrete Co., Thakeham Tiles, Marley Tiles at Storrington and the Nerus Brick & Tile Co. at Rye Harbour, all of which advertised in the 1930s. Fire bricks were produced at Pennybridge in Wadhurst from about 1924 by a firm which was known at first as Industrial Silica Ltd, then as Wadhurst Silica Ltd and in 1930 was taken over by the Sussex Brick Company.[16]

Another silica product, which gained in popularity around this time, was sand-lime bricks. These were made from a mixture of damp sand and approximately 6% of slaked lime and were first pressed into moulds and then heated under pressure in a steam chamber, or autoclave. Sand of the right quality was available in several localities in Sussex, particularly in West Sussex, where a broad belt of greensand lies close to the chalk. The best-known factory was the one in Midhurst, originally opened in 1913 by S. Pearson & Son, the family firm of Lord Cowdray, who owned the land on Midhurst Common from which the sand was extracted. The works was sold after World War 1 to a briquette manufacturer, who also took over Cocking lime works, three miles away, which supplied the fine-ground lime. Benjamin Cloke, who became the owner in 1926, was principally interested in dispatching the bricks by rail and selling them on the London market but some were used in Midhurst itself.[17]

As with the brick industry in general, the 1930s brought mixed fortunes. To begin with, stocks piled up in the works but the introduction of the 'Midhurst White' facing brick in about 1935 coincided with the revival of the market. Large quantities were sold in the Bognor area, where they undercut the price of hand-made stocks by almost 50%, with the result that some of the Bognor brickmakers were obliged to send their wares as far afield as Brighton for sale. Unfortunately the sand-lime bricks proved to have only poor resistance to the weather on the coast and many of the houses built with them subsequently had to have their walls rendered. In the late 1930s, however, Midhurst Whites prospered and the business became a public company in 1938. Unlike most other Sussex brickworks, the one at Midhurst was not obliged to close during World War 2 and it continued to operate successfully until the mid-1980s.[18]

11. RECONSTRUCTION AND RATIONALISATION

As during World War 1, the years between 1940 and 1945 saw the closure of most of the brickworks in Sussex. 'Blackout' regulations forced the immediate shut-down of all works where firing was carried out in clamps or open-topped kilns, as the glow would have provided a beacon for enemy aircraft. House-building ceased altogether but a few selected works were allowed to remain open because some bricks were required for the construction of air-raid shelters and bases for the armed forces and, later, for repairing bomb-damaged buildings. Alternative uses were once again found for some of the kilns and other buildings. At Crowborough brickworks, which had a large army camp nearby, a giant bakery was set up, supplying bread to military depots throughout the south-east of England. At Warnham, the section of the works where pressed bricks were made was allowed to continue production but the stock-brick yard and the adjoining railway sidings were taken over by the Canadian army and used as a centre for the assembly and repair of Churchill tanks. An anti-aircraft gun was set up on the site of the Depot Brickyard in Horsham and nearby Crossways Brickyard was used for a short time by the Royal Engineers as a bomb-disposal depot.[1]

The post-war period (1945-1959)

After the war there was an acute shortage of building materials. The need to rebuild the bomb-damaged cities and also to increase the nation's stock of housing led to the immediate re-opening of all of the larger pre-war brickworks. These had been maintained during the shut-down period from funds raised by a levy made on the firms which had remained in operation. However, manpower was now also in short supply and so the labour-intensive smaller brickyards and, in particular, the seasonal brickfields, which had flourished between the wars in the coastal area of West Sussex, were no longer considered viable. By 1951, according to the Occupation Tables in the report on the population census taken in that year, workers in the brickmaking industry in Sussex numbered 1,495. This is a reduction when compared with the figure of 1,841 employed in the industry in 1931 but, when the rationalisation and, above all, the increased mechanisation which had taken place within the intervening 20 years are considered, it is evident that brick production had, by this date, caught up with and probably overtaken pre-war levels.

Directories covering the whole county were no longer published after the war but an idea of the number of firms engaged in brickmaking can be obtained from lists which appeared in a publication called the *Quarry Managers' Journal*. In editions published in the 1920s and '30s there were fewer brickmakers listed than in *Kelly's Directories* for the same period, probably because some of the claypits at that date were still too small to merit inclusion. For example, the 1933 edition contained the names of 63 firms in Sussex, compared with the 73 which had advertised in *Kelly's Directory* in 1930. An edition of the *Journal* which appeared in 1944/5 contained the names of 51 firms. As many were still not back in production by this date, the entries probably only signified their intention to resume working as soon as they were permitted to do so.

In 1951 the number of firms was down to 34, divided fairly evenly between East and West Sussex. Most of them were working on sites where brickmaking had taken place before the war but the names of some of the firms had changed, revealing that several Sussex businesses were now controlled by companies based outside the county. The Keymer Brick & Tile Co. had already been taken over by the Maidenhead Brick & Tile Co. before the war. The Colhook Brick & Tile Works in Northchapel, near Petworth, was now run by R.G. Ward & Co., with registered offices in the city of London and W.T. Lamb & Sons, who had brickworks in Kent and Surrey, were now also running two yards in Pulborough, one at Codmore Hill, which they had acquired just before the war and a second, called Wamborough Brick & Tile Works, in the same area. In addition, the Lunsford Company, of Bexhill, though still trading under its own name, gave an office address in Horsham, which showed that it had come under the control of the Sussex and Dorking United Brick Companies, which, for some unaccountable reason, did not appear in the list.

By 1959, brick production had passed its post-war peak and had begun to fall off and the number of firms listed was reduced to 28. Three companies, which had been omitted in 1951, were now restored to the list but seven others had closed during the 1950s. The sites of some, such as the North Lane Brick Co. of Rustington, near Littlehampton and George Wells & Son, of Crawley Down,

were destined for re-development as housing estates but the remainder, which were all in country locations, had been forced to close in the face of competition from the bigger companies. The Hackenden Brick Co. of East Grinstead, whose name was included in the 1959 list, had in fact already shut down and the decision to close the Horeham Road Brickworks, which had earlier been absorbed into Sussex & Dorking United, was also taken around this time.

Sussex stocks

An interesting feature of the Sussex brickworks listed in 1959 is the variety of products they still had to offer. Most companies described their wares and although a few works, such as Agates at Horsham and H. Geall of Bognor, merely specified 'stock bricks' or simply 'bricks', others offered a wide range of products. The bricks included: red, purple and multi-coloured facings; hand and machine-made stocks; plain, rustic and slotted wire-cuts, engineering bricks and paving bricks. Ten of the companies were also manufacturing tiles – both hand and machine-made roofing tiles and, in one case, quarry tiles – as well as drainpipes and some flower pots. In addition there were sand-lime bricks and other products, such as concrete tiles, breeze blocks, fireplaces and briquettes.

Yet, in spite of this versatility, a preference in Sussex for traditional building materials is apparent from the fact that at least half of the brickworks were still producing 'stocks'. Various explanations for the term 'stock brick' have been advanced but it is generally agreed that it stems from the hand

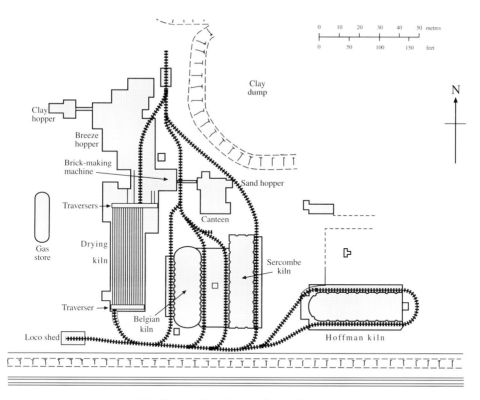

41. Plan of Crowborough Brickworks

moulder's use of a rectangular wooden stock, fixed to his bench, which formed the base of the mould. Gradually 'stocks' came to denote the products of clamp-burning yards, that is: bricks that had a proportion of fuel mixed in them. Finally, by extension, the term 'kiln stocks' was used to describe bricks which had fuel incorporated but were burnt, not in a clamp but in a kiln. In 1959, kiln stocks were being made at the works on Clapham Common and at Crowborough but the majority of stocks were still clamp-burnt.

The clamp, however, was undergoing a transformation. In most yards it was no longer unprotected from the weather but was housed under an open-sided shed, built either of steel or concrete, with a corrugated iron or asbestos roof which allowed some ventilation. Most works had at least two such sheds, so that one clamp could be set and fired whilst the other was cooling, preparatory to the bricks being drawn and sorted. These clamp sheds were large enough to hold a million bricks, or even more. 'Town ash' was now a thing of the past. Coke breeze was the fuel mixed with the clay and a larger grade of coke formed the bed on which the clamp was built. The use of protected clamps enabled the burning process to be more carefully controlled. The proportion of under- or over-burnt bricks, which had often been high in the old-style 'open' clamps, was now reduced to around 10%. It was also possible to exercise more control over the colour of the finished products, both

101

by varying the quantity of breeze incorporated and by careful positioning of the bricks in the clamp: bricks set in the reducing zones nearer to the centre of the clamp were darker when burnt than those in the oxidising zones at the sides. The finished products could then be sorted into light, medium and dark 'multis' (multi-coloured stocks).

Clamp brickyards were also introducing more mechanisation to streamline their procedures. Mechanical excavators in the claypit, the automatic mixing of clay with sand, breeze and water and machinery for grinding were now the order of the day. Although in some works, such as Cox's at Plumpton and Laybrook in Thakeham, hand-moulding was still retained, in others semi-automatic moulding, using a 3- or 4-mould Berry machine, had been introduced. Mixing and moulding were now generally carried out in covered working areas and bricks were dried in a heated chamber or tunnel-drier. All of this required capital expenditure and production had to be greatly increased to justify this.

The corporate giants: Redland and Ibstock

Demand for bricks had slackened from the mid-1950s onwards, as a result of the development of new building systems. For some time, breeze and concrete blocks had been increasingly used to replace common bricks for internal walls and rendered surfaces. Now reinforced concrete construction was favoured by architects for blocks of flats and public buildings, as well as for bridges and other engineering work, which had formerly required large quantities of bricks. In consequence, in the 1960s, the pace of closure speeded up and over the next ten years, the number of brickworks in Sussex was more than halved. Closures included such old-established companies as Benjamin Ware & Sons and the Nyewood Brick & Tile Works as well as the last surviving brickfields in Plumpton, Horsham and Bognor. Also the little estate brickyard at Ashburnham, a survival from an earlier age, was abandoned in 1968.

The only alternative to closure was amalgamation, so that companies could pool their resources and reduce administration and development costs. This was the course taken by the Sussex and Dorking United Brick Companies which, in 1958, controlled works in Sussex at Warnham, Southwater, Bexhill and Horam. Negotiations were begun with the Redland group and, in the following year, a merger was arranged. From now onwards, this company, which also owned works in Surrey and Kent, was to play a dominant role in brickmaking in the south-east. In Sussex, further acquisitions took place. In 1959, a firm with a very long history, E. & R. Norman of Chailey Potteries, was taken over, as was the works of the Hamsey Brick Co. a mile to the south; two years later, it was the turn of the Crowborough Brick Company.

Redland now proceeded to rationalise its operations. The aim was to offer its customers as wide a range of top quality bricks as possible, with each works concentrating on the production of a particular type of brick. To this end, the works at Chailey was converted for making stocks, with clamp sheds each designed to hold a million bricks. At Warnham a new works designed for the

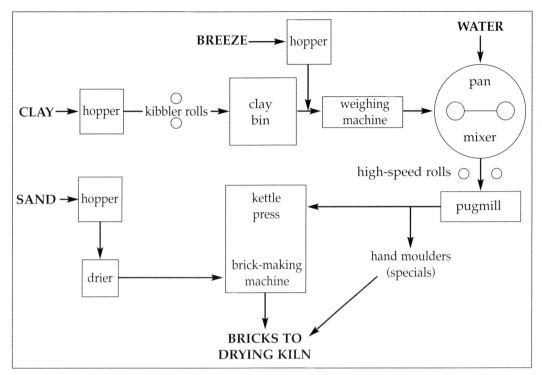

BREEZE ⟶ hopper

WATER

CLAY ⟶ hopper — kibbler rolls ⟶ clay bin

pan

weighing machine

mixer

high-speed rolls

SAND ⟶ hopper

kettle press

pugmill

drier

brick-making machine

hand moulders (specials)

BRICKS TO DRYING KILN

42. Chart showing machinery and procedures employed at Crowborough Brickworks in the 1970s

manufacture of wire-cuts, known as Holbrook, was built to the south of the existing ones in 1963. In the following year, the Wealden works, where stocks were made on another part of the site, was reorganised with new automatic moulding machinery and extended driers and clamps. Pressed bricks were still made at Warnham and at Southwater and the Crowborough works continued to turn out its own distinctive brand of purple kiln stocks. These measures enabled the company to hold and even increase its share of the market at a time when others were struggling and even failing to survive.

There was one other group of brickworks which came through the recession of the 1960s by adopting the course of amalgamation: the three works owned by Hudson's Ltd at West Hoathly, Laybrook and Horam. The oldest of these was the one alongside the Lewes to East Grinstead railway at Sharpethorne in West Hoathly. This had been opened in 1880, when the railway was under construction and acquired by W. Hudson in the late 1890s. The Laybrook works, at Goose Green in Thakeham, was started up in 1935 by a firm of builders from Storrington and was managed by the Laybrook Brickworks Co. until taken over by Hudson's in 1961. Both of these works made stock bricks, fired in clamps. The third works, at North Corner in Horam, operated under the name of Sussex Tileries and Brickworks from just before World War 1 until the 1960s, when it, too, was acquired by Hudson's. As the original name implies, the products here were bricks and tiles, both kiln-fired.

The parent company's main activity was in the field of sand and gravel extraction but also included warehousing, haulage and plant hire. When the opportunity arose, in 1967, of acquiring the patent of the Berry brickmaking machine, a subsidiary company, the Berry Engineering Co., was established, with headquarters in Brighton and workshops in its own section of the brickworks at West Hoathly. The range of equipment manufactured was rapidly extended so that not only moulding machinery but also box feeders, crushing rolls, mixers and conveyers could be supplied to the works within the group and to others outside it as well.

These activities were fully described in an article in the *British Clayworker* in July 1969, entitled 'A lesson in making old works viable', which set out the changes which had been made at the three brickworks. These were mainly designed to streamline and increase production and, at the same time, cut down the number of men employed as, by now, the high cost of labour was an important factor. Mixing and grinding were entirely performed by machinery, most of which was automatically controlled. For moulding, the semi-automatic Berry machines were used and these could now be serviced and repaired by the firm's own engineering department. Operatives were required to un-mould the bricks on to pallets and place these on racks on drier cars, which then ran along tracks through the tunnels of the oil-heated driers.

The innovation of the 1960s which made perhaps the biggest impact was the introduction of fork-lift trucks to transfer the cars from the driers to the clamp sheds and to remove the bricks from the sheds after firing. This speeded up operations and also eliminated any handling of the bricks between leaving the moulding machines and reaching the setters at the clamp, thus reducing the chance of damage. At West Hoathly there were two clamp sheds, one holding 1 million and the other about 1.7 million bricks, whereas Laybrook had a single concrete shed which housed almost 2 million bricks. As the fire was lit after two bays were filled, continuous operation by gangs of setters and drawers was possible. The skilled task of setting the bricks in the clamp was still performed manually, as was the sorting of the fired bricks into different categories according to colour and quality.

The old Sussex Tileries works at Horam had been partly rebuilt. Here the bricks were burnt in a two-chamber downdraught kiln, holding 25,000 bricks in each chamber. Another kiln of the same type was built to hold 30,000 per chamber and there were plans to reopen the section of the works where hand-made tiles were produced. However, contrary to expectations, there was no up-turn in the market and in 1971 the company was forced to suspend operations altogether at the Horam works. By the mid-1970s, the parent company was in deep financial trouble and, at the end of 1976, sold its subsidiary, Hudson Brick & Engineering, to the Leicestershire-based firm of Ibstock, which owned brickworks countrywide.

Swings of the pendulum

Brick manufacture has always been notoriously subject to fluctuating demand and, in the 1970s, when the country's economy was at a low ebb, there was further contraction in the industry. Most of the remaining independent brickworks were forced to close, including the one on Clapham Common which had been in existence for close on 250 years. The Keymer Brick & Tile Co., the only works still in operation in Burgess Hill, came under new management and stopped production of bricks altogether, concentrating on the higher-value product for which its remaining clay reserves were best suited, namely handmade clay tiles. Two small brickyards, at opposite ends of the county, survived by specialising in the production of handmade bricks for uses such as the restoration and extension of historic buildings as well as new projects for which the builders were prepared to pay the extra cost (about 30%) involved. The yard at Guestling, near Hastings, used two circular coal-fired downdraught kilns, each holding 30,000 bricks and the one at Pitsham, near Midhurst, had a single rectangular downdraught kiln and also burnt one clamp of the traditional 'open' type each year.

The other survivors were brickworks at Freshfield Lane in Horsted Keynes, at Rudgwick and at Ashpark near Plaistow, all of which used clamp firing. This yielded larger quantities of bricks for less capital outlay than did kilns. Indeed, in 1973, the Rudgwick Brickworks Co. had successfully pioneered and patented a method of firing clamps, using gas (LPG) instead of the traditional bed of coke. They claimed that installation costs could be recovered in from six to twelve months and that the system was quicker, cleaner

and yielded a higher proportion of first-quality bricks.

During the 1970s the big companies, too, were experiencing hard times. Redland, whose production at Warnham alone had been stabilised at 100 million bricks per year, saw stocks accumulate alarmingly. In 1978 it was decided to make use of the slack period to rebuild the works at Bexhill. The clay reserves at the Crowborough works, 15 miles to the north-west, were nearly exhausted and production there would have to cease in two years' time but there was still a market for the purple stocks for which it was renowned. Therefore the old Lunsford works at Bexhill was redesigned to make this type of brick, using automation and electronic controls wherever possible. The old kilns were demolished and the new works, renamed Ashdown, was built with all the brickmaking processes – clay preparation, moulding, drying, firing and packing – united under one roof. Setting, hitherto a manual operation, was carried out by an Aberson machine, which formed the green bricks into packs at the rate of 9,800 per hour. Fork-lift trucks transferred these packs to the chambers of the gas-fired continuous kiln, removed them after firing to the sorting station and finally collected the bricks, now strapped in packets of 370, and conveyed them to the stock.

In 1980 the works at Crowborough was duly closed down but there was still more rationalisation to come. Redland's pressed bricks were encountering increased competition from outside the county and in 1982 the decision was taken to close the pressed brick plant at Warnham and to shut down the works at

43. Gas-fired downdraught kiln in use at Lunsford Brickworks, Bexhill, up to 1978

Southwater altogether. A year later, the other big company, Ibstock Brick Hudsons, sold the patent of the Berry brickmaking-machine to Abersons and closed the engineering section of their works at West Hoathly. Soon after this, however, prospects began to improve. Prosperity had returned, especially to the south-east of England, and a building boom got under way. What was more, disenchantment with the concrete buildings which had been so popular in the 1960s now set in and bricks returned to favour. The slimming-down and reorganisation which had taken place began to pay dividends and truckloads of bricks were seen regularly on the roads once more.

The building boom of the 1980s quickly cleared the stocks of bricks which

had accumulated at the various works and was soon straining the capacity of the industry to meet demands. As in the 1930s, imported bricks from Belgium began to make their appearance in Sussex. The Midlands firm of Butterley Brick Ltd took over the Hastings Brickworks at Guestling with the intention of modernising it and increasing production. Early in 1988 Ibstock sought planning permission to build a new works at Horam to replace the one which had lain dormant since 1971. This encountered some local opposition, which caused a delay to allow revised plans to be drawn up and before these could be implemented, the pendulum swung the other way again: the country's economy had gone into recession and house-building ceased abruptly.

The 1990s saw further changes: several of the smaller brickworks changed hands and in 1996 Redland withdrew from Sussex, the works at Bexhill and Chailey being acquired by Ibstock and the largest operation, at Warnham, by the Ambion Brick Co.

Bricks and the environment

The 1980s not only saw the building of large numbers of new houses but also the conversion of many redundant farm buildings, including barns and oast houses, for residential purposes. Handmade bricks to match or blend with the existing fabric were available from both the small specialist brickworks, and some of the bigger works, such as West Hoathly, which retained a hand-made brick section. Hand-made clay tiles, which by this date had largely been superseded by the cheaper, machine-made, concrete variety, were nevertheless still being manufactured at the one remaining tileworks in the county, at Keymer. Even so, the demand for bricks and tiles suitable for conservation work was so great that a farmer at Kent Street, south of Sedlescombe, started production on his farm of hand-made bricks and tiles specifically for restoration and renovation purposes. Operating under the name of Aldershaw Tiles, the yard offered a range of plain and decorative peg tiles, tapered oast-house tiles, roof fittings and special bricks of various shapes and colours.

This renewal of interest in traditional materials, on the one hand, was balanced on the other by the efforts of the larger brick companies to offer an ever increasing range of new colours and textures of brick, thus encouraging architects to use their products imaginatively in modern building developments. In recent years this trend has produced some buildings of outstanding quality but also some rather ugly ones. Bricks in shades of salmon pink do not blend well with the colours of traditional Sussex brickwork, just as pantiles, which essentially belong to the east of England, strike a discordant note in a county where plain tiles have always been used in the past.

Concern for the environment has led, in some cases, to a rather ambivalent attitude to bricks and brickmaking. Whilst it is generally appreciated that bricks and tiles are more acceptable and durable building materials than plastic and concrete and therefore need to be readily available, public complaints are sometimes voiced about brickworks, the volume of traffic they generate and the effect of their claypits on the landscape. However, most of the big claypits are sited well away from habitation and are masked by belts of trees. One of the worked-out deep pits at Warnham is now serving a useful purpose as a landfill site and the methane gas collected is used, instead of fossil fuel, in the driers and kilns of the adjoining works. Furthermore, the widespread use of smokeless fuels has led to very much cleaner atmospheric conditions in the vicinity of the brickworks.

In the past, the various products of the Sussex brickyards, as displayed in the buildings of towns and villages, in country houses, farms and cottages, have contributed significantly to the landscape. It is to be hoped that, in the future, bricks and tiles made of Sussex clay will continue to be used, so that this character can be preserved.

APPENDIX 1: FROG-MARKED BRICKS

The practice of making a 'frog', or indentation, in the surface of a brick did not begin until the late 18th century and, in some brickyards, much later than that. The origin of the term is obscure but it appears to relate to the similar frog, or hollow, in a horse's hoof. The purpose of the frog was twofold: it reduced the weight of the brick, making it easier to handle and also served as a key for mortar, thus permitting thinner joints between courses of brickwork. For this reason the brick was always laid with the frog uppermost. Paving bricks, which were thinner than building bricks, having a depth of not more than 2in, rarely had a frog.

In order to form the frog, a wooden or metal projection was screwed on to the top of the stock on the moulder's bench. After the mould was filled with 'pug', the surplus material was struck off the top, leaving the surface flat, with the result that hand-moulded bricks only had a single frog. Some modern machine-made bricks, however, have two frogs, formed when the brick is subjected to pressure during moulding.

In many brickyards, especially where moulding was done by hand, the frog was unmarked, although the hollow formed might vary in depth or shape, so that the work of different moulders could be identified. Elsewhere, from the middle of the 19th century onwards, the practice grew up of including the maker's name or the company's trademark. This could take the form of a name or of initials or sometimes even of a symbol. Occasionally the place of manufacture was also included.

The following are some of the marks which have been used by brickmakers in Sussex. The sites of manufacture are indicated in brackets (numbers refer to the entries in the gazetteer).

The most widely-distributed are the ones produced by Redland Brick and its predecessors:

SUSSEX BRICK & ESTATES Co Ltd
S B E C
SUSSEX BRICK Co Ltd
SUSSEX & DORKING Utd BRICK Cos Ltd
} (Horsham 15 & 16)

WARNHAM S B C
WARNHAM R B
WEALDEN
} (Horsham 15)

SUSSEX BRICK & TERRACOTTA Co
SOUTHWATER
} (Horsham 16)

LUNSFORD BEXHILL
LUNSFORD (S & D Utd)
ASHDOWN – formerly marked CROWBOROUGH
ASHDOWN P – formerly marked PEVENSEY
} (Bexhill 10)

44. Frog-marked brick made c1880

Brick marks incorporating names include:

F. BERRY – BURGESS HILL	(Keymer 10)
BUTT	(Littlehampton 1)
DICKER	(Hellingly 16)
DREWETT LITTLEHAMPTON	
EASTBOURNE	(Eastbourne 4 & Hailsham 16)
GENT	(Lower Beeding 4)
HIGHLEY	(Balcombe 2)
JOHNSON & CO. }	(Keymer 15)
KEYMER	
LION	(Pagham 2)
LUDLAY	(Berwick 2)
ROWFANT	(Worth 7)
RYE }	(Rye 4)
SMITH.RYE	
SUMNER JUNR CRAWLEY	(Ifield 3)
TROJAN	(Selsey 4)

Bricks marked with initials which can be identified with reasonable certainty:

AC BOSHAM	(Bosham 2)
B & G HAILSHAM	(Hailsham 19)
CBC	(Berwick 2)
C C	(Rotherfield 16)
FLB	(Horsted Keynes 5)
G F – changed to H F	(Westham 3)
G H	(Hailsham 14)
H L	(Thakeham 4)
HWH	(West Hoathly 3)
H Y	(East Grinstead 12)
W M	(Warbleton 6)
ZP&S	(Rustington 3)

The only Sussex bricks known to have been marked with a symbol are those produced by the Wilmington Brick Co. which used as its trademark a representation of the Long Man, the primitive figure cut in the chalk of the Downs (Arlington 2)

Some tiles were stamped with the maker's name but fewer examples of these have been recorded. They include:

ALDERSHAW SUSSEX	(Battle 11)
W GRAVETT	(Hailsham 6)
LUNSFORD BEXHILL	(Bexhill 10)
TYHURST UCKFIELD	(Uckfield 3)

There is a collection of frog-marked bricks at Amberley Museum, many of which are of Sussex origin.

APPENDIX 2: BRICKMAKING TERMS

BAVIN	i. (West Sussex) A synonym for faggot (qv)
	ii. (East Sussex) A bundle of short twigs used to start the fire in a kiln or clamp
BEARING-OFF BARROW	A long barrow, fitted with springs, on which 30-36 'green' bricks were placed on two long planks for transport from the moulding table to the hacks. Alternative name: hack barrow
BRICK EARTH	i. A geological formation, found on the coastal plain of SW Sussex
	ii. A synonym for loam (qv)
BRICKFIELD	Name usually, but not always, applied to a site where bricks were clamp-fired
BRICKWORKS	i. A modem designation for a brickyard or
	ii. A large-scale enterprise where machinery is used and bricks kiln-burnt
BRICKYARD	A small-scale enterprise, where bricks were generally burnt in an updraught kiln
COMMON BRICKS	Bricks of second quality, used for internal walls
CONTINUOUS KILN	A series of connected chambers, each with its own hatch, or wicket, which permitted the operations of setting, pre-heating, firing, cooling and drawing to take place in sequence. In the Hoffmann kiln the chambers were arranged in a circle. Subsequent developments of the design, including the Staffordshire and the Belgian kiln, were rectangular
CROWDING BARROW	A barrow with a square horizontal platform and a similar vertical platform at the front, used to transport about 60 dried bricks per load from the hacks to the clamp or kiln
CUCKLE	A curved blade with a handle at each end, used to cut a 'clot' of pugged earth, sufficient to make one brick, off the heap on the moulding table
DOWNDRAUGHT KILN	A vaulted kiln, either round (beehive) or rectangular in shape, with an internal wall which deflected the hot gases upwards to the roof, whence they were drawn down through the bricks. A common chimney might serve two or more kilns of this type
DRAIN BRICK	Bricks used for drainage of marshy land were exempt from Brick Tax if clearly marked with the word 'Drain'
DRAIN TILE	A curved tile used in conjunction with a flat sole-plate for purposes of field drainage before round drainpipes became available
FACING BRICKS	First quality bricks, used for the facades of buildings
FAGGOT	A long bundle of brushwood or furze used to stoke a wood-fired kiln
GRAFT	A spade-like implement, consisting of three prongs joined at the tips, used for digging clay
HACK	A stack of 'green' bricks set out on edge in a double row to dry, generally in the open air
HEADER	The narrow end of a brick
HOMMICKER	i. A long-handled tool resembling a mattock, used to pull clay down from the stockpile (curf) and mix it to moulding consistency with added water.
	ii. The workman who performed this operation
LOAM	The coarse, sandy material used in the manufacture of bricks

PRESSED BRICKS	Bricks machine-moulded under pressure to give a smooth surface and additional strength
PUGMILL	A machine for mixing clay and other ingredients to the desired consistency for moulding cf Ch 8
STOCK	A rectangular piece of wood, bolted to the moulding table, over which the brick mould was placed
STRETCHER	The long face of a brick
STRIKE	A flat piece of wood used to remove surplus clay from the top of the mould and/or smooth the surface of the brick. Sometimes a wire bow was used to perform this task
TERRACOTTA	Unglazed moulded clay blocks, burnt at a high temperature and used to adorn buildings, either as an integral part of the fabric or as external ornament e.g. balustrades, urns and roof finials
WEALDEN KILN	cf Ch 5. This differs from the type known as a Suffolk kiln in only one respect: the loading hatch is at the opposite end to the firing tunnels, whereas in the Suffolk kiln it is on one of the sides
WIRE-CUTS	Bricks made by cutting a column of extruded clay with a taut wire. Modern wire-cuts are generally perforated

For an illustrated glossary of terms used in brickmaking and to describe bricks and brickwork, see Brunskill, *Brick Building in Britain*, 86-111.

45. Bricks set in a chamber of one of the continuous kilns at Warnham

111

LIST OF ABBREVIATIONS

BBS	British Brick Society	*QMJ*	*Quarry Managers' Journal – Directory of Quarries, Clayworks, Sand & Gravel Pits etc.*
BEGS	*Bulletin of the East Grinstead Society*		
BL	British Library		
CKS	Centre for Kentish Studies, Maidstone	Robson	Robson's *Directory for London & the Six Home Counties*
DBC	*Directory of British Clayworkers*	ROHAS	Rape of Hastings Architectural Survey
ESRO	East Sussex Record Office, Lewes	*SAC*	*Sussex Archaeological Collections*
HAARG	Hastings Area Archaeological Research Group	SAS	Sussex Archaeological Society
		SCM	*Sussex County Magazine*
HEH	Huntington Library, San Marino, California	SIAS	Sussex Industrial Archaeology Society
HMAG	Hastings Museum and Art Gallery*	*SIH*	*Sussex Industrial History*
Kelly	Kelly's *Post Office Directories*	*SNQ*	*Sussex Notes and Queries*
NGR	National Grid Reference	SRO	Surrey Record Office, Kingston
Pigot	Pigot's *London & Provincial Commercial Directories*	SRS	Publications of the Sussex Record Society
Pike	Pike's *Directories* for various localities e.g. Pike/Hastings	*SWA*	*Sussex Weekly Advertiser*
		VCH	*Victoria County History of Sussex*
PRO	Public Record Office, Kew	WSRO	West Sussex Record Office, Chichester

* Documents formerly held in Hastings Museum are now lodged at East Sussex Record Office.

NOTES AND REFERENCES

Detailed references relating to brickyard sites will be found in the 'Gazetteer' section, where these are listed under the name of the parish in which they were/are situated.

Introduction
1. J. Bond, S. Gosling & J. Rhodes, *The Clay Industries of Oxfordshire: Oxfordshire Brickmakers (1980)*; Cox, *Bedfordshire*, 49-58; Leslie, 'Ashburnham', 10-19.

Chapter 1
   In this chapter reference has been made to S.C.A. Holmes (ed), *British Regional Geology: The Wealden District* (4th ed. 1965) and to the more detailed *Memoirs of the Geological Survey* relating to different parts of Sussex, both the earlier volumes published between 1903 and 1928 and the later series published from the 1960s onwards.
1. Leslie, 'Ashburnham', 20
2. ESRO AMS 4439
3. D.E. Highley, 'The Economic Geology of the Weald' *Proceedings of the Geologists' Association* (1975), 561
4. WSRO Goodwood MS. E5476
5. Observations made by Wilfrid Beswick

based on examination of various samples of brick earth from the Hastings Beds and of bricks made from Wadhurst Clay found at a kiln site in Northiam (cf Northiam 3)
6. *VCH* **6** (1), 112; S.J. Twist, *Stock Bricks of Swale* (Sittingbourne 1984), 4; ESRO RAF 37/23 and BMW A2/29 f21
7. Shephard-Thorn et al, *Tenterden*, 106
8. For a fuller discussion of clamp-burning see Chapters 6 and 10

Chapter 2
1. BBS, 'Brick', 4
2. S. Foster in Rudling, 'Hartfield', 104
3. Brodribb, *Roman Brick*, 9, 26
4. Green, 'Itchingfield', 24-6; J. Rock, 'Ancient Cinder Heaps in East Sussex' *SAC* **29** (1879), 178; G. Brodribb, 'A Further Survey of Stamped Tiles of the Classis Britannica' *SAC* **118** (1980), 185-7; G. Brodribb & H. Cleere, 'The Classis Britannica Bath-house at Beauport Park, E. Sussex' *Britannia* **19** (1988), 267
5. W. Figg, 'On the Remains of a Roman Building Discovered At Wiston in 1848' *SAC* **2** (1849), 313-5; F.G. Aldsworth, 'A Roman Brick and Tile Kiln, Fernhurst' *SAC* **114** (1976), 328; Rudling, 'Dell Quay', 81-90

6. Gazetteer: Hurstpierpoint 1

7. Rudling, 'Hartfield', 194-200

8. HEH BA Vol 36.1474 (ex inf. C. Whittick); *SRS* **65**, passim; Streeten, 'Building Materials', 79

9. The evidence for the existence of tile kilns at Robertsbridge and Michelham depends on 16th-century references to a 'Tylehostfield' in *SRS* **47**, 130 and 'Le Tylehouse land' in Salzman, *Hailsham*, 253; Streeten, 'Building Materials', 93, 95, 97

10. M. Gardiner, G. Jones & D. Martin, 'The Excavation of a Medieval Aisled Hall at Park Farm, Salehurst' *SAC* **129** (1991), 93; L.F. Salzman, 'Documents Relating to Pevensey Castle' *SAC* **49** (1906), 15, 21; *SRS* **7** (1907), 173; Salzman, *Industries*, 123

11. *SRS* **10**, 236, 267; K.J. Barton, *Medieval Sussex Pottery* (1979), 170; PRO E179/189/45 (ex inf. C. Whittick) NB No attempt has been made to give modern equivalents for old currency (£ s d)

12. I.C. Hannah, 'Bishop's Palace, Chichester' *SAC* **52** (1909), 14; *SRS* **52**, 114; *VCH* **2**, 252; ESRO RAF Manor of Pebsham Account Rolls.

13. ESRO SAS/G 44/6 & 73

14. ESRO SAS/G 44/80

15. ESRO SAS/G 44/74 & 77; J. Brent, 'Alciston Manor in the later Middle Ages' *SAC* **106** (1968), 90

16. *VCH* **2**, 251; E.S. Eames and M. Gardiner, personal communications; Ponsonby, 'Monastic Tiles', 34-5

17. Gazetteer: Rye 1; J.I. Hadfield, 'The Excavation of a Medieval Kiln at Barnett's Mead, Ringmer' *SAC* **119** (1981), 89; Streeten, 'Building Materials', 95; 'Additions to SAS Museum July 1948' No 23, *SAC* **87** (1948), xli; P.S. Godman, 'Rolls of the Manor of Wiston' *SAC* **54** (1911), 153; L.F. Salzman, 'Early Churchwardens' Accounts, Arlington' *ibid.*, 91

18. S.E. Winbolt, 'Excavations at Sedgwick Castle' *SAC* **66** (1925), 113; The Marquis Curzon of Kedleston, *Bodiam Castle* (1926), 67, 136-142

Chapter 3

1. Salzman, *Industries*, 181; ESRO RYE 33/5; Farrant, 'Building Materials', 24 – quoting PRO E190/788/25

2. Holt, 'Early brickmaking', 165; inf. Eric Holden

3. W.D. Simpson, 'Herstmonceux Castle' *Archaeological Journal* **99** (1942), 110-122; D. Calvert, *The History of Herstmonceux Castle* (1982), 8-13

4. ESRO SAS/HC 180; ROHAS P27/2 (file in the Search Room at ESRO)

5. ESRO T266 (ex inf. C. Whittick); W.D. Scull, 'Old Buckhurst' *SAC* **54** (1911), 62; Holt, 'Early brickmaking', 164

6. Calvert, *op.cit.*, 13; Wight, *Brick Building*, 388; *VCH* **2**,151; I am indebted to Jeremy Goring for information about Sir Richard Guldeford

7. HEH BAT 55.1598; ESRO SAS/G16/8, 14

8. *SRS* **64**, passim; Mayhew, *Tudor Rye*, 32, 176-7

9. *VCH* **9**, 165; Wight, *Brick Building*, 389-90; D. Rudling in J. Farrant et al, 'Laughton Place: a Manorial and Architectural History, with an Account of Recent Restoration and Excavation' *SAC* **129** (1991), 106, 116; ESRO A2327/1/4/29

10. M. Howard in Farrant et al, *op. cit.*, 133-152

11. J. Farrant & J. Warren in Farrant et al, *op. cit.*, 155-160, 161-3; W.H. Blaauw, 'Brickwork at Laughton Place' *SAC* **7** (1854), 71

12. M. Biddle in Colvin et al, *King's Works*, 419-443

13. Bricks for the building of Nonsuch Palace in Surrey in 1538 (Colvin et al, *op. cit.*, 185) were delivered 'standing in the kilns' and the authors suggest that the 'kilns' were perhaps clamps which were dismantled when firing was complete

14. Holt, 'Early Brickmaking', 164; Wight, *Brick Building*, 387

15. H.R. Schubert, *History of the British Iron and Steel Industry* (1957), 196

16. *Ibid.* 197; CKS U1475 B8/2 – I am grateful to Gwen Jones for drawing my attention to this document

17. D.W. Crossley, *Sidney Ironworks Accounts 1541-1573* (Royal Historical Soc. 1975), 209 & 82-4;

18. ESRO ASH B643; E. Straker, *Wealden Iron* (1931), passim

19. Kenyon, *Glass*, 209

20. *VCH* **2**, 253; WSRO Cowdray MS. 285 f13v

21. J.A. Wooldridge, *The Danny Archives* (1966), x-xii, 74; W.H. Godfrey, 'The Estate of George Goring 1595' *SNQ* **1** (1926), 22
22. G. Batho, 'The Percies at Petworth' *SAC* **95** (1957), 8, 12; W.H. Godfrey, 'An Elizabethan Builder's Contract' *SAC* **65** (1924), 217.

Chapter 4

1. ESRO DAN 1126 228v
2. ESRO HIL 6/14/1; ADA 19, 40, 44 – I am grateful to John Kay for drawing my attention to these documents
3. ESRO ADA 46; M J. Leppard, 'Brickmaking' *BEGS* **44** (1988), 3
4. ESRO ADA 1
5. ESRO ADA 186-8 & W/INV 3098
6. ESRO ADA 117-8
7. ESRO SAS/A663-4 & QDD 6/E2; Beswick, 'Dicker', 2-10
8. *SRS* **9**, 62; *VCH* **6** (1), 112 & (2), 179, Aldsworth, 'Ebernoe', 219; *SRS* **72**, 91; WSRO QDD 16/W8
9. For a detailed description of the firing process see: Leslie, 'Ashburnham', 13-20
10. Aldsworth, 'Ebernoe', 219-24; Leslie, loc. cit.
11. ESRO XA 11/2, SAS/RF 15/17 & AMS 740
12. G. Batho, 'Petworth House 1574-1632' *SAC* **96** (1958), 108-134; WSRO PHA 6324 No 49 (ex inf. A. McCann)
13. ESRO A 4600/7
14. *VCH* **6** (1), 16; WSRO EpI/29/50/44
15. ESRO ASH 159/41 & ASH 1817 f 595/64 – I am indebted to David Crossley for this and subsequent references to bricks supplied to the ironworks
16. ESRO ASH 1178 f239, 1815 f456/219, 1653 & 1670-1732
17. Leslie, 'Ashburnham', 2-22; Harmer, 'Clay', 14-21
18. WSRO Goodwood MSS. EW2, 5476-5488
19. 1 am indebted to T.J. McCann for information about this family
20. WSRO Cowdray MS. 1813
21. ESRO A5257/C27.

Chapter 5

1. ESRO W/INV 1202; WSRO EpI/29/11/65
2. ESRO W/A11.206; WSRO EpI/29/216/11 & 16; ESRO W/INV 1619
3. Osborne, 'Bakers', 24-27; F.G. Aldsworth &

A.G. Down, 'Pottery in the Graffham area' *SAC* **128** (1990), 117-139
4. Baines, *Pottery,* 174; Beswick, 'Dicker', 4, 6
5. Baines, *Pottery*, passim
6. ESRO CAF 2/4 f123 and see gazetteer
7. *SWA*, 28 Mar 1774 and 14 Aug 1826; ESRO SAY 2831
8. Beswick, *Bricks and Tiles,* 7-8
9. ESRO CAF 2/4 & ALF 7/16; Kelly (1862); Wadhurst census returns (1871)
10. WSRO Par. 118/30/1; Kelly (1845); Daggett, *Toddington,* 89; Farrant, 'Building Materials', 25; inf. G. Mead; *Brighton Herald,* 30 Aug 1862
11. Neale, *Horsham,* 39; Pigot (1832-9); Kelly (1851-9); Baines, *Pottery,* 74
12. ESRO W/A40.85 & ADA 186; *SRS* **25**, 30, 135 and see gazetteer
13. Kelly (1867-87); ESRO PEV 390 & A4426/15
14. ESRO A 2300 (pt.); Kelly (1862-1903)
15. V. Hodsoll, *James Peerless, Builder* (Eastbourne LHS Factsheet 1, 1986)
16. Kelly (1878-99); Whitehouse, *Warnham,* 6; Pigot (1839); Kelly (1887-1907)
17. Kelly (1845); Baines, *Pottery,* 76; Kelly (1895-9)
18. Kelly (1859-90); Baines, *Pottery,* 74
19. Kelly (1882-1903).

Chapter 6

1. S. Farrant & J.H. Farrant, 'Brighton 1580-1820: from Tudor Town to Regency Resort' *SAC* **118** (1981), 339; Farrant, 'Building Materials', 24
2. ESRO A 4600/7
3. Farrant, 'Building Materials', 24; I.D. Margary, 'Militia Camps in Sussex' *SAC* **107** (1969), plate facing p 137
4. Gazetteer: Hastings 2 & 3
5. WSRO Goodwood MS. E5408; Venables & Outen, *Bognor,* 19
6. ESRO AMS 5575/27/5
7. ESRO A4600/7; J. Farrant, 'The Seaborne Trade of Sussex 1720-1845' *SAC* **114** (1976), 111
8. Watercolour in Blackburn Museum; O'Shea, 'Piddinghoe', 2-13
9. F. Kitchen, 'The Building of the Coastal Towns' Batteries' *SAS Newsletter* **45** (1985), 417
10. Beswick, 'Martello Towers', passim;

PRO MFQ 307/16B – I am indebted to
John Goodwin for drawing my attention
to this map

11. ESRO DB/B72/2 (ex inf. Margaret
    Whittick)
12. 1 am indebted to Ron Martin for
    information about mathematical tiles
13. F. Bentham Stevens, 'Brighton in 1846'
    SNQ **12** (1948), 4
14. Brunskill, *Brick Building*, 192-3; SWA,
    1 Apr 1805
15. Neale, *Horsham*, 40; ESRO QRE 947
16. WSRO Add. MS. 2996; Farrant, 'Building
    Materials', 25-6
17. Farrant & Farrant, *op. cit.*, 348
18. ESRO DB/B71/78; HMAG Corporation
    Minutes Vol 16 – 1 am indebted to
    Margaret Whittick for both of these
    references; R. Cooper, *Reminiscences of
    Eastbourne* (1903), 104.

Chapter 7

1. WSRO Add. MS. 2996; Kelly (1903-18)
2. *SWA*, 26 July 1790; ESRO A 5244; D.F.
   Gibbs & J.H. Farrant, 'The Upper Ouse
   Navigation 1790-1868' *SIH* **1** (1970/1), 23-
   40
3. WSRO QDP/W41
4. J. Hoare, *Sussex Railway Architecture* (1979),
   23
5. Neale, *Horsham*, 39-41
6. HALSP, *Railways*, 15-17
7. WSRO QDP/W89 & 113
8. ESRO GRA 17/49; M.J. Leppard, 'Brickmaking in East Grinstead: Additional
   Notes' *BEGS* **30** (Spring 1981)
9. ESRO PLU 1/4 f2l
10. Dobson, *Treatise*, 75-79
11. HALSP, *Railways*, 17
12. Neale, *Horsham*, 49
13. Beswick, 'Battle', 4
14. ESRO RAF 37/23
15. WSRO QDD 6/E3; B. Short (ed), A *Very
    Improving Neighbourhood: Burgess Hill 1840-
    1914* (1984), 38
16. Whitehouse, *Warnham*, 3, 7

Chapter 8

1. WSRO Goodwood MS. E5408; census
   returns for Rotherfield (1851); ESRO ASH
   1743
2. WSRO Goodwood MS. E5408; Farrant,

'Building Materials', 25; ESRO GBN 16/3
& A 5257/C27; ESRO A 2300 (pt) &
SAS/SM 168b

3. WSRO Cowdray MS. 1813; ESRO BAT
   2928d & ASH 1751-2; Hunt, *Mining
   Records*, 39-40; ESRO RAF/F/12/16
4. ESRO AMS 6214 & BMW A2/44
5. M. Beswick,'Brickmaking at Hawkswood
   in the 1880s' *Hailsham Historian &
   Naturalist* **2** (Nov 1987), 19-21; B. Short
   (ed), *Scarpfoot Parish: Plumpton 1830-1880*
   (1981), 33; Kelly (1874-99)
6. Henry Wolf, *Sussex Industries* (n.d. c1882),
   81
7. G.L. Remnant, 'Jonathan Harmer's
   Terracottas' *SAC* **100** (1962), 142-8
8. ESRO SAS/G/Acc1160; see Ch 3 Note 11
9. Wolf, *op. cit.*, 81-2
10. Baines, *Pottery*, passim; catalogue formerly
    in the possession of Robert Ware
11. Kelly (1899)
12. Foster, *Mines* (1896-1900): I am indebted to
    Paul Sowan of the Croydon Natural
    History and Scientific Society for
    supplying me with abstracts of these
    documents
13. Kelly (1874-1899); Pike/Hastings (1876)
14. Foster, cf note 12

Chapter 9

1. WSRO Ep II/5/5 f128-9 & II/5/6 f206;
   ESRO W/A11.206 & A17.57
2. ESRO HIL 6/14/1 & ADA 19, 20, 40; inf.
   John Kay
3. WSRO Ep II/5/11 f204-5; *SRS* **1**, 231;
   ESRO ADA 46; H. Warne, *The Heart of
   Burgess Hill: the History of the Brick and Tile
   Trade 1578-1855* (forthcoming)
4. WSRO Ep I/29/216/11, 16, 30;
   EpI/29/116/187 & Add. MS. 13420; *SRS* **9**,
   179 & **32**, 5, 76
5. G. Batho, 'The Percies at Petworth' *SAC* **95**
   (1957), 12; Kenyon, *Glass*, 209; WSRO
   EpI/29/150/12 & EpI/29/93/14, 52; G.H.
   Kenyon, 'Petworth Town and Trades' *SAC*
   96 (1958), 65; WSRO PHA 6324/49 (ex inf.
   A. McCann); WSRO LT Woolbeding (ex
   inf. J.C.V. Mitchell)
6. *SRS* **28**, 46; ESRO A 4426/6 & ALF 7/1-32
7. *SRS* **6**, 330; 'An 18th-century Brickmaker'
   SNQ **2** (1928), 90; ESRO SAS/A 663;
   W/A62.193, A72.106 & A78.822;

W/INV 3098; ADA 207; Pigot (1828); Kelly (1845-87)

8. Beswick, 'Dicker', 3, 4, 6-7; Kelly (1859-1927)

9. Beswick, 'Dicker', 5, 8-9; gazetteer: Wartling 2, Warbleton 5 & 6, Fletching 2, Westham 2, Willingdon 3, Bexhill 13; census returns for Uckfield (1851-71)

10. Gazetteer: Warbleton 4, Herstmonceux 4, Hailsham 9, Fletching 1, Maresfield 3 & 6, Westham 3; Beswick, 'Dicker', 3, 6

11. L.J. Maguire, A *Transcription of the Early Records of the Old Meeting House, Ditchling* (private pub. 1976); WSRO EpI/29/210/258; ESRO W/A66.307

12. *SRS* **35**, 351; Maguire *op. cit.*; ESRO AMS 5853/3; Emily Kensett, *History of the Free Christian Church, Horsham* (1921), 74, 86

13. *SWA*, 30 Jun 1815; Baines, *Pottery*, 125; Avery, *Burgess Hill*, 6, 2-13; *SRS* **75**, 76-77

14. WSRO EpII/25/3 (ex inf. E. Doff); ESRO NB 2/1-2 & NI 2/1, 6-7

15. Baines, *Pottery*, 110-121; inf. W. Norman (1978)

16. Gazetteer: Keymer 3 & 7, Clayton 5, Lower Beeding 4, Horsham 10; WSRO TDE 30; Kelly (1895-9)

17. Inf. G. Mead; Kelly (1851-87)

18. Bexhill census (1851); Martin, 'Frederic Martin'.

19. Kelly (1878-1938); inf. David Hawes (1991)

20. *SRS* **35**, 308, 320; Kelly (1851-90)

21. Gazetteer: Eastbourne 2 & 3, Hailsham 6

22. Gazetteer: Horsham 3 & 7; Kelly (1857-1938)

23. Kelly (1855-1922); ESRO PAR 228/1/3/1

24. Gazetteer: Uckfield 2 & 3; ESRO QRE 793 & PAR 286/12/1; inf. Helen McCurdy (née Ware)

25. ESRO TDE 6 & 33, ESRO ADA 126 & LT Uckfield; Kelly (1845, 1859)

26. Kelly (1862-66); *Uckfield Visitors' Guide* (1869); ESRO ADA 129-30

27. ESRO ADA 130-33; Kelly (1878); docs. held by Dawson Hart & Co., Uckfield

28. Docs. as 26; inf. H. McCurdy

29. As 27; ESRO BMW A2/136

30. Inf. H. McCurdy

Chapter 10

1. Woodeforde, *Bricks,* 146-50

2. Whitehouse, *Warnham*, 3-6

3. *Ibid.*, 5, 7

4. *Pictorial Trade Record* new series iv – copy in WSRO library

5. Beswick, *Bricks and Tiles*, 12; *Kent & East Sussex Courier,* 7 Mar 1980; Whitehouse, *Warnham,* 7

6. Paris, 'Partridge Green', 31-3; transcript of an interview with H.A. Simmons conducted by Geoffrey Mead in 1980; interview with Ben Foreman conducted by the author in 1989 – tape lodged at WSRO

7. OS maps 3rd edition (c1910)

8. A *Description of the Various Processes Employed by the Sussex Brick Company Limited* (n.d. c 1938), 6 – copy supplied by G.H.W. Coomber

9. *Ibid.*, 8

10. Whitehouse, *Warnham,* 9; W.R. Beswick 'Visit to Lunsford Brickworks' *SIAS Newsletter* **8** (Oct 1975)

11. Sussex Brick Co., *op. cit.*, 10

12. V. Mitchell & K. Smith, *Sussex Narrow Gauge* (2001)

13. Kelly (1927, 1930)

14. Whitehouse, *Warnham,* 8

15. Inf. G. Bradley-Smith (1989); Whitehouse, *Warnham,* 9; Kelly (1938)

16. Kelly (1924-38)

17. Inf. J.C.V. Mitchell (1985)

18. Inf. J.C.V. Mitchell & D. Hawes

Chapter 11

1. *Kent and East Sussex Courier,* 7 Mar 1980; Whitehouse, *Warnham,* 10; inf. G.H.W. Coomber

Most of the material for this chapter was collected by members of the SIAS Brick Study Group which met between 1978 and 1986 and by the author, in conversation with members of the staff of brickworks she has visited.

PART II
GAZETTEER OF BRICKMAKING SITES

INTRODUCTION

Note Many of the sites of former brickyards in the list which follows are in private ownership and permission should be obtained by anyone who wishes to inspect them. In most cases very little, other than a pit or pond and sometimes a scatter of brick and tile debris, remains to be seen.

The gazetteer is divided into two sections covering the counties of East Sussex and West Sussex, with boundaries as delineated in 1974.

The sites are listed under parishes, which are arranged in alphabetical order. For this purpose, boundaries are those which obtained c1840, when the majority of the tithe maps were drawn up. The names of municipalities and of civil parishes created since that date have been included, with cross references to the relevant 'old' parishes. As there have been a number of subsequent boundary revisions, readers are advised to consult entries for adjoining parishes as well as for the one(s) in which they have a particular interest. Reference maps are kept at the East and West Sussex Record Offices to show alterations in parish boundaries.

Within the parish groups, sites are numbered as far as possible in chronological order of the first known date of operation. It should be noted that unlocated sites are not listed: in many parishes brickmaking took place at a much earlier date than the one first mentioned in the gazetteer.

The format adopted for the arrangement of entries is, with minor variations, the one used by Alan Cox in his study of the Bedfordshire brickworks. The entries comprise:

A *description* of the site and its location

A six-figure National Grid *map reference*

The approximate *dates* when it was in operation

The names of *operators*, if known: these may include owners, lessees, managers and, in some cases, individual brickmakers

Products: this entry is only included if specific products were advertised or if there was a change from one type of product to another e.g. from hand-made, clamp-burnt stocks to kiln-fired wire-cuts

Present *condition* of the site: only included if the site has been inspected by a member of the Brick Study Group

Geology: included if the site is mentioned in one of the memoirs of the Geological Survey or has any particularly interesting features

Further information: miscellaneous details such as the kind of machinery used or the existence of inventories, catalogues, photographs etc.

References: maps are listed first, followed by documents in the two county record offices and other institutions (cf list of abbreviations), printed sources (cf bibliography) and the names of individuals who have furnished information (the date indicates when this was supplied).

Evidence for the existence of former brickyards has, in some cases, been adduced from field names marked on estate maps or listed in the schedules which accompanied the tithe maps. For this purpose, names such as Brick Kiln Field, Brick Clumps (clamps) Field and Brick Field have been accepted unreservedly, whereas Kiln Field and Claypit Field have been rejected, unless there was other evidence to link them with brickmaking, because they may have been associated with the practices of limeburning and marling, used extensively in the past. More problematical are names such as Brickhurst Wood, which may be of Saxon origin and so have no connection with brickmaking or, alternatively, may be a corruption of brick 'oste', a term used in the 15th and 16th centuries to signify a kiln. Similarly, Brickhouse and Tilehouse Fields are capable of two interpretations and have only been accepted if the older form of 'brickoste', or some other corroboration has been found. The name Tylers Field has usually been rejected because of the possibility that this merely indicates the name of a previous owner.

An attempt has been made to link the names of brickmakers published in various directories with known brickmaking sites but this has met with limited success. Postal addresses, particularly in the 19th century, could be very misleading (Herstmonceux, for example, received its letters via Hawkhurst, in Kent) and some brickmakers contrived to have two separate entries, one under their own name and another under the name of the firm that employed them. In a few cases, the names of brickmakers recorded on the decennial census returns have been included but it was found that quite often a brickmaker lived in one parish and worked in the adjoining one and so this material has not been used extensively.

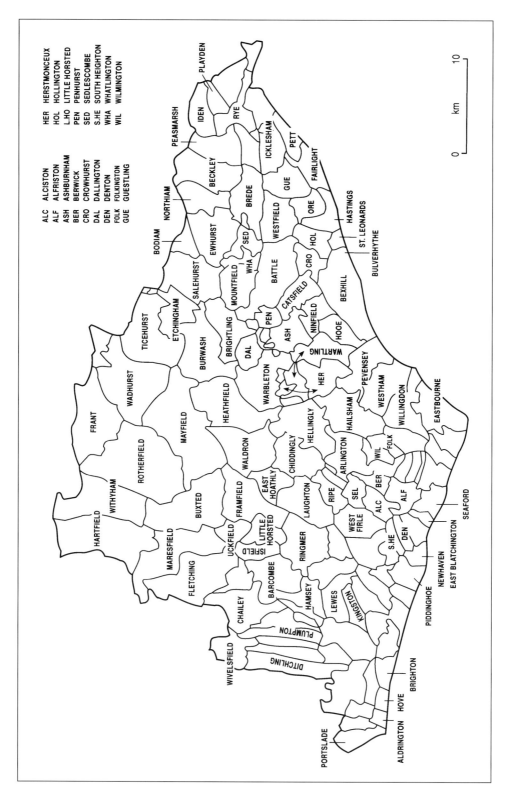

46. *East Sussex: parishes with brickyards listed in the gazetteer*

Documents listed under 'References' in this section are lodged at the East Sussex Record Office, Lewes, unless otherwise stated.

ALCISTON

1 Tile kiln ½ mile north of Alciston church
NGR: TQ 505 063
Date: Built in 1418, the tilery was still in existence in 1627 but had gone out of production by 1666. Tilehouse Field was marked on a map of 1822
Op.: Originally part of the Battle Abbey estate (cf Ch 2), it was leased to Ralph Sadyllar in 1536 and granted to Sir John Gage in 1540. John Peckden was the occupier before 1577, when the tilery was leased to Edward Newton. Other lessees included Jacob Awood in 1599 and Thomas Heaver and his son John, who were granted a 21-year lease in 1627
Prod.: By 1599 bricks were being made as well as tiles
Refs: SAS/G16, 44/73-80 & G/Acc 917, 920, 929/1.

ALDRINGTON

1 Brickyard on the north side of Shoreham Road (present-day Kingsway) SE of Wish Barn
NGR: TQ 276 045
Date: Probably in operation by 1828 and listed on the tithe award of 1843
Op.: The tenants in 1843 were Messrs Cheeseman, who advertised as Geo. Cheeseman & Son with various depots in Brighton between 1828 and 1874
Refs: TDE 78; Pigot (1828-39); Kelly (1846-'/4).

2 Brickyard on the Hove boundary
NGR: TQ 279 048
Date: 1840s and 1850s
Op.: The tenant in 1843 was William Nicholson, who was listed as a brickmaker and innkeeper in Brighton in 1851
Refs: TDE 78; census (1851) (ex inf. G. Mead).

3 Brickfield on the site of the present-day recreation ground between New Church Road and Marine Avenue
NGR: TQ 272 049
Date: 1860s to 1880s
Op.: James Holes (cf Portslade 2) advertised in 1882 and George, Charles and Henry Burn were brickmakers in the 1870s and '80s
F.Inf.: A photograph of Aldrington Brickworks c1870 was published in 1952
Refs: OS 25in 65/12 (1874); PAR 228/1/2/1 & 3/1; *SCM* **26** (1952), 170; Kelly (1882).

4 Brickfield between Old Shoreham Road and present-day Rowan Avenue
NGR: TQ 272 061
Date: 1890s and early 1900s
Op.: Mrs Charlotte Washington advertised from 1895 to 1903
Refs: OS 6in 65 NE (1898); Kelly (1895-1903).

5 Brickfield on the east side of Coleman Avenue between New Church Road and Portland Road
NGR: TQ 274 053
Date: In existence by 1895 and closed c1920
Op.: Edmund John Ockenden advertised in 1895 and 1899, when the brickfield was known as Gothard's. The name then changed to the Wish Brickfield Co., with George Freeman as manager
Prod.: Clamp-burnt bricks
F.Inf.: 52 men were employed in 1897. A tramway was used to transport brick earth from the pit to the moulding area. Cottages for the workers were built in Grange Road and Bolsover Road
Refs: OS 25in 65/12 (1898, 1911); Kelly (1895-1918); Foster, *Mines* (1898-1901); Pike/Brighton (1902-20); inf. C.C. Randall (1979).

6 Brickfield on the north side of New Church Road on the Portslade boundary
NGR: cTQ 266 053
Date: Early 20th century
Op.: Horace Frank Ockenden gave his address as Worcester Villas from 1905 to 1911
Refs: Kelly (1899); Pike/Brighton (1905-11) (ex inf. G. Mead).

7   Brickyard on the site of the sports ground south of Queens Parade, Hangleton Road
    NGR: TQ 271 064
    Date: Not known
    Geol.: Woolwich and Reading Beds
    Ref.: Young & Lake, *Brighton & Worthing*, 73.

ALFRISTON

1   Brickyard on the west side of North Street
    NGR: TQ 521 033
    Date: In existence by 1803, the yard appears to have gone out of use before 1842, when only Brick Kiln Cottages and Brick Kiln Brook, on the opposite side of the road, were listed on the tithe award. The word 'Brickilns' on the map of 1875 refers to the cottages, where remains of a kiln were found during alterations
    Op.: John Back was a brickmaker here in 1803, as was Robert Boodle in 1804 and 1808. In 1813 the owner was John Chapman, of Lewes, and the foreman Henry Back
    Refs: TDE 15; OS 25in 68/14 (1875); LPL/1/E3; *SRS* **25**, 206 & **26**, 442; *SWA*, 5 Jul 1813; F. Pagden, *History of Alfriston* (1899).

ARLINGTON

1   Brick kiln at Knockhatch east of Michelham Priory
    NGR: cTQ 573 094
    Date: Early to mid-16th century; land called Kell was mentioned in a valuation of the Priory in 1535 and may possibly be identified with the Brickhouse or Bricoste Croft, otherwise Knockhatch, referred to in a deed of 1587
    Refs: Salzman, *Hailsham*, 245-6, 258; E. Straker's transcript of CKS U267 T141/1 (ex inf. E. Doff).

2   Brickyard at the corner of Bayley's Lane on the Wilmington boundary
    NGR: TQ 553 070
    Date: In existence by 1803, listed on the tithe award of 1843 but as Old Brick Kiln in 1874; the brickyard was revived in the 1930s and closed in the 1950s.

    Op.: Bartholomew Osborn (cf Hailsham 3) was a brickmaker in Arlington in 1803. George Gosden was running the yard by 1841 and advertised from 1855 to 1862. The Wilmington Brick Co. advertised from 1930 to 1951, when the foreman was a Mr Gurr
    Geol.: Weald Clay
    Refs: TDE 51; OS 25in 68/7 (1874); LPL/1/E3; census (1841); Kelly (1855-62, 1930-38); *QMJ* (1933-51); Lake et al, *Lewes*, 35; inf. Maurice Thornton (1982).

ASHBURNHAM

1   Tile kiln
    Location not known.
    Date: In existence in 1362
    Ref.: Salzman, *Industries*, 123

2   Brick kiln SW of Ashburnham Furnace
    NGR: cTQ 683 168
    Date: 'The waste called Brickekell' and Brickekell Wood were mentioned in a deed of 1647
    Ref.: ASH/B643 (ex inf. D. Crossley).

3   Brickyard SW of Ashburnham Forge
    NGR: TQ 686 159
    Date: Probably in existence by 1682; the kilns were pulled down when a new brickyard (site 4) was opened in 1841
    Op.: Owned by the Ashburnham estate: John Harmer advertised for a journeyman brickmaker in 1791, John Sands was in charge from 1801 to 1826 and Silas Sands from 1828 to 1837
    F.Inf.: Bricks and tiles were supplied for use at the ironworks
    Refs: TIDE 68; ASH 160-1733, 1806, 1817; *SWA*, 9 May 1791.

4   Brickyard SE of Court Lodge
    NGR: TQ 684 161
    Date: Opened in 1841; closed in 1968
    Op.: Owned by the Ashburnham. estate: four generations of the Barden family were in charge between 1841 and 1955 when Jack Harmer, the last foreman of the yard, took over
    Prod.: Building and paving bricks, roof tiles and fittings, agricultural drainpipes and flower pots

Cond.: The double up-draught kiln is still in existence (2001) although its condition has deteriorated

F.Inf.: A detailed account of the brickyard, with photographs, was published in 1971, as was a description of tilemaking in 1981

Refs: OS 25in 57/1 (1874 et seq); ASH 1737-71; Leslie, 'Ashburnham', 2-22; Harmer, 'Clay', 14-20.

BARCOMBE

1 Brickyard on the bank of the river Ouse east of Pikes Bridge

NGR: TQ 435 147

Date: In use when the Upper Ouse Navigation was under construction in 1791 and listed as Upper and Lower Brickyard on the tithe award of 1839

Op.: The owner/occupier in 1839 was Russell Gray

Refs: TDE 134; A 5244.

2 Brickyard on the east side of the road south of Town Littleworth

NGR: TQ 412 176

Date: A kiln was marked on a map of 1829 and Brickyard Farm and Brickyard Wood to the north were named in 1873

Op.: Henry Novis, a brickmaker, was living in this area in 1841

Refs: SAS/SH 389; OS 25in 40/10 (1873); census (1841).

3 Brickfield on the west side of the railway west of Barcombe Cross

NGR: TQ 415 158

Date: In use when the Lewes to East Grinstead railway was under construction in 1880

Ref.: GRA 17/49.

BATTLE

1 Tile kiln SW of Battle Abbey

NGR: TQ 739 149

Date: First mentioned in a document of c1280, the tilery was still in existence in 1539 and Tile Kiln Field was marked on a map of 1724

Op.: Operated directly by the Abbey until the early 16th century. John Trewe was granted a 10-year lease in 1520

Prod.: Mainly roofing tiles but bricks were mentioned in 1520

Refs: BAT 4421/7; HEH BA Vol 36.1474 & Vol 55.1598 (ex inf. C. Whittick); *SRS* **65**, passim; Streeten, 'Building Materials', 79-97.

2 Tile kiln on Telham Hill
Exact location not known

Date: 13th century

Ref.: [Duchess of Cleveland], *History of Battle Abbey* (1877), 3 (footnote).

3 Brickfield north of Netherfield Place

NGR: TQ 717 182

Date: Probably in use when most of the house was rebuilt c1670: marked on an estate map of 1797

Refs: ASH 1170/33; inf. D. & B. Martin (1989).

4 Brickyard(s) on the east side of Hastings Road

NGR: cTQ 763 152 & TQ 767 147

Date: The yard was in existence by 1719, had probably been resited by 1773 and went out of use c1797

Op.: i. John Furner was taxed on the brick-kiln house and land in 1719 and was succeeded in 1722 by Robert Furner, who was granted a licence to dig clay in 1728. By 1740 his heirs had sold the property and from 1743 to 1761 it was in the hands of Walter Alleyn.
ii. William Gutsell paid rates from 1773 followed by James Bourner from 1783 to 1797

Refs: BAT 4421/9; RAF 52; TDE 158; BAT 20; PAR 236/30/1/1-4.

5 Brickyard on the north side of Telham Lane

NGR: TQ 753 142

Date: 18th century. Brick Kiln Field was marked on a map of 1724

Op.: A licence to dig clay was granted to William Hammond, ironmonger, in 1723 and renewed by other members of the family until 1764

Refs: BAT 4421/10; BAT 20 & 140

6 Brickyard on the south side of Hastings Road at Starrs Green

NGR: TQ 762 150

Date: Opened c1784, still in use in 1859 but abandoned by 1873

Op.: Samuel Gutsell, a brickmaker, bought

a cottage in the area in 1784 and advertised in 1797. Christopher Smith was the tenant in 1854, when the Telham Court estate, to which the yard belonged, was advertised for sale but the brickmaker may have been Thomas Bourner (cf site 7) who advertised in 1845 and 1855

Refs: TDE 158; RAF 37/70 Box 140; *Universal British Directory* (1797); Kelly (1845, 1855).

7   Brickyard at the corner of Hastings Road and Little Hemmingfold Lane
NGR: TQ 769 144
Date: Opened some time after 1790 and marked on maps of 1825, 1859 and 1873
Op.:   James Bourner (cf site 4) bought the land in 1790 and had erected a brick kiln before he sold the property to the Beauport Park estate in 1825. He continued as tenant and Thomas Bourner was rated for the brickyard in the 1830s. The yard was to let in 1851 and the new tenants, Eldridge and Stubberfield, advertised in that year, followed by Frederick Tree in 1859
Refs: A 5046; TDE 158; OS 25in 57/8 (1873); PAR 236/30/1/6; Kelly (1851, 1859); *Sussex Agricultural Express*, 19 July 1851.

8   Brickyard on the north side of Little Hemmingfold Lane
NGR: TQ 769 145
Date: Probably opened in 1805. Two kilns were shown on the map in a sale catalogue of 1832 and the site was still listed as Brickyard in 1859 and 1872
Op.:   Samuel Gutsell (cf site 6) was granted a lease, including the right to dig earth and clay for brick and tile-making, in 1805 and was rated for the yard until 1833. By 1851 it was under the same management as site 7
Refs: RAF 52; TDE 158; PAR 236/30/1/4, 6; A1684 SHE.

9   Brickyard on Marley Farm
Exact location not known
Date: In operation up to 1853 but super-seded shortly afterwards by site 10
Op.:   Owned by the Battle Abbey estate

Prod.:   New machinery for making tiles and drainpipes was installed in 1853
Refs: BAT 2954; Beswick, 'Battle', 4.

10 Brickworks on the west side of the railway north of Marley Lane
NGR: TQ 755 159
Date: First used when the Hastings line was under constuction c1850, opened as a commercial brickyard in 1853 and still in operation in 1901
Op.:   Owned by the Battle Abbey estate. George Archer was a brickmaker living at the 'railway hut' in 1851. Charles Hutchings was paid for work in the brickyard in 1853 and Aaron Foord and Thomas Samways in 1854. From 1886 to 1888 the foreman was Frederick Martin
F.Inf.:   The site had its own railway siding. Bricks were burnt in a Scotch kiln
Refs: TDE 158; OS 25in 57/4 (1873, 1899); BAT 2954-5, 2486-9; sale catalogue (1901) in Battle Museum; census (1851); Beswick, loc. cit

11 Brickyard at Aldershaw Farm west of Kent Street, Sedlescombe
NGR: TQ 788 152
Date: Opened c1985 and still in operation (2001)
Op.:   R. & B. Williams, trading as Aldershaw Tiles
Prod.:   Mainly hand-made roofing tiles, with some mathematical tiles and bricks for restoration work.
Geol.:   Clay is dug from a deep pit in the Wadhurst Clay (782 152) used in the 19th century by sites 7 and 8
Ref.:   *Kent & East Sussex Courier*, 20 Nov 1992.

12 Brick kiln in Phipp's Gill on the Battle Abbey estate
NGR: cTQ 732 152
Date: 16th or early-17th century: Brickhill/Brickhiln Copse was the name given to present-day Phipp's Gill in documents of c1640 and 1660. Kilnfield to the SW (730 149) marked on a map of 1721 may be linked to this
Refs: BAT 4419 & 4421/7; HEH BA 67/34

BECKLEY

1 Brickyard south of Church Shaw near the Northiam boundary

NGR: TQ 839 236

Date: 18th century: listed as Brick Kiln Field on a parish survey of 1815. Sale particulars of 1817 mention clay suitable for making bricks and tiles but the yard was no longer active at that date

Op.: The Standen family were tenants in the 18th century and John Standen supplied bricks for Northiam school house in 1729, possibly made on this site

Refs: PAR 237/6/1; GBN 5/4; FRE 8181/8.

2 Brickyard south of Four Oaks

NGR: TQ 863 238

Date: The brick kilns were mentioned in a document of 1768. Listed as Brick Kiln Field in 1815 when the yard had probably been superseded by site 6

Op.: As site 6 in 1815

Refs: PAR 237/6/1; GBN 3/1.

3 Brick kiln west of Little Gate Farm

NGR: TQ 851 220

Date: Brick Kiln Field was listed on the survey of 1815

Op.: Samuel Reeves was the owner/occupier in 1815

Ref.: PAR 237/6/1.

4 Brick kiln on the south side of Whitebread Lane NW of Four Oaks

NGR: TQ 857 244

Date: Brick Kiln Field was listed on the survey of 1815

Op.: Thomas Elphick was the tenant in 1815

Ref.: PAR 237/6/1.

5 Brickyard on the north side of the road in Beckley village

NGR: TQ 850 240

Date: In existence before 1806, still in operation in 1839 but abandoned in the 1850s, when a Methodist chapel was built on the site

Op.: John Thamsett (Tampsett) supplied bricks and tiles for Northiam schoolhouse in 1806 and 1807 and for Beckley School in 1808. He was the owner/occupier in 1815 and 1839. In 1841 the brickmaker was Stephen Paine, who advertised in 1851

Refs: PAR 237/6/1; TDE 34; FRE 8182/12, 19 & 8183/7; census (1841); Kelly (1851).

6 Brickyard on the south bank of the River Rother at Knelle Dam

NGR: TQ 853 269

Date: In existence in 1815 and marked as Brick & Tile Works on the map of 1872, by 1898 the yard had been moved to the south (853 267). It had ceased operation by 1940

Op.: Owned in 1815 by the Peasemarsh Place estate. H. Catt advertised as a brickmaker in Beckley in 1851, followed by R. Paine from 1859 to 1867. In the 1930s the yard was in the hands of M.P. Harris & Co. (cf Northiam 6)

Cond.: The buildings remained for some time after the war

Refs: PAR 237/6/1; TDE 34; OS 25in 31/8 (1872, 1898, 1910); Kelly (1859-67); inf. C. Bloomfield (1986).

BERWICK

1 Brickyard near Berwick church

NGR: cTQ 518 049

Date: 19th century

Ref.: Rev. E.B. Ellman, *Recollections of a Sussex Parson* (1912), 262 (ex inf. E. Doff).

2 Brickworks on the edge of Ludlay Coppice on the west side of the road from Berwick station to Upper Dicker

NGR: TQ 527 075

Date: Marked on maps from 1874; closed in 1965

Op.: Owned by the Gage estate: David Lusted was employing 2 men and 2 women here in 1881. O. Funnell advertised in 1899. In 1901 his lease was taken over by W. Marchant, who was succeeded in 1913 by Alfred Pettit & Son. They advertised until 1927, followed by E. & A. Marshall from 1930 to 1938. After the war the yard was run by the Ludlay Brick & Tile Co. Ltd

Prod.: Clamp-burnt bricks up to World War 2. c1950 the yard was converted from seasonal to all-the-year-round working with a Berry moulding machine, a heated drying-shed and Scotch kilns.

F.Inf.: An inventory of implements and plant taken in 1913 included a horse-drawn pugmill. There was a 2ft-gauge tramway from the claypit to the works prior to closure. The site was surveyed by members of SIAS in 1984 and the buildings were demolished in 1986

Geol.: Upper beds of the Weald Clay

Refs: OS 25in 68/6 (1874, 1899, 1910, 1928); census (1881); Kelly (1899-1938); *QMJ* (1927, 1951-9); BMW C11/9 (pt); A2/254; White, *Lewes*, 29; Chalkpits Mus., *Industrial Railways*; inf. P. Laker (1986).

3 Brickworks on the north side of the railway at Berwick Station
NGR: TQ 524 070
Date: Said to have been in existence by 1881; first advertised in 1903 and closed c1958
Op.: Owned by the Gage estate and operated by the Cuckmere Brick Co. Ltd; in 1929 the company director was A. Avard of Eastbourne and the manager W.L. Laker
Prod.: Common wire-cuts, sand-faced wire-cuts and hand-moulded red facing bricks. Bricks were supplied for the building of St Andrew's Church, Eastbourne.
F.Inf.: The steam-engine formerly used to power the machinery had been replaced by oil-engines by 1929. A circular kiln was used for hand-made bricks and a continuous kiln for commons. A photograph of Mr Laker and the workmen accompanied a magazine article of 1929
Geol.: Weald Clay at the junction with the Lower Greensand
Refs: OS 25in 68/6 (1910, 1928); Kelly (1903-1938); *QMJ* (1927-51); White, *Lewes*, 29; 'Cuckmere Brick Co., Berwick' *SCM* **3** (1929) 479; Lake et al, *Lewes*, 33; inf. P. Laker (1986).

BEXHILL

1 Brick kiln on Worsham Farm
NGR: TQ 755 088
Date: Brickhoste Croft was mentioned in a lease of 1606 and can be identified with Little, Middle and Upper Brickhurst Fields on a map of 1791
Refs: AMS 5828/2; RAF 25/25.

2 Brickyard on the west side of Buckholt Lane
NGR: TQ 742 094
Date: Brick Kiln Field was marked on a map of the manor of Ingrams of 1753. A brickyard was opened a little to the north in the late 19th century and closed c1928
Op.: James Carey was the brickmaker in the latter period
Prod.: In the 1920s one of the products was fired clay for use as hardcore
Refs: A 1745; TDE 141; OS 25in 70/3 (1899, 1909); inf. Peter Carey (1990).

3 Brickfield on the coast west of Cooden
NGR: TQ 694 061
Date: Marked 'D' on a sketch-map of 1805 and as Brick Yard Field and Pond on the tithe award of 1839, this was one of the sites used to make bricks for the Martello towers in 1805-6
Op.: Mr Dalloway, contractor to the Board of Ordnance
Refs: PRO MFQ 307/16B; TDE 141; Beswick, 'Martello Towers', 23.

4 Brickyard at Sidley Green
NGR: TQ 737 092
Date: In operation by 1794 and closed in the 1940s
Op.: John Crowhurst had been succeeded in 1839 by Henry Reeves, who advertised until 1867. Albert Adams had taken over by 1874 and was followed by James Adams in 1895 and Stephen and George Adams from 1913 onwards
Prod.: Bricks, tiles and earthenware
F.Inf.: A tile inscribed 'Edward Barn made this tile being the first made at Sidley in the year 1794' and a photograph taken c1900 are in Bexhill Museum
Refs: TDE 141; OS 25in 70/3 (1873, 1899, 1909, 1930); Kelly (1855-1934); *QMJ* (1927-44); Baines, *Pottery*, 68.

5   Brickyard east of The Highlands
    NGR: TQ 731 094
    Date: In operation in 1839, the site had
           reverted to scrub by 1873. In 1899
           Highlands Brick Works was marked
           slightly to the south of the old
           workings
    Op.:   The occupier in 1839 was Thomas
           Larkins of Woodsgate Farm. The
           brickmaker in 1851 was Spencer
           Eastwood
    Refs: TDE 141; OS 25in 70/3 (1873, 1899);
           census (1851).

6   Brick and tile works on the north side of
    Pebsham Lane
    NGR: TQ 757 090
    Date: In existence from the 1840s and still in
           operation in 1909
    Op.:   John Martin was the brickmaker in
           1851, Henry Freeman in 1861 and 1871
           and George Freeman in 1881
    Prod.: The Freemans lived at Pipe Kiln
           Cottage, which suggests that agricul-
           tural drainpipes formed an important
           part of the output of the works
    Refs: OS 25in 70/4 (1873, 1899, 1909);
           census (1851-81).

7   Brickfield on the east side of Sea Road south
    of the railway
    NGR: TQ 745 074
    Date: The claypit was marked on the map of
           1873
    Op.:   Possibly Charles Mercer in 1851
    Refs: OS 25in 70/7; census (1851); L.J.
           Bartley, *The Story of Bexhill* (1971), 93.

8   Brickworks north of Whydown Road
    NGR: TQ 712 094
    Date: In existence by 1881 but disused by
           1909
    Op.:   Thomas Ransome was a brickmaker at
           High Woods in 1881. Alfred Ford
           advertised in 1887 and George
           William Veness from 1890 to 1899
    Refs: OS 6in 70 NW (1898) 25in 70/2 (1909);
           census (1881); Kelly (1887-99).

9   Brickfield at the corner of Ashdown Road and
    Dorset Road
    NGR: TQ 750 077
    Date: 1880s: the claypit was filled in to make
           a cricket ground in the late 1890s
    Op.:   Thomas Dyer and George Ballard

were brickmakers in 1881, probably
working on this site
    F.Inf.: Steam-driven machinery was used as
           Henry Jarrett gave his occupation in
           1881 as 'engine driver, brick factory'
    Refs: Census (1881); Bartley, *op. cit.*, 93, 132.

10 Brickworks on the north side of Turkey Road
    NGR: TQ 720 094
    Date: Opened in 1888, marked on maps
           from 1898 onwards and still in
           operation (2001)
    Op.:   Henry E. Cruttenden, of St Leonards,
           advertised in 1899 followed by
           Jackson & Adeney from 1903 to 1922
           and the Lunsford Co. Ltd until 1938.
           After the war the works was run for a
           time by M.P. Harris (cf Northiam 6)
           before being acquired by the Sussex &
           Dorking Brick Co., which then became
           part of the Redland Group. Now
           owned by Ibstock Brick Ltd
    Prod: As well as bricks and tiles, output up
           to 1940 included architectural terra
           cotta, chimney pots and finials, flower
           pots, vases and other ceramic ware, as
           recorded on a film made in 1938. The
           works now produces only kiln-fired
           stocks
    Geol.: Wadhurst clay, from which 'Pevensey'
           bricks are currently made, and
           Tunbridge Wells Sand, used for
           'Ashdown Crowborough' multi-
           coloured stocks
    Refs: OS 6in 70 NW (1898) 25in 70/2 (1909,
           1930, 1939); Kelly (1899-1938); *QMJ*
           (1927-59); Bartley, *op. cit.*, 93, 145;
           Bexhill Observer, 1 Aug 1936; *SIAS
           Newsletter* **8**, Oct 1975; film in the
           possession of I.G.C. Dowsett of
           Eastbourne; inf. T.D. Brand (1993).

11 Brickfield south of Woodville Road
    NGR: TQ 736 072
    Date: 1890s
    Ref.: Bartley, *op. cit.*, 93.

12 Brickworks between Ninfield Road and St
    Mary's Lane
    NGR: TQ 727 099
    Date: In operation by 1899 and closed just
           after World War 2
    Op.:   G. Baker from 1903 to 1920 followed
           by Alfred Spiers & Son. They sold the

business in the late 1920s to White Bros, who advertised from 1930 to 1938

F.Inf.: A typical row of brickworkers' cottages had been built on the south side of Ninfield Road by 1909

Refs: OS 25in 57/15 & 70/3 (1899, 1909, 1930); Pike/Hastings (1903-20) (ex inf. D. Padgham); Kelly (1930-34); *DBC* (1938); inf. P. Carey (1990).

13 Brickworks on the west side of Peartree Lane
NGR: TQ 717 103
Date: In existence by 1907, closed for a time, then revived in the 1930s
Op.: William Knowles advertised at Lunsford Cross in 1907 and Goldsmith's Brickyard was listed in Peartree Lane from 1932 to 1938
Refs: OS 25in 57/14 (1909, 1930); Kelly (1907); Pike/Hastings (1932-8) (ex inf. D. Padgham).

14 Brickworks between Watermill Lane and Kiteye Wood
NGR: TQ 734 104
Date: Early 20th century
Op.: S. & G. Adams (cf site 4) in 1909
Refs: OS 25in 57/15 (1909); Pike/Hastings (1909) (ex inf. D. Padgham).

15 Brickworks on the north side of Broadoak Lane
NGR: TQ 730 085
Date: 20th century: the claypit was marked on maps of 1930 and 1939
Op.: Members of the Carey family (cf site 2): Stephen Carey advertised from 1913 to 1938
Refs: OS 25in 70/3 (1930, 1939); Kelly (1913-15); *QMJ* (1927); *DBC* (1938); Bartley, *op. cit.*, 93; inf. Peter Carey.

EAST BLATCHINGTON

1 Brickfield on the west side of present-day Kimberley Road
NGR: TV 472 995
Date: Opened in 1882 and possibly still in operation in 1930, as a photograph in Seaford Museum is captioned: Rough Sea by Buckle Brickworks 1930
Op.: Lutley & Mannington (cf Hailsham 9) were granted a lease of 6 acres of land

'with liberty to get and work common brick clay and sand chalk into bricks' in 1882. [ ] Funnell was the brickmaker in 1893 and George Allen advertised in 1895

Prod.: Hand-made clamp-fired bricks
F.Inf.: Brickmaking plant, including 2 steam-powered pugmills, was offered for sale in 1883
Cond.: Brick debris was still visible in the gap between the entrance to the caravan site and Kimberley Road c1980
Refs: HIL 7/12/1, 2; SAS/SM 168b; Kelly (1895); Seaford Museum photo ref. 6470a; inf. Joan Astell (1980).

BODIAM

1 Brickyard on the demesne land of the manor of Bodiam
Exact location not known
Date: In existence before 1672 when the Brickkell Pond was drained; a yard was still in operation in 1747
Op.: Ralph Gladdish made bricks for William Byrd, the vicar of Bodiam in 1682 and William Boys, brickmaker, made his will in 1747
Refs: AMS 5691/2/20; A 2696 (ex inf. G. Jones); W/A57.501.

BREDE

1 Brick kiln south of Furnace Lane
NGR: TQ 838 207
Date: Brick-kiln Farm and Brick Kiln Field were mentioned in a lease of 1818
Refs: TDE 17; SAS/FB 245.

2 Brickyard and pottery on the south side of Pottery Lane
NGR: TQ 818 187
Date: The pottery was in existence by the mid-18th century and brick and tile kilns by the 1790s; closed in 1892.
Op.: Owned by Henry Richardson from the mid-1700s until his death in 1798. Mr Eldridge was the master potter and brickmaker in 1795. Thomas Weller and his descendants ran the works throughout the 19th century
Refs: TDE 17; OS 25in 44/10 (1873); A4426/6; Baines, *Pottery*, 56-69.

3 Brick kiln on the north side of the present-day Powdermill Reservoir
NGR: TQ 802 198
Date: Brick Kiln Field was listed on the tithe award of 1846
Op.: Spencer Crisford, the tenant in 1846, was also tenant of a brickyard in Sedlescombe (qv)
Refs: TDE 17.

4 Brickyard on Brook Lodge Farm
NGR: cTQ 805 183
Date: Mid-19th century
Op.: Owned and worked by Henry Smith, who also owned the brickyard south of Brede Bridge (cf Westfield 4)
F.Inf.: Bricks stamped 'DRAIN', which must have been made before the abolition of the brick tax in 1850, have been built into walls near the farmhouse
Ref.: E. Austen, Brede: *The Story of a Sussex Parish* (1946), 10.

5. Brick and tile works on Reysons Farm
NGR: TQ 832 193
Date: Marked only on the map of 1873
Op.: Seymour Apps advertised from 1874 to 1899
Refs: OS 6in 44 (1873); Kelly (1874-99).

6 Brickworks in Round Wood north of Broad Oak
NGR: TQ 826 202
Date: Marked only on the map of 1929
Ref.: OS 25in 44/7 (1929).

BRIGHTLING

1 Brick kiln SE of Socknersh Manor
NGR: TQ 700 231
Date: Brick Kiln Meadow was listed on the tithe award of 1838
Refs: TDE 47.

2 Brickyard on the northern edge of Purchase Wood
NGR: TQ 674 207
Date: In existence by 1700; closed by 1797
Op.: Thomas Wimble in 1700 and John Wimble in 1723
Refs: AMS 3501; RAF/F/4/1; W/INV 1655.

3 Brickyard in Brightling (Rosehill) Park
NGR: TQ 686 196
Date: Brick Kiln Field, marked on an estate map of c1836, was probably the site of

brickmaking when the house was built in the early 18th century
Op.: Owned by the Fuller estate
Ref.: SAS/RF 15/12/1.

4 Brickyard west of the road from Oxleys Green to Fontridge Lane
NGR: TQ 687 223
Date: In operation by 1838; closed in 1940
Op.: Owned by the Fuller estate: the brickmaker between 1850 and 1874 was John Relf
Prod.: Bricks, tiles and drainpipes: Relf's notebooks for the years 1869-1874 list the contents of each kiln burnt
F.Inf.: The double Wealden-type kiln and the water-driven pugmill were surveyed and recorded in 1969
Refs: TDE 47; OS 25in 43/1 (1874 et seq); RAF/F/12/16, 17; PAR 254/1/2/2; Draper & Martin, 'Local Industry', 55-7.

BRIGHTON

1 A number of brickmaking sites near the Hove boundary south of Western Road
NGR: cTQ 301 042
Date: Brickmaking was taking place in this part of the Wick estate from at least the 1720s. Two groups of kilns were shown on a sketch map of Brighton camp drawn in 1793. From the 1830s the centre of operations moved westwards into Hove
Op.: Henry Hill made bricks and tiles for Stanmer House here between 1723 and 1727. George Sharp and [ ] Sweet-enham advertised as brickmakers in Brighton in 1798. Thomas Budgen, a builder, rented a brickyard at Wick from c1808 to 1811 and a brickmaker of the same name was living in Middle Street in 1821 and died in 1826. William Hall gave his address as Norfolk Square in 1832
Refs: I.D. Margary, 'Militia Camps in Sussex' *SAC* **107** (1969), plate facing p137; A4600/7; W/A75.907; *Universal British Directory* (1798); Farrant, 'Building Materials', 24-5; Brighton Baptisms 1813-1823 in Brighton Reference Library & Swaysland's *Brighton Directory* (1832) (ex inf. G. Mead).

2 Brickyard in Richmond Terrace east of Lewes Road
NGR: TQ 315 048
Date: 1820s
Op.: [Amon] Wilds the elder, a builder (cf Lewes 2), paid rates for the yard in 1824
Ref.: Brighton Poor Rate Book (ex inf. G. Mead).

3 Brickyard on the south side of Viaduct Road
NGR: cTQ 313 054
Date: 1840s; a complaint was made in 1846 about the nuisance caused
Op.: Possibly Edward Pattenden, who gave his address as Brunswick Place North in 1843
Refs: DB/B60/12 (ex inf. Margaret Whittick); Leppard's *Brighton Directory* (1843) (ex inf. G. Mead).

BULVERHYTHE

1 Brickyard near the Bull Inn
NGR: TQ 769 081
Date: Marked 'E' on a sketch map of 1805: a kiln in the same area, on land belonging to the Pebsham estate, was marked on railway plans of 1839
Op.: Mr Dalloway, contractor to the Board of Ordnance in 1805; John Barton was the tenant in 1839
Refs: PRO MFQ 307/16B; QDP/E171/3; Beswick, 'Martello Towers', 23.

BURWASH

1 Brickyard on the west side of the Stonegate road at Burwash Common
NGR: TQ 639 236
Date: In existence by 1791 when there was a brick kiln on Gutsoll (Goodsoal) Farm; listed on the tithe award of 1839
Op.: Solomon Stubberfield (cf St Leonards 2) was a brickmaker here in 1839, when he was in dispute with William Daw about the sale of his brickmaking implements. Obadiah Daw, brickmaker, was a witness in the case and probably worked in the yard subsequently
Refs: TDE 157; A4919/10/261: QRE 866.

2 Brickyard on the south side of High Street west of the Bear Inn
NGR: TQ 673 246
Date: In existence in 1826, when it was offered to let; by 1839 the site had been levelled for use as a bowling green
Refs: TDE 157; *SWA*, 25 Sept 1826.

3 Brickworks on the west side of Spring Lane near the junction with High Street
NGR: TQ 669 246
Date: In operation by 1855 and closed c1900
Op.: John Parsons advertised from 1855 to 1878. James Keeley and his son William were working here by 1881 and the latter advertised from 1890 to 1899 before moving to site 4.
Prod.: Bricks, tiles and drainpipes: spare parts for the tile and pipe machines were supplied by the Hurst Green foundry in 1887 and 1896
Refs: OS 6in 29 (1875) 25in 29/12 (1898); AMS 6214; census (1871-91); Kelly (1855-99).

4 Brickworks on Claws Farm on the east side of Shrub Lane
NGR: TQ 683 261
Date: In existence by 1861, the yard is said to have closed in 1912-13 but was marked on maps up to 1937
Op.: Probably Thomas Edwards in 1841; George Edwards was working here in 1861, followed in 1871 by George Keeley, who was foreman in the brickyard assisted by his sons John, Robert and Henry. George and Henry were still there in 1881, when the yard appears to have been owned by Thomas Lambert Gillham, farmer and brickmaker., of Biggs (now Eatonden Manor) Farm in Ticehurst, who advertised in 1882, followed by his exors from 1890 to 1899. In 1901 William Keeley (cf site 3) took over
Refs: OS 25in 30/5 (1875-1937); census (1841-91); Ticehurst census (1881-91); Kelly (1882-1907); Shephard-Thorn, *Tenterden*, 56; Draper & Martin, 'Local Industry', 57; R.H. Charters, 'Making bricks in 1901' *Recologea Papers* Vol 5 No 4 (Robertsbridge 1976), 58-9; inf. Norman Bishop (1993).

5   Brickworks on the west side of Belle Alley Hill
    NGR: TQ 677 244
    Date: In operation by 1871 and marked on maps from 1875 to 1937
    Op.:   Daniel Robinson was described as brickmaker and landowner in 1871. The site was acquired by Rudyard Kipling in 1906 as part of the Batemans estate
    Refs: OS 25in 30/9 (1875, 1898, 1909, 1937); AMS 5982/10/1, 2; census (1871); Draper & Martin, 'Local Industry', 57.

6   Brickworks on the south side of Spring Lane at Southover
    NGR: TQ 654 256
    Date: Marked only on the map of 1875
    Ref.: OS 6in 29 (1875).

BUXTED

1   Brickyard on New House Farm
    NGR: TQ 499 243
    Date: Listed on the tithe award of 1841
    Op.:   The owner/occupier in 1841 was John Olive
    Ref.: TDE 135.

2   Brickworks at Hastingford
    NGR: TQ 525 253
    Date: The brickworks was in operation from c1870 to c1900 but bricks for Hastingford Farm, built c1600, were also made in the locality
    Op.:   John Potter was the master brickmaker in 1871 and 1881. Henry Tyhurst & Son of Uckfield (qv) advertised as brickmakers here from 1882 to 1895 followed by John Preston Smith in 1899
    Prod.: Bricks and roofing tiles
    F.Inf.: Sand for brickmaking was brought from the Abergavenny estate at Hadlow Down
    Refs: OS 25in 28/10 (1875, 1899); census (1871-81); Kelly (1882-99); inf. Sir F. Sowrey (1989).

3   Brick kiln (?) on the north side of the stream near Stonehouse Cottages
    NGR: TQ 485 284
    Date: Uncertain: the cottages were built c1872

Cond.: Waster bricks were found in a mound beside the stream in 1977
Refs: Inf. C.F. Tebbutt (1977) & Sir F. Sowrey (1989).

4   Brickworks on the west side of Gordon Road
    NGR: TQ 498 233
    Date: Marked only on the map of 1874
    Ref.: OS 25in 28/13 (1874).

CATSFIELD

1   Brickworks on the west side of Watermill Lane
    NGR: TQ 733 116
    Date: 1930s
    Op.:   Crisford & Roberts
    Prod.: Kiln and clamp bricks
    F.Inf.: The pugmill was powered by a Ruston & Hornsby oil engine
    Refs: OS 25in 57/11 (1939); inf. Mr Crisford of Horam (1980).

CHAILEY

1   Brickyard at South Chailey on the east side of Green Lane
    NGR: TQ 392 174
    Date: Opened in the late 17th century, extended to the north and east in the 19th and 20th centuries and still in operation (2001)
    Op.:   Richard Calchin had two brick-kilns on South Common in 1711. John Pulman acquired the site in 1721 and sold it to George Colvin in 1734. In 1762 John Billinghurst (cf Ditchling 2) became the owner and in 1792 his trustees sold the yard to Richard Norman, who was already working there. The business was then managed by successive generations of the Norman family (cf Ch 9) until it was sold to Redland Bricks Ltd in 1959. Now owned by Ibstock Brick Ltd
    Prod.: Kiln-fired bricks, tiles and drainpipes with glazed and unglazed pottery and mathematical tiles added to the range in the 19th century; since 1960, clamp bricks only
    F.Inf.: A lime kiln was also in existence in 1762. The pugmills were powered by a Marshall steam engine in the early 20th century

Geol.: Weald Clay
Refs: TDE 136; OS 25in 40/9 (1873, 1899, 1910); W/A40.85; ADA 186-8; Pigot (1828-39); Kelly (1845-1938); *QMJ* (1951-59); White, *Lewes*, 29; Baines, *Pottery*, 118-121; inf. Wallace Norman (1978).

2 Brickyard at South Common to the north of site 1
NGR: TQ 392 179
Date: Probably the site of brickmaking for the Hooke estate in the 1730s and again in 1754-5, when building work was in progress. The yard then operated continuously until c1900
Op.: John Siffleet was granted a licence to dig clay in 1754 and died in 1759. The yard was taken over by Thomas Alcorn and run thereafter by members of the Alcorn family, the last to advertise being William in 1887. The site was then acquired by the Normans (cf Site 1)
Prod.: Kiln-fired bricks and tiles
Refs: TDE 136; OS 25in 40/9 (1873, 1899); Hook 16/2, 6-7; W/INV 3098; ADA 187-8; SAS/HC 525; Pigot (1828-32); Kelly (1845-87).

CHIDDINGLY

1 Brickyard on Limekiln Farm near the Chalvington boundary
NGR: TQ 538 113
Date: In operation by 1754, marked on maps up to 1898 but as Old Kiln only in 1910
Op.: Richard Guy, who supplied bricks for building operations at Glynde Place in 1754, was succeeded by his son Walter in 1796. Thomas Guy advertised in 1859 and 1862 followed by Gaius Guy from 1867 to 1882
Refs: TDE 105; OS 6in 55 (1875) 55 SE (1898, 1910); Kelly (1859-82); Beswick, 'Dicker', 3-4, 6; Lusted, 'Glynde', 48.

2 Brickyard on present-day Brickfields Farm SW of Golden Cross
NGR: TQ 534 123
Date: In operation from before 1755 until the early 1900s
Op.: William Funnell, who sold bricks to Thomas Turner of East Hoathly in 1755, was granted the land as

copyhold in 1765. By 1800 the yard was in the hands of the Guy family (cf site 1). The tenant in 1844 was Thomas Richardson. James White, the tenant in 1852, was insolvent by 1856. The brickmaker from 1895 to 1903 was George Kennard
Refs: TDE 105; Kelly (1895-1903); Vaisey, *Turner*, 10; BUR 2/1/17, 50, 51; Beswick, 'Dicker', 3-7.

3 Brickyard on Millhouse Farm on the west side of the Dicker
NGR: TQ 540 120
Date: In existence by 1773; closed in the 1880s
Op.: William Funnell the younger was granted the copyhold in 1773. The site was sold to Richard Guy (cf Site 1) in 1789 and was operated as part of the family business until some time after 1844. John Guy advertised from 1859 to 1867, the yard passed to his son John in 1870 and Mrs John Guy advertised in 1882
F.Inf.: There was a lime kiln as well as a brick kiln on the site in 1773
Refs: TDE 105; OS 6in 55 (1875); Kelly (1859-67, 1882); BUR 2/1/200; Beswick, 'Dicker', 4, 6.

4 Brick Works on the south side of the Lewes road at Lower Dicker
NGR: TQ 542 122
Date: In operation from before 1857 to 1884
Op.: James White (cf site 2) handed over to Benjamin White (cf Laughton 2) in 1857. The latter advertised from 1859 to 1882
Refs: OS 6in 55 (1875); RAF/F/2/1; Kelly (1859-82); BUR 2/1/57; Beswick, 'Dicker', 7.

5 Brick and tile works north of Parsonage Farm
NGR: TQ 545 147
Date: Opened in 1882 and closed c1904; there may have been brickmaking at an earlier date as 'Pit and Shaw' are marked on this site on a map of 1777
Op.: John Benge (cf Waldron 3) advertised for 'a man to kiln bricks' in 1882 and Charles Benge advertised from 1895 to 1903
Refs: A 2449/5; OS 6in 55 NE (1898, 1910); *Sussex Advertiser*, 7 Mar 1882, Kelly (1895-1903).

CROWBOROUGH *see* ROTHERFIELD, WITHYHAM

CROWHURST

1   Pottery and brickyard on the east side of Old Forewood Lane
    NGR: TQ 758 133
    Date: In operation by 1892, marked on the map of 1899 but disused by 1908
    Op.:   James Walder & Son, builders, of Hastings, advertised from 1895 to 1903
    Refs: OS 25in 57/8 (1899, 1908); Kelly (1899-1903); Baines, *Pottery*, 66.

DALLINGTON

1   Tile kiln on Padgham Farm
    NGR: TQ 657 181
    Date: Marked Kiln Field on a map of 1793
    F.Inf.:   Tile wasters were found in a bank by the pond in 1980
    Refs: ASH 2364; inf. Colin Rose (1980).

DANEHILL *see* FLETCHING, HORSTED KEYNES

DENTON

1   Brickworks north of The Drove
    NGR: TQ 451 018
    Date: Marked only on the map of 1910
    Ref.:   OS 25in 78/3 (1910).

2   Brickworks west of the junction of Avis Road and Avis Way
    NGR: TQ 449 022
    Date: Marked only on the map of 1928
    Op.:   Denton Brick Co. Ltd advertised in 1930
    Refs: OS 25in 78/3 (1928); Kelly (1930).

DITCHLING

1   Brick kiln near Inholms Farm
    NGR: TQ 327 195
    Date: The 'brickhouse' was mentioned in a will of 1742
    Op.:   [ ] Brand at some time prior to 1742
    Ref.:   W/A56.343 (inf. H. Warne).

2   Brickyard and pottery on the east side of Ditchling Common
    NGR: TQ 340 181
    Date: c1740 until 1940
    Op.:   John Billinghurst was a brickmaker in Ditchling in 1740, probably on this site. After his death in 1791, John Caffin and Francis Foster, potters and brickmakers, took over the business. When their partnership was dissolved in 1815, Foster continued alone and was succeeded in 1820 by William Gravett, a potter, who also advertised as a brickmaker from 1845 to 1855. He was followed by George Chinery from 1859 to 1871. In 1873 the site was leased to Henry Johnson, who transformed it into the Ditchling Terra Cotta Works, run after 1875 in conjunction with the Keymer Brick & Tile Works (cf Keymer 15)
    Geol.:   Weald Clay
    Refs: SAS/Aber 44; MP 24; TDE 103; OS 25in 39/11 (1875, 1910); *SWA*, 30 Jun 1815; Kelly (1845-1938); census (1861-71); White, *Brighton & Worthing*, 14; Baines, *Pottery*, 123-33.

3   Brickfield south of Jane's Lane
    NGR: TQ 327 198
    Date: The Brickfield (329 197), on Little Oathall Farm, was listed on the tithe award of 1843 and a brickfield was marked to the NW of this on the map of 1874
    Op.:   Henry Wells was the tenant in 1843
    Refs: TDE 103; OS 25in 39/6 (1874).

4   Brickworks in Nye Lane
    NGR: cTQ 330 145
    Date: 1920s
    Op.:   The Ditchling Brick Co. advertised in 1927
    Ref.:   Kelly (1927).

EASTBOURNE

1   Brickyard on the south side of present-day Firle Road
    NGR: TV 618 997
    Date: Marked on maps of 1805 and 1816
    Op.:   John Mann, a building contractor, who made bricks for the Board of Ordnance in 1805. He was listed as the

owner in 1816 and was assessed on brick sheds and kilns in 1818

Refs: PRO MFQ 307/16B; GIL 30 & 127; TDE 85; GIL 432 & DE/B11/1 (ex inf. V. Hodsoll); Beswick, 'Martello Towers', 26.

2   Brickyard on the NE side of present-day Bourne Street
NGR: TV 616 995
Date: In existence by 1810, marked on a map of 1816 but as 'old brickyard' in 1841
Op.: Samuel Gravett was assessed on a cottage and brickyard between 1810 and 1821
Refs: GIL 30 & 127; TDE 85; DE/B11/1 (ex inf. V. Hodsoll).

3   Brickyard on the SW side of present-day Whitley Road
NGR: TV 618 999
Date: Listed as Rick Yard (sic) on the tithe award of 1841 and marked on the map of 1874
Op.: Samuel Gravett, son of another brickmaker of that name (cf site 2), advertised at Sea Houses from 1832 to 1845. In 1841 he was the tenant of this site, which was owned by H.B. Gorringe. By 1855 the brickmakers were Hain & Gravett. S. Gravett advertised in 1862 and Mrs Gravett in 1867
F.Inf.: A licence to dig brick earth was granted to the owner T.J. Gorringe in 1849 and renewed in 1867
Refs: TDE 85; OS 25in 80/6 (1874); GIL 366; Pigot (1832-9); Kelly (1845-67).

4   Brickfield at Rose Lands
NGR: TQ 622 005
Date: 1860s to 1880s
Op.: Eastbourne Brick Co. Ltd had a registered office in Seaside Road in 1866. Albert Tompsett advertised in 1878 and 1882
Refs: OS 25in 80/6 (1874); SAS/LM 113.

5   Brickfield on Seaside near the junction with Lottbridge Drove
NGR: TQ 625 008
Date: In existence by 1866, marked on the map of 1874 but by 1899 the brick earth was exhausted and the brickfield had been moved to the

north (cf Willingdon 2)
Op.: James Peerless, a builder, leased the land from the Devonshire estate in 1860 and bought brickmaking machinery in 1879. He died in 1890 but the firm of J. Peerless advertised as brickmakers here until 1899
Refs: OS 25in 80/6 (1874, 1899); A6011; Kelly (1890-99),

6   Brickfield on the site of present-day York Road and Hyde Road
NGR: TV 608 988
Date: Latter part of the 19th century
Op.: Possibly Henry Climpson, a master brickmaker who was living in Back Town Street in 1861
Refs: Census (1861); R. Cooper, *Reminiscences of Eastbourne* (1903), 104.

see also: WILLINGDON

ETCHINGHAM

1   Brickfield on the south side of present-day Fysie Lane
NGR: TQ 715 271
Date: 16th century: still called Upper and Lower Brick Fields in 1839
Op.: Probably John Saxby, who supplied bricks and tiles to the Roberts estate in Ticehurst in 1574. His widow was the tenant of The Brickefeildes in 1597
Refs: TDE 127; *SRS* **53**, 200, 205; *SRS* **71**, 141.

2   Brick kiln east of Haremere Hall
NGR: TQ 724 266
Date: Listed as Brick Kiln Field on the tithe award of 1839; the kiln was probably in use when the house was enlarged in 1616 and again in 1682
Refs: TDE 127; *SRS* **53**, 100.

3. Brick kiln at Elphicks on the east side of the road from Hurst Green to Flimwell
NGR: TQ 726 289
Date: Listed as Brick Kiln Field in 1839
Op.: Owned by the Roberts estate
Ref.: TDE 127.

4   Brickyard on the south side of the road from Swiftsden to Ticehurst
NGR: TQ 725 286
Date: The brick kilns were in existence by 1779 and were shown on the tithe map

of 1839; marked as Tile Works on maps from 1873 to 1937

Op.: Daniel Austin between 1841 and 1861

Refs: TDE 127; OS 25in 30/3 (1873, 1897, 1909); census (1841-61); L.J. Hodson & J.A. Odell, *Ticehurst: the story of a Sussex parish* (1925), 19; Draper & Martin, 'Local Industry', 58.

5 Brickyard west of Old Shoyswell Manor Farm

NGR: TQ 684 273

Date: Probably in existence well before 1839 when the yard was shown on the tithe map: marked on the map of 1875 but disused by 1899

Op.: Owned by the Shoyswell estate: the brickmakers were Joseph Mann in 1841, George Keeley in 1861 and George Edwards in 1871

Refs: TDE 127; OS 6in 30 (1875) 30 NW (1899); census (1841-71).

EWHURST

1 Tile kilns in Wellhead Wood south of Robertsbridge Abbey

NGR: i. TQ 756 233 ii. 757 230 iii. 760 226

Date: i. 13th century: nib-tiles found at nearby Drigsell grange during excavations resemble fragments found at this site. The adjacent field was called Tylehostfeilde in 1567 and Tile Croft in 1811
ii. 14th or 15th century: peg-tile wasters from the site measure 160mm x 15mm
iii. Called Tile Croft on a map of 1811

Op.: Richard le Tyghelere was living in Ewhurst in 1296 and may have been employed by the abbey

Refs: BAT 4435/18, 19; *SRS* **47**, 130, 149; *SRS* **10**, 13; G. Jones, 'Field Report' *Recologea Papers* Vol 7 No 4 (Robertsbridge 1981), 70.

2 Brickyard SE of Ewhurst Green

NGR: TQ 798 244

Date: 17th century, or earlier: Bricke Kelfeilde and Brick Clampefeilde to the east are shown on a map of 1635

Ref.: BAT 4420.

3 Brick kiln on Sempstead Farm

NGR: TQ 805 236

Date: Brick Kiln Field was marked on a map of 1784 and listed on the tithe award of 1843

Refs: AMS 6001; TDE 139.

4 Brick kiln on the south side of the road east of Staplecross

NGR: TQ 787 224

Date: Brick Kiln Field was marked on maps of 1801 and 1843

Op.: The owner in 1801 was Thomas Daws

Refs: Acc 654/1; TDE 139.

5 Brickyard east of the road from Staplecross to Cripps Corner

NGR: TQ 783 219

Date: In operation in the late 18th and early 19th centuries: the brick kiln was listed on a terrier of 1817

Op.: Possibly the Henley family: a tile bearing the names Jeremiah and Thomas Henley and the date 1762 has been found at Staplecross

Cond.: A description and diagram of the site were published in 1981

Refs: PAR 324/7/1; Jones, *op. cit.*, 71; inf. G. Jones (1983).

6 Brick and tile works on Marchants (Newhouse) Farm south of the road from Staplecross to Horns Cross

NGR: TQ 813 219

Date: Opened c1840, marked on the map of 1872 but disused by 1899

Op.: Owned by the Mannington family: the brickmakers were Stephen Catt in 1841 and Benjamin and Horace Russell in the 1870s

Prod.: Brickyard accounts for the years 1850 to 1855 list bricks, roof tiles and drainpipes. A bill head in the Perigoe Museum, Northiam, includes 'Jacobins' which appear to have been a variety of paving brick

Refs: OS 25in 44/2 (1872, 1899); BAT 2928; census (1841, 1871); inf. G. Jones (1981).

7 Brickworks on the west side of the road south of Staplecross

NGR: TQ 780 221

Date: In existence by 1882; closed 1914

Op.: Aaron Sellman advertised as a farmer and brickmaker from 1882 to 1907

Prod.: Bricks, tiles and drainpipes; spare parts for the pipe-machine were purchased from Hurst Green Foundry in 1895. The bricks for St Mark's Church, built in 1906, were said to have been made here

Refs: OS 25in 44/1 (1897); AMS 6214; Kelly (1882-1907); inf. G. Jones.

8 Brick clamp north of the road from Staplecross to Northiam

NGR: cTQ 783 226

Date: Bricklamp (sic) Field was named on a map of 1656

Op.: The property was sold by Thomas Sheather to William Brayban in 1725

Ref.: Acc 165/1329-1342.

FAIRLIGHT

1 Tile kiln SW of Tilekiln Farm

NGR: TQ 844 114

Date: There was a tilemaker in Fairlight in 1619: Tile Kiln Field was listed on a survey of 1811

Op.: John Wollage took two apprentices to learn the trade of tilemaking in 1619

Refs: BAT 4437; OS 1in 5 (1813); PAR 353/33/17-18.

2 Brickyard south of Pett Road on Hole Farm

NGR: cTQ 85 13

Date: A licence to burn bricks and tiles was granted in 1630

Op.: The tenant of 'Webbes' (Hole Farm) in 1630 was T. Alchorn

Refs: A 4728/4; Manor of Robertsbridge Court Book at Sheppard & Son, Battle f143v (ex inf. C. Whittick).

3 Brickyard near Fairlight church

NGR: cTQ 860 119

Date: A small yard was in use here in the 1920s

Geol: Ashdown Sand

Ref.: White, *Hastings*, 92.

WEST FIRLE

1 Brickyard on the east side of the lane leading to Loover Barn

NGR: TQ 467 082

Date: In existence by 1803 and listed on the tithe award of 1843

Op.: Owned by the Firle estate: the brickmakers were George Deary in 1803 and Thomas Feast in 1841

Refs: TDE 36; LPL/1/E3; census (1841).

FLETCHING

1 Brickyard on the common at Piltdown

NGR: TQ 449 220

Date: In existence before 1706 and closed c1870

Op.: Abraham Parker the elder, the owner from 1675, was a brickmaker when he made his will in 1706. Thomas Stevenson, first mentioned in 1760, paid land tax on the brick kiln in 1875 and was the owner of a cottage near the brick kiln, formerly Parker's, in 1796. He was followed by his son George, who died in 1846, and grandson George, who advertised until 1867

Refs: TDE 145; M252/266; W/A47.44; AMS 2686; census (1841-61); Kelly (1855-67); *SRS* **77**, 80

2 Brickyard on the north side of the road west of Sheffield Green

NGR: TQ 406 248

Date: In operation by 1775, the kiln was on the south side of the road (TQ 407 246) c1816 but the yard was marked on the opposite side from 1840 to 1910

Op.: John Billinghurst (cf Ditchling 2 & Chailey 1) was making bricks for the Earl of Sheffield in the 1770s and. 1780s for work at Sheffield Place and for building the Sheffield Arms. The tenant in 1840 was Richard Markwick (cf Maresfield 5) but the brickmaker in 1841 was Reuben Goldsmith, who was still living in Brickyard Cottage in 1871. By 1881 Henry Setford had taken over and his family were the brickmakers until the yard closed

Prod.: Bricks, tiles and drainpipes; a sketch of the kiln was made by George Holroyd in 1815

Geol.: Upper Tunbridge Wells Sand

Refs: TDE 145; OS 6in 27 (1875) 25in 27/10 (1899, 1910); SPK/E3/1, 4, E13/5 & F1/3; census (1841-81); Bristow & Bazley, *Tunbridge Wells*, 98; inf. A. Fayle (1981).

FOLKINGTON

1 Brick Field north of Wootton Manor
NGR: TQ 565 058
Date: Field name on the tithe award of 1839
Ref.: TDE 100

FOREST ROW *see* EAST GRINSTEAD, HARTFIELD

FRAMFIELD

1 Tile kiln on the north side of Gatehouse Lane
NGR: TQ 500 207
Date: 17th century; marked as Kiln Plat on a map of 1785 and excavated in 1929
Refs: AMS 4456; H.W. Keef, 'Seventeenth Century Tile Kiln, Framfield' *SNQ* **2** (1929), 181.

2 Brick kiln on Palehouse Common
NGR: cTQ 500 185
Date: Probably in existence in 1709, the kiln was first mentioned in 1746
Op.: Nicholas Clarke, brickmaker, of Framfield married Elizabeth Ticehurst of Ringmer in 1709 and was presented at the Manor Court in 1746 for building a kiln
Refs: PAR 461/1/1/5 (ex inf. John Kay); ADA 117 f 139.

3 Brick kiln on Blackboys Common
NGR: cTQ 526 202
Date: Probably in existence by 1713, the kiln was first mentioned in 1746
Op.: Members of the Brooker family supplied bricks for the almshouse in 1713 and 1724. David Brooker was described as a brickmaker in 1741 and Edward Brooker was presented for building a kiln in 1746
Refs: ADA 117 ff 81 & 139; PAR 343/31/1/1.

4 Two brick kilns in Barnet Wood
NGR: TQ 525 190
Date: Two kilns were in existence in 1746. One was short-lived but the other, listed as Great Brick Kiln Field on the tithe award of 1841, continued in use until the 1850s
Op.: James Fielder and Richard Carter had both built kilns by 1746. There is no mention of Carter's holding after 1751. Stephen Fielder inherited the other in 1758 and on his death in 1802 it passed to John Durrant. The brickmaker in 1841 and 1851 was Thomas Cole
Prod.: Thomas Turner of East Hoathly bought tiles from Fielder's kiln in 1758
Refs: TDE 6; ADA 117-124; Vaisey, *Turner*, 162; census (1841-51).

5 Brick kiln on Highland Common
NGR: TQ 496 218
Date: The kiln was in existence by 1756 and the holding was still described as Brick Kiln Place in 1839 but as Kiln Field only on the tithe award of 1841
Op.: The site was granted, out of the common, to William Durrant in 1757
Refs: TDE 6; ADA 118-125.

6 Brickworks on the south side of Eastbourne Road at Mount Ephraim
NGR: TQ 488 191
Date: c1880 until the 1940s
Op.: Stephen Stevens advertised from 1882 to 1907 followed by Reuben Stevens from 1913 to 1944
Refs: OS 6in 61 NW (1899, 1911); Kelly (1882-1924); *QMJ* (1927-44).

FRANT

1 Brick kiln west of the pond bay on Gun Farm, Eridge
NGR: TQ 557 352
Date: Listed as Brick Kiln Plat on a terrier of c1800
Refs: ABE 27E.

2 Two brick kilns on the Abergavenny estate at Eridge
NGR: TQ 568 360 & 559 357
Date: Brick Kiln Field NE of Eridge Castle was marked on a map of c1800 and another Brick Kiln Field, at the entrance to the park, was listed on the tithe award of 1846. Both were probably used at different times to supply building materials for the estate
Refs: ABE 27E; TDE 63.

3 Brickyard in Shernfold Park
NGR: TQ 596 353
Date: In use when a new house was being built in the 1790s and listed as Brick Field in 1846

Op.: Thomas Tebbut was making bricks for Shernfold in 1795

Refs: TDE 63; H.S. Eeles, *Frant: a Parish History* (1947), 194.

4 Brickyard on the south side of Wadhurst Road

NGR: TQ 596 342

Date: In use at some time between 1805 and 1833 and listed as Brick Kiln Field in 1846

Op.: General Alexander Beatson, one of whose 'sidelines was the making of bricks at Knowle Farm'

Refs: TDE 63; Eeles, *op. cit.*, 161.

5 Brickyard on the property formerly called Delvidere, now Woodside

NGR: cTQ 591 342

Date: Listed as Brick Kiln and Yard in a conveyance of 1837

Ref.: AMS 593-4.

6 Brickyard on the edge of Higham Wood SE of Bells Yew Green

NGR: TQ 612 359

Date: In existence by 1841, listed in 1846 and marked as Brick Works on the map of 1873

Op.: Part of the Bayham Abbey estate; the brickmaker in 1841 was John Batchelor and the tenant in 1846, I. Roper

Refs: TDE 63; OS 6in 7 (1873); census (1841).

7 Brickyard on the south side of Hawkenbury Road (now in Kent)

NGR: TQ 600 383

Date: Listed in 1846 and marked on the maps of 1873 and 1899

Op.: The tenants in 1846 were John Crundwell and others; the brick maker in 1858 was William Francis; William Brooker advertised from 1878 to 1887 and Henry Marchant, of Benhall Mill, from 1895 to 1918

Prod.: In 1858 the products were kiln, clamp and paving bricks, drain and socket pipes and tiles

Refs: TDE 63; OS 6in 7 (1873) 7 SW (1899); Hunt, *Mining Records*, 39; Kelly (1878-1918).

8 Brickworks between Benhall Mill Road and the railway

NGR: TQ 594 378

Date: Marked only on the map of 1873

Ref.: OS 6in 7 (1873).

9 Brickfield on the west side of Eridge Road south of Strawberry Hill

NGR: TQ 568 373

Date: Marked only on the map of 1873

Ref.: OS 6in 6 (1873).

GROOMBRIDGE *see* WITHYHAM

GUESTLING

1 Brick kiln on Fairlight Down

NGR: 841 125

Date: In existence by 1740, marked on a map of 1795 and described in a survey of 1811

Op.: John Dann paid rent for a kiln and some waste ground on Fairlight Down in 1740. The tenant in 1811 was William Weller

Refs: BAT 4433, 4437; SAS/RF 15/23.

2 Brick kiln NE of Broomham

NGR: TQ 856 155

Date: Listed as Upper & Lower Brick Kiln Fields on a valuation of the estate made in 1833 and on the tithe award of 1842

Refs: TDE 40; A 5257/C31.

3 Brickyard west of Guestling Green

NGR: TQ 849 138

Date: In existence by 1833 and marked on the map of 1873

Op.: The tenant in 1842 was John Bray Furminger, who surrendered his lease in 1846. East Sussex Brick & Tile Co. (manager: H. Murray) advertised in 1890 and 1895, possibly working on this site

Prod.: Bricks, roof tiles and drain tiles in 1846

Refs: TDE 40; OS 25in 58/8 (1873); A5257/C27, 31; Kelly (1890-95).

4 Brickworks on the east side of the railway south of Doleham Halt

NGR: TQ 836 163

Date: Marked only on the map of 1909

Ref.: OS 25in 58/8 (1909).

5 Brickworks on the east side of Fourteen Acre Lane

NGR: TQ 841 158

Date: Marked Brick & Tile Works on the

map of 1909, not in use in 1929, re-opened in the 1930s, closed during the war, revived afterwards and still in operation (2001)

Op.: The Guestling (Sussex) Brick & Estate Co. advertised in 1938. In 1981 the owner of what was then Hastings Brickworks Ltd was George Chaplin and the works manager Keith Watson, whose family was said to have started the yard. The works, owned by Butterley Brick Ltd in the 1990s, now trades independently as Sussex Brick Ltd.

F.Inf.: Up to 1981 the hand-made bricks were still being burnt in two coal-fired circular kilns. These have been replaced by gas-fired intermittent kilns

Refs OS 25in 58/3 (1909, 1929); Kelly (1938); *QMJ* (1944/5); *SIAS Newsletter* **23**, July 1979; *Sussex Express*, 23 Oct 1981.

HADLOW DOWN *see* BUXTED, MAYFIELD

HAILSHAM

1 Tile kiln in Tilehurst Wood to the west of Hempstead Lane
NGR: cTQ 575 097
Date: The Tylehouse land, formerly belonging to Michelham Priory, was mentioned in a conveyance of 1587
Cond.: There are a number of pits in the wood and some tiles were found in the 1960s
Refs: Salzman, *Hailsham*, 253; SAS/PN 311; inf. A. Hibbs (1987).

2 Brickyard on Brownings Farm east of the road from Hailsham to Polegate
NGR: TQ 580 076
Date: Mid-18th to mid-19th century
Op.: Probably the workplace of John Carey, described as a brickmaker in 1772, who made his will in 1787. Bartholomew Osborn from before 1817 until at least 1842
Refs: TDE 140; W/A65.364; RAF 37/76; Pigot (1839); *SRS* **25**, 78; Salzman, *Hailsham*, 60.

3 Brickyard north of present-day Factory Lane
NGR: TQ 582 092
Date: In existence by 1826, still in operation in 1860 but closed shortly afterwards
Op.: Stephen Goldsmith of Hellingly owned land, including the brick kiln, in 1826. John Barber was the tenant in 1842
Refs: TDE 140; AMS 2973.

4 Brickyard at Summerhill on the west side of Coldthorn Lane
NGR: TQ 583 075
Date: In existence by 1851; closed c1874 when the buildings were shown although the yard was not named on the OS map
Op.: Jonathan Terry until 1855, when he sold the utensils, including the pugmill and a tile machine to Trayton Smith (cf Herstmonceux 2), who was living in the area in 1851 and advertised between 1862 and 1874
Refs: OS 25in 69/5 (1874); census (1851-71); BUR 2/1/39; Kelly (1862-74).

5 Brickyard on the west side of the former railway south of Hailsham station
NGR: TQ 589 091
Date: From before 1855, when a valuation of the yard was made, to c1880
Op.: The owner was Mr F. Ellman and Thomas Turner was the outgoing tenant in 1855. William Beeny, a coal merchant, advertised as a brickmaker from 1859 to 1874. By 1876 the owner was Mr John Mercer
Prod.: Kiln and clamp bricks
F.Inf.: A lease of 1863 listed: brickyard, shed, ozier bed, brick kilns and ponds and excavations, tramway sidings and metals
Refs: OS 25in 69/1 (1874); census (1861-71); Kelly (1859-74); BUR 2/1/46, 210, 270; inf. A. Hibbs.

6 Brickworks on the east side of Battle Road at Harebeating
NGR: TQ 594 108
Date: In existence by 1861, closed c1914
Op.: William Gravett in 1861, followed by his widow from 1895 and son William from 1903
Prod.: Clamp, kiln, coping and splay bricks and roofing tiles
Refs: OS 25in 56/13 (1899, 1910); census (1861-81); Kelly (1874-1913); Pike/Eastbourne (1886).

7   Brickfield between the railway and Station
    Road, Polegate
    NGR: TQ 587 048
    Date: Marked on the map of 1875; closed in
           1880
    Op.:   William Beeny (cf site 5)
    Refs: OS 25in 69/9 (1873); inf. A. Hibbs.

8   Brickfield south of the railway and east of the
    A22
    NGR: TQ 577 048
    Date: Marked on the map of 1874 and as
           Brick Works in 1899
    Op.:   Possibly Leonard Huggett in the 1890s
    Refs: OS 25in 68/12 (1874, 1899); Kelly
           (1895-99).

9   Brickworks at Hawkswood (Hawklands)
    NGR: TQ 589 112 - 591 110
    Date: A composite site occupied by at least
           four separate brickyards: the first was
           in operation by the late 1870s and the
           last remained active until 1927
    Op.:   i. Lutley & Mannington advertised in
           1878 and 1882. In 1883 the partnership
           was   dissolved   and   Douglas
           Mannington (cf East Blatchington 1)
           managed the yard until c1887. Samuel
           Cornford,   previously   the   yard
           foreman, advertised from 1890 to 1899
           followed by Mrs Cornford until 1907
           ii. Esau Taylor, a brickmaker living in
           Hellingly in 1881, advertised from
           1886 to 1899
           iii. Stephen Guy from 1886 to 1893,
           when he sold to O. Mitchell, who
           advertised from 1895 to 1903; by 1915
           the yard was in the hands of William
           Guy, who advertised it for sale but
           continued brickmaking until 1927
           iv. Thomas Edenborough advertised
           from 1895 to 1903
           v. A.E. Nicholson also advertised in
           1895
    Prod.: The Mannington ledger for 1882-4
           lists kiln and clamp bricks, paving
           bricks and red and black roofing
           tiles. Esau Taylor made bricks, tiles
           and pottery
    Refs: OS 25in 56/9, 13 (1899, 1910);
           SAS/SM 168b; Kelly (1878-1927);
           Pike/Eastbourne (1886); *Sussex
           Express*, 11 May 1919; M. Beswick,

'Brickmaking at Hawkswood in the
1880s' *Hailsham Historian and
Naturalist* **2** (Nov 1987), 19-21; inf. A.
Hibbs (1981).

10 Brickworks at Oaklands on the west side of
    Ersham Road
    NGR: TQ 585 082
    Date: From 1874, when the pond was dug
           and the clamp ground prepared, to
           c1900
    Op.:   William Gravett (cf site 6) was paid for
           work done in 1874. Albert Tompsett,
           brickmaker, was in dispute with his
           neighbour Albert Dann in 1877. Dann
           advertised as brickmaker and market
           gardener in the 1890s
    Prod.: Red facing, paving and ornamental
           bricks, tiles and drainpipes
    Refs: OS 25in 69/1 (1899); BUR 2/1/238;
           Eastbourne Chronicle, 23 Jun 1877; Kelly
           (1878, 1895-99); inf. A. Hibbs.

11 Brickworks between Battle Road and the
    former Harebeating Mill
    NGR: TQ 594 106
    Date: c1880 to c1900
    Op.:   Several brickmakers were living in the
           area in 1881. Noah Funnell advertised
           in the 1890s
    Refs: OS 25in 56/13 (1899); census (1881);
           Kelly (1895-99).

12 Brickyard on Nightingale Farm east of the
    road from Hailsham to Polegate
    NGR: TQ 578 066
    Date: c1880 to c1900
    Op.:   Four brickmakers living at Starvecrow
           in 1881 were probably working here.
           D. Stevens advertised in 1889 and
           Benjamin Stevens in the 1890s
    Refs: OS 25in 68/8 (1898); census (1881);
           Kelly (1895); inf. A. Hibbs.

13 Brickworks on the site of present-day
    Brookside Avenue, Polegate
    NGR: TQ 577 052
    Date: Opened c1880 and marked on the
           maps of 1899 and 1909
    Op.:   Stephen   Message,   listed   as   a
           brickmaker in 1881, was involved in
           the development of the Polegate
           Estate and lived in Havelock House,
           Victoria Road, built with bricks from
           his own yard. He died in 1924

Refs: OS 25in 68/12 (1899, 1909, 1928); A4426/15; Kelly (1890); inf. Mrs K. Slater (née Message).

14 Brickworks on the west side of Coldthorn Lane
NGR: TQ 585 080
Date: Opened in the 1890s and still marked on the map of 1950
Op.: James Gurr advertised from 1927 to 1934 apparently followed by Southdown Brickfields Ltd in 1938, although Gurr's name still appeared in a directory of 1944
Geol.: Weald Clay
Refs: OS 25in 69/1 (1899, 1910, 1928, 1937, 1950); Kelly (1927-38); *QMJ* (1927-44); Lake et al, *Lewes*, 35; inf. A. Hibbs (1991).

15 Brickworks on the north side of Hawkswood Road
NGR: TQ 593 112
Date: c1890 until 1940s
Op.: Thomas Rich bought the site in 1889 and advertised from 1899 to 1915; exors of Thomas Rich from 1922 onwards
Refs: OS 25in 56/9 & 13 (1911, 1932); Kelly (1899-1938); *QMJ* (1927-44); inf. A. Hibbs.

16 Brick and tile works west of the former railway south of Coppards
NGR: TQ 584 068
Date: Opened in 1897 and marked Brick Works (disused) in 1909; revived after World War 1 and continued until c1970
Op.: Henry Marchant was the manager for the Eastbourne Brick Co., which advertised in Polegate in 1903. Post-World War 1 it was run by Polegate Brick & Tile Co. followed by Southdown Tileries Ltd from 1925 to 1934, when it came under the control of Keymer Brick & Tile Co. (qv)
Prod.: Some bricks but mostly roofing tiles
Geol.: Weald Clay
F.Inf.: A family photograph album (in Eastbourne library) contains snap shots of the works in 1924/5, when extensions were in progress. The works had its own railway siding at this date

Refs: OS 25in 69/5 (1909, 1928, 1950); Kelly (1924-38); *QMJ* (1933-59); White, *Lewes*, 32; Lake et al, *Lewes*, 35; inf. A. Hibbs.

17 Brickworks on the north side of Station Road, Polegate
NGR: TQ 584 051
Date: Marked only on the map of 1898
Op.: Andrews & Towner in 1903 and James Andrews in 1907
Refs: OS 25in 69/9 (1898); Kelly (1903-7).

18 Brickworks in Brook Street, Polegate
NGR: TQ 577 050
Date: First marked in 1899 and displaced to the west when the by-pass was constructed in the 1930s
Op.: Benjamin Gurr in 1907 and Thomas Gurr from 1913 to 1938
Geol.: Weald Clay
Refs: OS 25in 68/12 (1899, 1909, 1928, 1937); Kelly (1907-34); *DBC* (1938); White, *Lewes*, 32; Lake et al, *Lewes*, 35.

19 Brickworks on the west side of Station Road, Hailsham
NGR: TQ 591 087
Date: Opened 1903 and still marked on the map of 1950
Op.: Burtenshaw & Green from 1919 onwards. Henry Marchant (cf site 16), the works manager, received an award for 60 years service to the brickyards in 1930
Prod.: Clamp bricks and some cement tiles
Geol.: Mottled brownish Weald Clay
F.Inf.: A tramway linking the works to the railway line and an engine shed are shown on the map of 1928
Refs: OS 25in 69/1 (1928, 1937, 1950); Kelly (1924-38); *QMJ* (1927 44); White, *Lewes*, 31; Lake et al, *Lewes*, 35; inf. A. Hibbs.

see also: HELLINGLY

HAMSEY

1 Brickyard at Lower Tulleyswells Farm, Cooksbridge
NGR: TQ 397 137
Date: In existence by 1808, marked on a map of 1827 and listed as Brick Field,

though probably out of use, in 1838

Op.: Owned by the Shiffner estate; the brickmakers were John and Joseph Back, who supplied bricks for the building of the County Hall in Lewes between 1809 and 1811. Richard Verrall took over in 1813

Refs: Shiffner 2854(2); TDE 111; QAH 1/7/E3; *SWA*, 25 Jan 1813.

2 Brickyard north of Hewinstreet Farm
NGR: TQ 396 159
Date: In existence in 1821, marked on a map of 1827 and in almost continuous operation until 1990

Op.: Owned by the Shiffner estate; the brickmakers were Thomas Best and his sons Andrew and George from at least 1821. Thomas died in 1835 and from 1841 to 1874 the yard was managed by William Bristow. Benjamin Ware, of Uckfield (qv), advertised in 1878 followed by Trayton Stevens in 1882. In 1889 Stevens was in partnership with James Chandler of Lewes (qv), then Chandler, a builder, advertised on his own from 1895 to 1915. By 1927 the yard was in the hands of the Hamsey Brick Co. It was sold to Redland Bricks Ltd in the 1960s

Prod.: Kiln and clamp-fired bricks, tiles and drainpipes were being made in 1889 when an inventory of the yard was taken. In 1960 the products were clamp bricks and hand-made, multi-coloured facings

Geol.: Weald clay

Refs: Shiffner 2854(6); TDE 111; OS 25in 40/13 (1873, 1899, 1910, 1932); W/A78.822; BMW A2/29 ff21-30; *SRS* **25**, 38; Pigot (1828); census (1841-51); Kelly (1855-1938); *QMJ* (1927-59); White, *Lewes*, 28; Lake et al, *Lewes*, 33.

HANGLETON *see* ALDRINGTON

HARTFIELD

1 Tile kiln east of Cansiron Lane
NGR: TQ 456 383
Date: AD 100-130 when the Roman ironworks were in operation

Prod.: Roofing tiles, box-flue tiles and flat tiles (bricks)

Ref.: Rudling, 'Hartfield', 191-230.

2 Brick clamps near Bolebrook Castle
NGR: TQ 473 378
Date: Brick Clamps Pit Field was shown on a map of 1799, probably marking the site where bricks were made when the castle was built in the late 15th century and again when the present house was built c1600

Refs: AMS 5786; *SNQ* **7**, 164, 207; Armstrong, *Sussex*, 41.

3 Brickyard SE of Newbridge
NGR: TQ 458 326
Date: In operation by 1731 when the grant of copyhold included a brick-kiln and two workshops and the liberty to dig clay to make bricks and tiles. The kiln was still mentioned in 1842 but was no longer in use by that date

Op.: The grantee in 1731 was John Hudson but the brickmaker was probably William Langley, who took apprentices in 1733 and 1741. In 1773 Hudson sold the yard to a brickmaker, Thomas Langdon, who advertised it for sale in the following year and sold it to Thomas Swaysland in 1776. In 1808 it was acquired by the church-wardens and overseers of the parish, one of whom was Abraham Spencer (cf site 4), presumably to provide work for the poor. Two years later it was sold to George Fitness

Refs: TDE 149; ADA 82-4, 87; *SWA*, 21 Mar 1774; *SRS* **28**, 109, 126.

4 Brickyard at Souters's Hole west of Chuck Hatch
NGR: TQ 467 329
Date: Opened in 1792, marked on maps from 1825 to 1898 but disused by 1910

Op.: The grantees in 1792 were Abraham and Joseph Spencer but the brickmaker was William Mitchell, who made his will in 1798 and died in 1815. Abraham Spencer sold the yard to the De La Warr estate in 1808 but continued to pay for brick earth taken from the forest until 1820. By 1842 the brickmaker was Thomas Divall, who was succeeded by his son William and grandson Leonard

Prod.: Kiln bricks, roofing tiles and agricultural drainpipes

Refs: *SRS* **72**, 174; TDE 149; OS 25in 16/8 (1875, 1898, 1910); ADA 83-4; CAF 2/4; W/A72.317; inf. Ralph Muggeridge, grandson of Leonard Divall (1980).

5 Brick kiln on Faulkners Farm, south of Colestock crossroads

NGR: TQ 476 389

Date: The brick kiln was marked on a map of 1795 but had gone out of use by 1842, when the site was listed as Brick Kiln Mead

Cond.: The field has a very uneven surface and there is a large scatter of waste bricks and tiles

Refs: *SRS* **72**, 108, 174; TDE 149; inf. C.F. Tebbutt (1978).

6 Brickfield on the east side of Shepherds Hill at Little Parrock

NGR: TQ 448 341

Date: In existence by 1842 and closed in the 1950s

Op.: [ ] Divall (cf site 4) was the tenant in 1842. Robert Edwards advertised from 1862 to 1882, succeeded by John Waters in the 1890s and Job Luxford, a builder of Forest Row, by 1913. After World War 1 the yard was owned and run by H. & E. Waters, also builders of Forest Row

Geol.: Wadhurst Clay

Cond.: There was a sizeable claypit visible and still some stacks of tiles in 1978

Refs: TDE 149; OS 25in 16/3 (1875, 1898, 1910, 1931); Kelly (1862-1924); *DBC* (1938); Bristow & Bazley, *Tunbridge Wells* 67; inf. C.F. Tebbutt (1978) & E.C. Byford (1984).

7 Brick kiln south of the road from Colemans Hatch to Wych Cross

NGR: TQ 438 321

Date: Called Brick Kiln Farm in 1845, when the brickyard was no longer active, identified on the map of 1875

Refs: OS 6in 16 (1875); Kelly (1845).

8 Brick kiln on Kilnwood Farm, Cotchford

NGR: TQ 477 344

Date: pre-1900

Ref.: Inf. C.F. Tebbutt (1978).

9 Brickfield at Upper Hartfield

NGR: TQ 464 343

Date: Marked on maps from 1910 to 1961

Op.: Charles Alcock

Prod.: Clamp bricks

Refs OS 25in 16/4 (1910, 1931) 6in 16 NE (1961); inf. C.F. Tebbutt (1978).

10 Brickworks between Posingford Wood and Newbridge stream

NGR: TQ 470 338

Date: 1930s

Op.: P.T. Muggeridge, builder, and Capt. Nunn who traded as Posingford Brick Co. Ltd

Prod.: Hand-made, clamp-fired, multi-coloured stock bricks

F.Inf.: The pugmill was driven by a Lister paraffin engine

Refs: Kelly (1938); inf. R. Muggeridge (1980).

HASTINGS

1 Brickfield on Clive Vale Farm in the parish of All Saints

NGR: TQ 837 112

Date: A close called Brickfeild was mentioned in a deed of 1642

Refs: Map in J.M. Baines' notes on brickmaking in Hastings library; HMAG XX 94/1

2 Two brick kilns in the parish of St Clement

NGR: TQ 824 101 & 828 106

Date: 18th century

Op.: Owned by the Collier estate: the tenant in 1750 and 1766 was John Perry

Refs: HMAG MA 287; SAY 2776.

3 Brick kiln in the vicinity of the present-day railway station

NGR: cTQ 815 055

Date: 18th and 19th centuries. Earlier brickmaking in the same area may be indicated by the field names Upper and Lower Bricketts on a map of c1750

Op.: Priory kiln was owned by Edward Milward in 1773. He employed John Breach as his brickmaker between 1790 and 1804. From 1806 to 1811 the kiln was leased to a Mr Weller

Prod.: Bricks and tiles

Refs: AMS 5880; *SWA*,19 Jul 1790; HMAG MIL/G12 & ABS/D158; Baines, *Pottery*, 73.

4   Brickfield at the southern end of Alexandra Park
NGR: TQ 817·102
Date: In use when the railway was under construction in 1849 and advertised for sale in 1850
Op.: In March 1849, William Hoof, of Kensington, Co. Middx, contractor of public works, obtained two licences to dig clay to make bricks and tiles, at this site and another higher up the valley (814 104). Thomas Dunn, a Hastings builder who, in April 1849, was granted a licence to dig clay on the intervening parcel of land, also acquired one of the railway brickyards in 1850
Geol.: Alluvium: much of the area is now occupied by the boating lake and other ponds
Refs: MIL F7/69, 70, 71; HALSP, *Railways*, 17; *Hastings & St Leonards News*, 29 Mar 1850; census (1851); inf. D. Padgham (2001).

5   Brick and tile works on the site now occupied by Silverdale School
NGR: TQ 799 113
Date In operation by 1856 and closed c1890
Op.: John Howell, a builder, with John Martin (cf Bexhill 6) as brick maker in the 1850s. Aaron Ford was a brickmaker at Silverhill when he made his will in 1878. Draper & Marchant (cf Hollington 3) advertised in Sedlescombe Road in 1887
Prod.: Bricks, tiles, drainpipes and chimney pots in 1858
Refs: OS 25in 58/14 (1873); Hunt, *Mining Records*, 40; HMAG HW 127; Kelly (1887); Martin, 'Frederic Martin', 34.

6   Brickworks at the north end of present-day Linton Road
NGR: TQ 811 100
Date: Marked only on the map of 1874
Ref.: OS 25in 58/14 (1874).

7   Brickworks on the north side of the Ridge at Baldslow
NGR: TQ 800 132

Date: Known as Beauport Brickworks, the yard was marked on the maps of 1873 and 1897 and run down as operations were transferred to site 10
Op.: James and Frederic, sons of John Martin (cf site 5) worked here in the 1870s. J.C. Kenward used this site from at least 1890 until 1894 and was succeeded in 1897 by Cheale & Co., millers, of Ore
Refs: OS 25in 58/10 (1873); Pike/Hastings (1890-97) (ex inf. D. Padgham); Martin, 'Frederic Martin', 34.

8   Brickworks on the site of present-day Freshwater Avenue
NGR: TQ 814 108
Date: 1875 to the early 1900s
Op.: Stephen Message was granted a lease of the eastern part of the site in 1875 and of the western part in the following year and advertised from 1878 to 1901
F.Inf.: The agreement stipulated a minimum production on the combined site of 3,000,000 bricks each year, on which a royalty of 3s per 1,000 was charged. In 1877 a complaint was made about nuisance caused by the burning of bricks and the tipping of rubbish on the site
Prod.: Clamp and kiln-fired bricks
Refs: OS 25in 58/14 (1899); VID 5/13/2; Kelly (1878-99); Pike/Hastings (1882-1901) (ex inf. D. Padgham).

9   Brickworks between site 8 and St Helens Road
NGR: TQ 809 106
Date: Opened in 1876 and marked on the map of 1899
Op.: J.G. Hickman, the tenant of Hole Farm, was granted permission to make bricks on the land in 1876. In 1894 his lease of the brickfield was transferred to Peter Jenkins, who advertised as a brickmaker from 1882 to 1899
F.Inf.: The agreement was for a minimum of 500,000 bricks per year
Refs: OS 25in 58/14 (1899); VID 5/13/2; Kelly (1882-99).

10 Brickworks on the east side of Harrow Lane
  NGR: TQ 799 125
  Date: Opened in 1894 as the successor to site 7 and marked as Beauport Brick Works on the maps of 1899 and 1909
  Op.: J.C. Kenward followed by J. Cheale & Co. (cf site 7) in 1897-8 and H.H. Arnold from 1899 to 1907. For most of this period the manager was J. Holyer. From 1908 to 1910 the yard was in the hands of W. Holdoway
  Prod.: Pottery was made as well as chimney pots and a wide range of bricks and tiles
  Refs: OS 25in 58/10 (1899, 1909); Foster, *Mines* (1898-1901); Pike/Hastings (1899-1910) (ex inf. D. Padgham); Baines, *Pottery*, 78-9.

see also: HOLLINGTON, ORE, ST LEONARDS

HEATHFIELD

1 Brick kiln on the west side of Newick Lane near the Mayfield boundary
  NGR: TQ 595 235
  Date: Late 17th and early 18th centuries; listed as Brick Croft Field and Shaw on the tithe award of 1841
  Op.: Probably the workplace of John Ellis, who supplied tiles for Brightling Forge in 1668. The supplier in 1692, Thomas Pankhurst, paid tithe from 1717 to 1731 on a farm 'at the Brickkiln belonging to John Baker of Mayfield Esq.'
  Refs: TDE 16; PAR 372/6/1 (ex inf. E. Doff); P. Lucas, *Heathfield Memorials* (1910), 73.

2 Brickfield on the east side of the road at Hale Hill
  NGR: TQ 598 185
  Date: Marked on a map of 1707 and listed as Brickfield Shaw in 1841
  Op.: The owner in 1707 was Thomas Fuller and bricks may have been made here for Heathfield Furnace, which was rebuilt by John Fuller in the 1690s
  Refs: Lucas, *op. cit.*, 172; TDE 16.

3 Brickyard on Runtington Manor Farm west of the former railway
  NGR: TQ 578 194
  Date: Shown as The Kelfield on a map of 1709, listed as Brick Yard in 1841 and marked on maps from 1875 to 1910
  Op.: John Young was the owner in 1709. William Barrow, the tenant in 1841, advertised from 1851 to 1862. John Harmer had taken over by 1867, followed by James Harmer from1899 to 1907
  Refs: AMS 5711; TDE 16; OS 25in 42/5 (1875, 1898, 1910); Kelly (1851-1903).

4 Brickyard on Heathfield Down north of Heathfield Park
  NGR: TQ 590 217
  Date: Probably in operation before 1752; a brick kiln was advertised for sale along with the old Half Moon Inn in 1774 and the copyhold of the kiln and a piece of wasteland was granted in 1804. The yard had gone out of use by 1818 and only the field names Old Brickyard Land and Brick Kiln Slip remained in 1841
  Op.: Possibly Bartholomew Gorely, brickmaker, of Heathfield, who became the tenant of another brickyard in Laughton in 1752. The grantee in 1804 was John Thomson
  Refs: TDE 16; SAS/A 663 & 667; *SWA*, 28 Mar 1774.

5 Brickfield on the Common, now Alexandra Road
  NGR: TQ 587 208
  Date: c1885 to 1907
  Op.: George Rumary, a builder, who was developing land near the new railway station in 1885. He lived at Cave Cottage alongside the brickfield
  Prod.: Clamp-fired bricks
  Refs: Kelly (1887-1907); inf. Mrs Rumary (1978).

6 Brickworks at Dewbush Farm on the east side of Vines Cross Road
  NGR: TQ 597 171
  Date: Marked on the maps of 1899 and 1910, the yard went out of production at the beginning of World War 1
  Op.: Sylvan Harmer, the son of John Harmer (cf site 3) advertised from 1899 to 1907
  Prod.: Kiln-fired bricks

Refs: OS 25in 42/13 (1899, 1910); census (1871); Kelly (1899-1907).

7 Two Brickfields on the north side of Hore Beech Lane, Horam
NGR: TQ 586 169 & 587 168
Date: Both were marked on the map of 1899 but the western one only remained in 1910 and was still in operation in 1927
Op.: Clement Turner advertised in 1913 and 1915
Prod.: Clamp-fired bricks
Refs: OS 25in 42/13 (1899, 1910); Kelly (1913-15); *SNQ* **1** (1927), 74.

8 Brickworks south of the Burwash road
NGR: TQ 625 226
Date: In operation by 1886. Marked on the map of 1898 but as Old Kiln in 1909
Op.: Owned by the Tottingworth Park estate
Prod: Kiln and clamp bricks, roofing tiles and land drains
F.Inf.: A gardener's notebook contains details of bricks etc made and payments to workmen in 1886
Refs: OS 25in 29/15 (1898, 1909); A6238.

9 Brickworks east of Mill House Farm on the Burwash boundary
NGR: TQ 635 233
Date: Marked only on the map of 1909
Ref.: OS 25in 29/15 (1909).

10 Brickworks on the north side of Ghyll Road
NGR: TQ 583 207
Date: Opened c1900 and marked on the map of 1910
Op.: Heathfield Brick & Tile Co. Ltd, manager: Thomas Stephens
F.Inf.: In 1905 the brick earth was valued at 1s per cubic yard and the buildings were said to have cost about £260
Refs: OS 25in 42/5 (1910); BMW/A2/16; Kelly (1903).

11 Brickfield at Horam Bridge on the east side of Waldron Gill
NGR: TQ 582 177
Date: Marked only on the map of 1910
Ref.: OS 25in 42/9 (1910).

12 Brick and tile works at North Corner, Horam
NGR: TQ 590 159
Date: In existence by 1913; production ceased in 1971

Op.: Sussex Tileries & Brickworks Ltd: in 1913 the owner was T.M. English and in the 1930s the managing director was G.C. Seaton. In the 1960s the works was acquired by Hudsons (cf West Hoathly 3) and modernised but closed in 1971. The owners, Ibstock Brick Hudsons Ltd, were refused permission to open a new brickworks to the west in 1989
Prod.: Roofing tiles marketed under the name of Coverwell, common bricks, fireplaces and briquettes (1959)
Cond.: The site had been cleared except for a steel-framed building, sheeted in corrugated asbestos in 1989
Geol.: Wadhurst clay
Refs: OS 6in 42SW (1932); Kelly (1913-38); *QMJ* (1927-59); White, *Lewes*, 21; 'A Lesson in Making Old Works Viable', *British Clayworker*, July 1969.

see also: WALDRON

SOUTH HEIGHTON

1 Brickyard at the north end of present-day New Road
NGR: TQ 447 025
Date: Opened in the late 1890s and closed c1914
Op.: C. Cooke advertised from 1899 to 1913
Refs: OS 25in 78/3 (1899); Kelly (1899-1913).

HELLINGLY

1 Brick kiln west of Carters Corner Place (formerly Barton House)
NGR: TQ 606 126
Date: Probably the site of brickmaking in 1647-9 and marked on a map of 1671
Op.: Leves and his partner (cf Herst-monceux 2) were paid for making bricks in 1647
Refs: AMS 740; SAS/RF 15/17.

2 Brickyard(s) on the east side of Coldharbour Road at Upper Dicker
NGR: TQ 557 103
Date: Brickmaking was taking place in the neighbourhood of Starnash from the 17th century onwards. The yard at Upper Dicker, first mentioned in 1767, continued in operation until the 1930s

Op.: Probably William Sargent prior to 1720, Thomas Wood from before 1767 to 1776, Thomas and James Peckham from 1776 to 1799; after this the yard was in the hands of Benjamin Goldsmith and successive members of his family. Stephen Goldsmith was the owner in 1856, when the brickmaker was Henry Goldsmith. On Stephen's death in 1876, the yard was sold to George Collins, although James Goldsmith was still the brickmaker in 1887. Harry Page took over c1900

Prod.: Kiln-fired bricks and tiles and pottery; in the 20th century paving bricks were a speciality

Cond.: The footings of a circular kiln can be seen in the garden of Kiln Cottage

Geol.: Weald Clay

Refs: TDE 5; OS 6in 55 (1874) 55 SE (1899, 1911); W/INV 1202; BUR 2/1/49, 270; Kelly (1862-1930); Pike/Eastbourne (1886); *QMJ* (1927); *DBC* (1938); White, *Lewes*, 29; Beswick, 'Dicker', 2-6, 9.

3 Brickyard on the north side of the road at Lower Dicker
NGR: TQ 564 114
Date: In existence by 1708, offered for sale in 1813, after which date it was probably abandoned; listed as Kiln Plot on the tithe award of 1842
Op.: Edward Wenham before 1758, followed by his son William, who paid land tax on the brick kilns in 1785, and other members of the family
Refs: TDE 5; *SWA*, 12 Apr 1813; Beswick, 'Dicker', 3, 8; *SRS* **77**, 108.

4 Brickyard on the south side of the road west of Boship Green
NGR: TQ 569 111
Date: Active in the 18th and early 19th centuries but listed as Old Brickyard in 1842, when it had been superseded by a new yard to the west (568 112). This later became known as the Dicker Pottery but bricks and tiles still formed part of the output until c1930
Op.: George Goldsmith in the early 19th century, followed by Uriah Clark from 1843
Prod.: Kiln-fired bricks and tiles, drainpipes,

chimney pots and ornamental fittings as well as pottery
Geol.: Weald Clay
Refs: TDE 5; OS 6in 55 (1874) 55 SE (1899, 1911); Kelly (1874-82); Pike/ Eastbourne (1882); White, *Lewes*, 29; Beswick, 'Dicker', 2, 5-6, 8; inf. L.R. Smith.

5 Brickyard on Old Pottery Farm on the east side of Coldharbour Road
NGR: TQ 563 108
Date: In operation from c1765 until c1850
Op.: William Cuckney from 1765 to 1787, members of the Mitchell family in the early 1800s and Stephen Goldsmith in 1842
Prod.: Principally pottery, with some bricks and tiles
Refs: *SRS* **72**, 174; TDE 5; *SWA*, 13 Feb 1826; Beswick, 'Dicker', 3, 9.

6 Brickyard on Price's Farm on the west side of Coldharbour Road
NGR: TQ 559 108
Date: From c1775 to the early 1800s
Op.: Richard Price in 1800
Ref.: Beswick, 'Dicker', 5, 9.

7 Brickyard on the west side of Coldharbour Road NE of site 6
NGR: TQ 561 111
Date: In operation from c1798; the kiln was mentioned in 1806 and was still in use in 1855. The yard was offered for sale in 1862 but remained unsold. It was abandoned by 1874
Op.: James Goldsmith, followed by George Goldsmith and his son John who was insolvent in 1856
Refs: TDE 5; BUR 2/1/42, 59, 105; Beswick, 'Dicker', 5, 9.

8 Brickyard on the west side of present-day Mansers Lane
NGR: TQ 561 114
Date: In use for a few years only from c1800
Op.: Robert Goldsmith
Ref.: Beswick, 'Dicker', 5, 8.

9 Tile yard (Boship Pottery) on the north side of the road opposite site 4
NGR: TQ 570 113
Date: In existence as a pottery from c1820, listed as Tileyard in 1842 but pottery

and drainpipes only were made after c1850

Op.: Several generations of the Miller family

Refs: TDE 5; OS 6in 55 (1874) 55 SE (1899); Beswick, 'Dicker', 8.

10 Brickfield at Lower Dicker between Coldharbour Road and Mansers Lane
NGR: TQ 563 113
Date: Marked only on the map of 1898
Refs: OS 6in 55 SE (1899); Beswick, 'Dicker', 8.

11 Brick and tile works on the west side of Hawks Road, Hailsham
NGR: TQ 585 105
Date: Marked on the map of 1873; closed by 1880
Op.: Uriah Clark (cf site 4)
Refs: OS 6in 56 (1873); sale partics. of 1873 (ex inf. A. Hibbs).

12 Brickyard on the east side of London Road, Hailsham
NGR: TQ 584 105
Date: 1880s: referred to as a former brickyard in 1892
Op.: The tenant in 1892 was Oscar Funnell
Ref.: Sale partics. (ex inf. A. Hibbs).

13 Brickworks at Leap Cross on the west side of London Road, Hailsham
NGR: TQ 584 104
Date: c1903 to c1922
Op.: Walter Langley
Refs: OS 6in 56 SW (1911); Kelly (1903-1922).

14 Brickworks at Rucklands on the west side of London Road, Hailsham
NGR: TQ 583 107
Date: Opened in 1900 and closed in the 1940s
Op.: Owned by Joseph Martin, an Eastbourne builder: the brickmaker was his brother Frederic, who was joined in 1919 by his son Gordon
Geol.: Weald Clay
Refs: OS 6in 56 SW (1911); Kelly (1907-38); QMJ (1927-44); White, Lewes, 31; Lake et al, Lewes, 35; Martin, 'Frederic Martin', 35; R. Martin, 'The Rucklands estate' Hailsham Historian and Naturalist Vol 2 No 3 (1992), 47-50.

15 Brickworks on the west side of Hackhurst Lane
NGR: TQ 557 118
Date: 1920s and 1930s
Op.: Sussex Stock Brick Co. in 1938
Prod.: Clamp-fired stocks
Refs: Kelly (1938); White, Lewes, 29; Lake et al, Lewes, 33; Beswick, 'Dicker', 7; inf. L.R. Smith.

HERSTMONCEUX

1 Tile kiln on the west side of Foul Mile north of Cowbeech
NGR: cTQ 619 160
Date: Tiles were made on land called Luxtrood in the late 14th century. This probably lay in the vicinity of two plots called Brick Earth Land, listed on the tithe award of 1839
Op.: Robert Bernard was sued for making tiles negligently in 1394. James Goldsmith (cf Warbleton 6) was the owner/occupier in 1839. He and his successors took tile clay from this site for use in the Warbleton yard
Refs: TDE 89; PRO CP40/533 m149 (ex inf. C. Whittick); inf. D. Calvert.

2 Brickyard south of Herstmonceux Castle
NGR: TQ 646 100
Date: The bricks were made on site when the castle was built in the 1440s. Thereafter bricks were made intermittently for repairs and alterations. The last brickyard was in operation in 1839 but closed c1850
Op.: John Leves and Thomas Browning made bricks for Lord Dacre in 1645-6. In 1839 and 1841 the occupier was Trayton Smith
Refs: TDE 89; XA 11/2; census (1841).

3 Brickyard and pottery on the west side of the road from Bodle Street to Windmill Hill
NGR: TQ 650 133
Date: Listed as a brickyard on the tithe award of 1839
Op.: John Siggery, a potter, was working here in 1835. In 1839 the tenant was his widow, Ann, who was also a potter
Refs: TDE 89; Baines, Pottery, 24, 167.

4　Brickworks on the west side of Victoria Road, Windmill Hill

NGR:　TQ 647 126

Date:　Opened c1860, marked on the maps of 1874 and 1899 but disused by 1910

Op.:　Edward Beeny, a farmer and miller, was also listed as a brickmaker in 1861. George Franks was the brickmaker in 1871 and by 1881 the yard was in the hands of John Cornford. In 1896 William Stevens was the tenant of the brickyard with Cornford living in a cottage nearby. Edward Bradford advertised as a brickmaker in Herstmonceux in 1903, probably on this site

Refs:　OS 25in 56/11 (1874, 1899, 1910); A4887; census (1861-81); Kelly (1903).

5　Brickworks on the south side of Chilsham Lane

NGR:　TQ 633 133

Date:　In existence by 1903, offered for sale in 1906 and closed during World War 1

Op.:　William Thomas Dawes jun. advertised in 1903

Refs:　OS 25in 56/7 (1909); Kelly (1903); sale catalogue in the possession of Philippa Heal.

EAST HOATHLY

1　Brickyard on Heasmans Farm

NGR:　TQ 527 163

Date:　Marked as Kiln Field on a map of 1788 and as Kiln Plat and Brick Yard on the tithe award of 1839

Op.:　Richard Hope was a brickmaker in East Hoathly throughout the second half of the 18th century, possibly working on this site. The owner/occupier in 1839 was Matthew Martin

Refs:　A 4113 (NRA 7); TDE 48; Vaisey, *Turner*, 333.

HOLLINGTON

1　Tile kiln near the end of present-day Carpenter Drive

NGR:　cTQ 785 119

Date:　The name Tile Kiln Farm was first used in the parish overseers' accounts in 1667. Kiln Field, shown to the west of the farmhouse on the tithe map of 1843, seems the most probable site for the kiln

Refs:　TDE 4; PAR 380/30/1.

2　Brickyard on the east side of Breadsell Lane

NGR:　TQ 777 124

Date:　In operation by 1843 and marked on the map of 1873

Op.:　The yard was part of the Crowhurst estate of Thomas Papillon Esq.

Refs:　TDE 4; OS 25in 58/9 (1873); Hunt, *Mining Records*, 39.

3　Brickworks on the west side of Hollington Lane

NGR:　TQ 795 117

Date:　In operation by 1851, marked on the map of 1873 and closed c1890

Op.:　James Marchant was a brickburner here in 1851, Draper & Marchant advertised from 1874 to 1882 and John Marchant in 1887

Refs:　OS 25in 15/13 (1873); census (1851); Kelly (1874-87); Pike/Hastings (1878) (ex inf. D. Padgham).

4　Two brickfields adjoining Old Church Road

NGR:　TQ 793 118 & c792 119

Date:　Abandoned by the 1880s

Refs:　*Hollington Methodist Church Centenary Booklet* (1987); inf. D. Pagham (1993).

5　Brickworks on the east side of Sedlescombe Road North

NGR:　TQ 796 123

Date:　Opened in 1876, marked on maps from 1899 to 1938 and known at different times as Ashdown Brickyard and Harrow Brick & Tile Works

Op.:　Frederick Cruttenden, a builder, leased the site in 1876 and was in financial difficulties in 1887. Padgham & Hutchinson were the tenants from 1900 to 1903, followed by James Martin & Son in 1904 and 1905 and Frank Murray & Co. from 1906 to 1920. G.B. & A. Collins (cf site 8) advertised in 1928 and 1938

Refs:　OS 25in 58/9 (1898, 1908, 1928, 1938); A2300; Pike/Hastings (1900-1920); Kelly/Hastings (1928); *DBC* (1938); inf. David Padgham (1990).

6 Brickfield on the site of present-day Harlequin Gardens
NGR: TQ 794 126
Date: Opened c1890 and marked on the map of 1898
Op.: Charles Hughes (cf St Leonards 3)
Refs: OS 25in 58/9 (1898); inf. D. Padgham.

7 Brickfield on the south side of Beauharrow Lane
NGR: TQ 793 128
Date: Marked only on the map of 1898
Op.: Arthur Henry White advertised in the 1890s and H.R. Soar in the early 1900s
Refs: OS 25in 58/9 (1898); Kelly (1890-5); Pike/Hastings (1901-2) (ex inf. D. Padgham).

8 Brickfield at the corner of Battle Road and Beauharrow Lane
NGR: TQ 791 127
Date: Marked on the maps of 1898 and 1908 and closed c1927
Op.: John Holyer (cf Hastings 10) in 1899 and 1900 followed by H. Lipscombe from 1903 to 1916 and G.B. Collins from 1917 to 1926
Refs: OS 25in 58/9 (1898, 1908); Pike/Hastings (1899-1926).

9 Brickworks between Sedlescombe Road North and Harrow Lane
NGR: TQ 798 129
Date: Marked on the maps of 1899 and 1909
Op.: Charles Hughes (cf site 6) from 1904 to 1911
Refs: OS 25in 58/10 (1899, 1909); Pike/Hastings (1904-11).

10 Brickfield on the site of present-day Kingsley Close
NGR: TQ 793 123
Date: Known as the Lower Yard to distinguish it from the Top Yard (site 8), it was opened c1900 and closed c1935
Op.: Hard Brick Co. (manager H. Marchant) from 1900 to 1909 followed by J.H. Marchant until 1919 and Mrs Marchant in 1920. Henry Ransom advertised from 1927 to 1931, followed by Brazil & Frost, who made breeze bricks from 1932 to 1934
Refs: OS 25in 58/9 (1908, 1928); Pike/Hastings (1900-20, 1928-34); *QMJ* (1927); inf. D. Padgham (1991).

HOOE

1 Brick(?) kiln on the east side of present-day Whydown Road
NGR: TQ 701 104
Date: The kiln was shown on a map of 1757 and the field was listed as Upper Kiln Field on the tithe award of 1839
Refs: P382/6/2; TDE 93.

2 Brickyard north of the Ninfield road at Hooe Common
NGR: TQ 694 108
Date: Possibly in operation in 1757, when a kiln was marked in the corner of what was then Lime Kiln Field. A brick kiln was included in a lease of 1815 and the name had changed to Brick Kiln Field in 1839. The brickworks was shown on the map of 1873 but was disused by 1899
Op.: William Rich was the tenant in 1839. Levi Lemmon (cf Ninfield 2) advertised as a brick- and tilemaker from 1855 to 1862. Jesse Message was a brickmaker here in 1871, followed in 1881 by Jesse Honeysett
F.Inf.: A sketch of the ruins of the brick kiln and lodge made in 1899 accompanied a note about the yard and its products written in 1935, when the site was called Brickyard Farm
Refs: P382/6/2; TDE 93; OS 25in 57/13 (1873, 1899); Acc 165/1012; Kelly (1855-62); census (1871-81); *SCM* **9** (1935), 670.

3 Brickyard on Kiln Lane
NGR: TQ 679 090
Date: Late 18th and early 19th centuries
Op.: John Blackman advertised for a tilemaker in 1792. J. & S Blackman were the tenants of land including Kiln Field in 1839 and a brickmaker called Joseph Hasler was living at 'late Blackmans' in 1851
Refs: TDE 93; *SWA*, 2 Jul 1792; census (1851).

4 Brick kiln NW of Holmes Farm
NGR: TQ 699 099
Date: Brick Kiln Field was marked on a map of 1810
Ref.: BMW/C10/3/9.

HORAM *see* HEATHFIELD, WALDRON

LITTLE HORSTED

1 Brickyard on the line of the Uckfield by-pass NW of its junction with Lewes Road
 NGR: TQ 471 192
 Date: Uncertain
 Ref.: C.F. Tebbutt & A.G. Woodcock, 'The Proposed Maresfield and Uckfield Bypasses' *SAC* **121** (1983), 191.

HOVE

1 Brickyards in the area of present-day Brunswick Square
 NGR: cTQ 297 043
 Date: This part of the Wick estate (cf Brighton 1) was used for brickmaking from the 1770s; brick kilns were marked on a map of 1825
 Op.: Thomas Scutt and Richard Kent, a builder, were in partnership from 1778 but ran separate brickyards after 1790. The brick kilns were mentioned in Scutt's will of 1794. Samuel Webb was a brickmaker at Wick in 1812 and George Webb was a brickmaker when he made his will in 1822
 Refs: *SRS* **72**, 174; *SWA*, 1 Feb 1790; AMS 5575/27/5; A4194/12-A1; W/A81.3; 'Catalogue of Sussex Pottery' *SAC* **46** (1903), 61.

2 Brickfields in the area of Adelaide Crescent
 NGR: cTQ 293 044
 Date: From before 1822 until the 1860s: a map of 1844 shows that the earliest brickfield on the site of Adelaide Crescent had been redeveloped but a brickfield was still in operation to the west. The church of St John the Baptist was built in 1851 on the site of a former brickfield
 Op.: Frederick William Lillywhite (cf Westhampnett) was a brickmaker in Hove from 1822 to 1837. His son John was foreman to George Stephens, who advertised in the 1830s. John Clayton, first mentioned as a brickmaker in 1820, was working in this area by 1836 and his son James advertised from 1851 to 1862

 Refs: PAR 386/1/2/1; Brighton Baptisms 1813-23 (ex inf. G. Mead); Pigot (1834-9); Kelly (1851-62); H.C. Porter, *History of Hove* (1897), 52, 59, 150; J.Middleton, *History of Hove* (1979), 48-9; R.Tibble, 'The Church of St John the Baptist, Hove' *Sussex History* **25** (Spring 1988), 27.

3 Brickfield on the south side of present-day Nizells Avenue
 NGR: TQ 298 051
 Date: Probably 1830s and 1840s
 Op.: Thomas Fowle, a brickmaker in 1829, advertised in 1832 and was living in Temple Street in 1840
 Cond.: Now tennis courts
 Refs: PAR 386/1/2/1; Pigot (1832); *SRS* **25**, 155; Young & Lake, *Brighton & Worthing*, 73; inf. G. Mead (1990).

4 Brickyard on the site of present-day Connaught Road
 NGR: TQ 285 048
 Date: In operation by 1845 and continued until the late 1860s
 Op.: Samuel Strong advertised from 1845 to 1867
 Ref.: Kelly (1845-67).

5 Brickyard in Hove Street
 NGR: cTQ 283 045
 Date: In operation by 1851
 Op.: John Bartlett advertised in 1851 and furnished the builders W. & B. Field of Brighton with 300,000 bricks @ 17s 6d per thousand in the same year
 Refs: Kelly (1851); Brighton Ref. Lib. mss (ex inf. R. Martin).

6 Brickfield on the east side of Hove Drove (now Sackville Road)
 NGR: TQ 285 054
 Date: Marked on the map of 1873
 Op.: Possibly John Bartlett (cf site 4), who advertised in 1875
 Refs: OS 6in 65 (1875); Folthorp's *Directory* (1875) (ex inf. G. Mead).

7 Brickfield at the corner of Hove Drove and Old Shoreham Road
 NGR: TQ 285 059
 Date: Marked on the map of 1873
 Op.: Probably Austin & Lee (Lynn), who advertised from 1866 to 1887
 Refs: OS 6in 65 (1875); Kelly (1866-87).

HURST GREEN *see* ETCHINGHAM, SALEHURST

ICKLESHAM

1   Brickfield near Camber (Winchelsea) Castle
    NGR: cTQ 919 185
    Date: In use when the castle was materially enlarged in 1538-9
    Ref.: Colvin et al, *King's Works*, 416-449.

2   Two brickfields on Castle (formerly Sheephouse) Farm
    NGR: The first is uncertain and the second cTQ 916 176
    Date: In use when the Martello towers were under construction in 1805 and 1806
    Op.: Mr Dalloway, contractor to the Board of Ordnance, had a brickfield on the castle lands in 1805 and his successor Mr Trimmer made bricks on land adjoining the Rye Marsh in the following year
    Ref.: Beswick, 'Martello Towers', 20-27.

3   Brickfield on the north side of the road from Icklesham. to Winchelsea
    NGR: TQ 896 170
    Date: Listed on the tithe award of 1845, by which date it was in use as a hop garden
    Ref.: TDE 8.

4   Brick kilns west of Icklesham village
    NGR: TQ 873 164
    Date: Described as 'site of brick kilns' in 1845
    Op.: The tenant in 1845 was Henry Farncombe sen.
    Ref.: TDE 8.

5   Brick kilns on the south bank of the River Brede west of Langfords Bridge
    NGR: TQ 860 178
    Date: A double kiln was marked on the tithe map of 1845
    Op.: The owner/occupier in 1845 was Thomas Cooper Langford
    Ref.: TDE 8.

6   Brickyard to the west of Knockbridge Farm
    NGR: TQ 875 157
    Date: 19th century
    Ref.: Inf. Zoe Vahey (1989).

7   Brickyard between Harbour Road and the river at Rye Harbour
    NGR: TQ 939 193
    Date: Marked only on the map of 1872
    Ref.: OS 25in 45/11 (1872).

8   Brickworks on the south side of Woodhouse Lane
    NGR: TQ 884 160
    Date: Marked on the maps of 1872 and 1899
    Refs: OS 25in 59/1 (1872, 1899).

9   Brickworks on Elms Farm at the corner of Pett Lane
    NGR: TQ 885 159
    Date: 1920s and 1930s: the kiln was still standing in 1942
    Refs: *VCH* **9**, 184; inf. Zoe Vahey (1989).

IDEN

1   Brick kiln to the west of Moat Farm
    NGR: cTQ 896 240
    Date: Brickmaking for Mote Manor was taking place in 1466-7: Brickoaste Brooke was marked on a map of 1634 and Great and Little Brickoaste Fields on a terrier of 1647
    Refs: SAS/HC 227 & 180/3-4.

2   Brickyard on Corkwood Farm
    NGR: TQ 903 250
    Date: According to local tradition a kiln was in existence from the 1780s: marked as Brickworks on the map of 1875
    Op.: Henry Carter was the brickmaker in 1861
    Prod.: Bricks, tiles and land drains; a brick marked DRAIN, found nearby, must have been made prior to 1850
    F.Inf.: The kiln was built into sloping ground near the bank of the River Rother. In 1992 the arch of one of the firing tunnels was visible and some of the fire bars were found
    Refs: OS 25in 32/10 (1875); census (1861); inf. R. Regendanz (1993).

3   Brick kiln on the west side of Main Street
    NGR: TQ 917 237
    Date: Erected after 1801 to make bricks for the terrace of five cottages to the south and demolished c1832 when the present-day April Cottage was built

Op.: The owner was William Fisher, innkeeper
F.Inf.: The kiln is shown on the plan as circular
Refs: A496/25; DAP Box 2 – manor of Iden Rectory docs.

4 Brickyard on the west side of Wittersham Road
NGR: TQ 916 249
Date: In existence in 1826 and listed on the tithe award of 1843
Op.: Green & Co. advertised in 1839; in 1843 the tenant was John Care
Prod.: Kiln-fired bricks and tiles; in 1843 there was a pottery adjoining the brickyard
Refs: TDE 147; *SWA*, 31 Jul 1826; Robson (1839).

ISFIELD

1 Brickyard west of the road from Lewes to Uckfield SW of Rose Hill
NGR: TQ 455 163
Date: In existence by 1724 and closed in the early 1800s
Op.: John Alcorn from before 1724 until 1775, followed by his son John. Thomas Best (cf Hamsey 2) was the owner from 1795 to 1801. Abraham Shaw, a brickmaker and shopkeeper who was declared bankrupt in 1806, may have worked on this site
Refs: SAS/HC 520-536; ADA 207; 'An 18th Century Brickmaker' *SNQ* **2** (1928), 90; *SWA*, 2 Jun 1806.

2 Brick and tile works on Horsted Lane
NGR: TQ 458 173
Date: 1870s and 1880s
Op.: Stephen Jeffery was the brickmaker in 1871 and William Cox the principal brick- and tilemaker in 1881
Refs: OS 6in 40 (1875); census (1871-81).

KINGSTON BY LEWES

1 Brickyard
Location not known
Date: The yard closed in 1829
Prod.: Kiln-fired bricks, tiles and drainpipes
Ref.: *Brighton and Hove Herald*, 9 Mar 1829.

LAUGHTON

1 Brick kiln north of Laughton Place
NGR: TQ 485 122
Date: Probably the site of brickmaking for Laughton Place in the 1530s; The Brick-oste Fieldes were marked on a map of 1641
Ref.: A2327/1/4/29.

2 Brickyard west of Halland Park Farm
NGR: TQ 507 161
Date: Probably the site of brick and tilemaking for the coach-house which was built in the late 17th century
Op.: Owned by the Pelham estate
Ref.: Lewes Coroners' Inquests 1959/48B; I. Nairn & N. Pevsner, *Sussex* (1965), 514.

3 Brickyard north of Broomham on the east side of the road to Whitesmith
NGR: TQ 524 129
Date: Probably in existence in 1752, listed on the tithe award of 1841 and marked on maps from 1875 to 1911
Op.: Bartholomew Gorely, a brickmaker, had land in this area in the 1750s. Benjamin Morris was the owner and Henry Haffenden the brickmaker in 1841, followed by Benjamin White in 1851, Jesse Hall in 1855-6, Edward Clark between 1859 and 1863 and various members of the Hinckley family from 1867 to 1903
Prod.: Kiln-fired bricks and tiles
Refs: TDE 27; OS 25in 55/6 (1875-1911); ESRO SAS/A 663; census (1841-81); Kelly (1851-1903); BUR 1/2/52, 132.

4 Brickfield on the east side of the road from Averys Oak to Laughton Common
NGR: TQ 495 141
Date: Late 18th or early 19th century
Op.: Possibly James Saunders in the 1770s
Refs: A 2327/1/4/31 map 3; SAS/A 664; CHR 7/2/2.

5 Brickyard on Laughton Common
NGR: TQ 493 143
Date: In operation by 1754 and listed as Brickyard Field and Pond on the tithe award of 1841
Op.: George Alcorn supplied bricks to the Glynde estate in 1754 and died in 1770

Refs: TDE 27; SAS/A 663; W/A62.193; Lusted, 'Glynde', 48.

6 Brickyard on Laughton Common SE of site 5
   NGR: TQ 495 142
   Date: In operation by 1775; closed c1930
   Op.: Joseph Back supplied bricks to the Pelham estate at Halland between 1775 and 1789. By 1841 the yard was owned by the estate and the brickmaker was Richard Funnell. Samuel Moppett advertised from 1859 to 1874, followed by his son George until 1895. A Mr Phillips was the last tenant c1930
   Prod.: Kiln-fired bricks and tiles
   Refs: TDE 27; OS 25in 55/1 (1875, 1898, 1911); SAS/A 664, 666; AMS 2132; census (1841-81); Kelly (1859-95); inf. Angela Snelgar (1983).

7 Brickyard on the west side of Pound Lane
   NGR: TQ 503 133
   Date: In operation by 1841, marked on the maps of 1875 and 1898 but as Old Kiln in 1911
   Op.: Various members of the Turner family between 1841 and 1861. William French, who bought the yard from the exors of Henry Turner in 1873 and sold it to Sir James Duke Bt in 1890, advertised from 1878 to 1895
   Prod.: Bricks, tiles and agricultural drainpipes, as shown in an inventory of 1872
   F.Inf.: The yard was advertised for sale in 1872 with 'a vein of excellent light-working brick earth'. The accompanying plan shows the kiln, sheds and pugmill
   Refs: TDE 27; OS 25in 55/5 (1875, 1898, 1911); census (1841-81); BUR 2/1/216; Acc 6790/5; Kelly (1878-95); sale particulars in the possession of Mrs Snelgar.

8 Brickyard and pottery at Whitesmith
   NGR: TQ 525 141
   Date: In operation by 1805: Brick Earth Field was marked just over the boundary in Chiddingly (527 144) on an early 19th-century survey. The pottery was shown on the map of 1875 and as disused in 1898 but bricks were being

made until 1915
   Op.: Jesse Hall (cf site 3) and four other members of his family were listed as potters in 1851. Peter Kennard advertised as a brickmaker from 1899 to 1907 followed by Frederick & Warden Kennard in 1915
   Refs: A2327/1/4/31 map 19; OS 25in 55/6 (1875, 1898); census (1851); Kelly (1899-1915); Baines, *Pottery*, 37, 169.

LEWES

1 Brickfield in the parish of St John Without, near the East Chiltington boundary
   NGR: TQ 391 149
   Date: Marked on a map of 1623
   Ref.: AMS 4811.

2 Brick kiln on the corner of Lancaster Street and North Street
   NGR: TQ 416 105
   Date: Marked on a map of 1799
   Op.: Probably Amon Wilds, a builder who was developing the area at this date
   Refs: LEW C2/3/1; inf. Colin Brent.

3 Brickyard between North Street and the River Ouse
   NGR: TQ 416 107
   Date: In existence by 1823: the kiln was marked on a map of 1824 and the yard was still listed in 1844
   Op.: Owned by Thomas Chatfield, a coal merchant
   Refs: PM 29(A); TDE 22; *SWA*, 16 Jun 1823.

4 Brickworks on The Brooks (formerly in the par. of South Malling)
   NGR: TQ 420 106
   Date: In operation by 1907 and marked on maps of 1910 and 1932
   Op.: James Chandler, builder, of Lewes, who also had a brickyard at Hamsey (qv)
   Refs: OS 25in 54/14 (1910, 1932); Kelly (1907); *QMJ* (1927).

MARESFIELD

1 Brickfield on the east side of Old Forge Lane
   NGR: TQ 459 258
   Date: Le Brickefeilde was mentioned in a survey of 1564 and again in 1653, when the adjacent Brickhost Gate was also listed. Brickmaking may have

ended when the ironworks ceased operation in the 17th century but the field name was still in use in 1840

Op.: Owned by members of the Hoode (Hode, Hoth) family from 1560 to 1815

Refs: TDE 151; ADA 94; J.R. Daniel-Tyssen, 'Parliamentary Surveys of the County of Sussex 1649-1653' *SAC* **24** (1872), 207, 213; Cleere & Crossley, *Iron*, 374; inf. C. Hobbs.

2 Brickfield in Pippingford Park

NGR: TQ 446 312

Date: Listed on the tithe award of 1840; bricks were probably made when the ironworks were in operation in the 18th century

Prod.: Bricks and roofing tiles were found when the furnace was excavated

Refs: TDE 151; D.W. Crossley, 'Cannon manufacture at Pippingford, Sussex c1717' *Post-medieval Archaeology* (1975), 24-5.

3 Brickyard on the north side of Tylers Lane

NGR: TQ 454 261

Date: Brickmaking was taking place in this area from the early 18th century. The yard was listed on the tithe award of 1840 and marked as Brick & Tile Works on the map of 1875

Op.: Robert Diplock, described as a bricklayer in 1705 when he bought land at nearby Clayfields, was a brickmaker in 1721. Edmund Smith and his son Jarrett, the tenant and brickmaker respectively in 1840, were said to have enclosed the land 'many years since' when granted the copyhold in 1852. Jarrett's son John, who had taken over by 1861, advertised until 1878 and was still brickmaking in 1881

Refs: TDE 151; OS 6in 27 (1875); ADA 81, 87-89 (ex inf. C. Hobbs); census (1841-81); Kelly (1851-78).

4 Brickyard near the windmill at Nutley

NGR: TQ 449 290

Date: Brick Kiln Farm was advertised for sale in 1752 and Brickhouse Mead and Brick Yard Field were listed on the tithe award of 1840

Op.: John Cheeseman was the tenant prior to the sale in 1752. Later that year John Streatfeild was taxed for the brick kilns followed by Richard Stevenson from 1756 to 1765. There were various occupiers over the next twenty years but after this the brick kilns were no longer mentioned.

Refs: TDE 151; ELT & LT Maresfield; *SWA*, 24 Feb 1752.

5 Brickyard south of Cackle Street

NGR: TQ 452 264

Date: The brickyard was in existence by 1817. It was listed on the tithe award of 1840 and marked as Brick & Tile Works on the map of 1875

Op.: Richard Markwick, originally a carpenter from Uckfield, ran the yard from c1817 until his death in 1862, when it was acquired by John Smith (cf site 3)

Refs: TDE 151; OS 6in 27 (1875); CAF 2/4 ff12, 123; ADA 87; census (1841-51); Kelly (1851-62).

6 Brickyard on the Maresfield Park estate

NGR: TQ 462 252

Date: Marked on a map of Lampool Farm in a survey of 1820

Ref.: PAR 420/26/1.

7 Brickyard at the eastern end of School Lane, Nutley

NGR: TQ 447 283

Date: In operation by 1826, listed on the tithe award of 1840 and in use until c1900

Op.: James Dives, the miller, had enclosed ½ acre for a brickyard prior to 1826. The tenant in 1840 was James Bourner and in 1851, Benjamin Minns, of the Shelley Arms, but the brickmakers were members of the Stevenson family (cf site 4). William Stevenson was the foreman of the brickyard in 1861 and 1871 and John and Henry Stevenson were brickmakers in 1881. From at least 1874 management was in the hands of William Turner & Sons and William Turner jun. became the owner in 1887

Prod.: Clamp- and kiln-fired bricks, tiles and land-drains

Refs: TDE 151; OS 1in (1831) 25in 27/3

(1874); CAF 2/4; QDD/6/E15; census (1861-81); Kelly (1867-95); unpub. memoirs of Harry Walter (c1950).

8 Brickworks at Marlpits, Nutley
NGR: TQ 448 287
Date: Known as the upper yard to distinguish it from the lower yard (site 7), it was marked on the map of 1898 and closed c1920
Op.: William Turner (cf site 7) followed by his son Albert
Prod.: Clamp bricks only during the last few years
Geol: Ashdown Beds
Refs: OS 25in 16/15 (1898, 1910); Kelly (1890-1918); Bristow & Bazley, *Tunbridge Wells*, 53; Walter *op. cit.*

MARK CROSS *see* ROTHERFIELD, WADHURST

MAYFIELD

1 Brick kiln south of Old Place
NGR: TQ 588 274
Date: Marked Brickhouse Field on a map of c 1640; a kiln may have been sited here in 1456 when roofing tiles were made for the Archbishop's Palace
Refs: AMS 5831; *VCH* **2**, 252.

2 Brick kiln west of Old Mill Farm
NGR: TQ 585 245
Date: Listed as Brickhouse Field on the tithe award of 1844; bricks may have been made here for the ironworks in the early 17th century
Refs: TDE 133.

3 Brick kiln on the east side of Newick Lane SW of Cranesden
NGR: TQ 584 260
Date: Marked Brickhouse Field on a map of c1750
Ref.: AMS 744.

4 Brickyard north of Lake Street
NGR: TQ 598 295
Date: Marked on a map of 1754
Op.: The owners were William and Sampson Moon
Ref.: BMW/C24B/1.

5 Brick kiln NW of Great Trodgers Farm
NGR: TQ 582 292

Date: Brick Kiln Field was listed on the tithe award of 1844 by which date the field was in use as a hop garden; the name survives as Brick Kiln Wood
Refs: TDE 133; OS 1:25,000 TQ 52 (1959)

6 Brickyard on the west side of Rotherfield Lane
NGR: TQ 579 273
Date: Active in the 18th century, marked only as Great and Little Brick Kiln Fields in 1826 but revived at some time between 1844 and 1871 and marked on the map of 1875
Op.: John Parks paid tithe for the Brick Kell from 1713 to 1730; George Parkes, probably a descendant, was a farmer and brickmaker in 1871 and advertised in 1878 and 1882
Refs: AMS 5713/5/2; TDE 133; OS 25in 29/1 (1875); KIR 32/3 f113; census (1871, 1881); Kelly (1878-82).

7 Brickyard on Brickkiln Farm at Hadlow Down
NGR: TQ 542 250
Date: In existence by 1785 and in operation until 1926
Op.: Owned by the Hadlow House estate: the brickmaker in 1843 was Michael Baker. Nicholas Stapeley advertised and bought parts for a drainpipe machine in 1895, by which time Thomas Barden (cf site 10) was working in the yard. He was succeeded by his sons Adam and David, who ran the works until it closed
Prod.: Building and paving bricks, roof tiles and drainpipes were sold in 1871
Refs: KIR 32/8 & 9; TDE 133; OS 6in 28 (1875) 25in 28/11 (1910); SM/D13 446; BUR 2/1/212; AMS 6214; Kelly (1895); *SRS* **77**, 156; inf. Bertram Barden (1992).

8 Brickyard on Northover (formerly part of Allens) Farm
NGR: TQ 568 241
Date: A kiln was marked on a map of c1803 and the yard was listed on the tithe award of 1844 and marked on the map of 1875
Op.: James Blackford in 1871 and 1881
Refs: AMS 5403; TDE 133; OS 25in 28/12 (1875); census (1871-81).

9   Brickyard on the west side of Newick Lane near the Heathfield boundary
    NGR: TQ 594 239
    Date: In existence by 1839, listed in 1844 and marked on the map of 1874
    Op.: Owned by the Kirby estate; the brickmaker from 1839 to 1881 was James Saunders (for an earlier brickyard on this estate cf Heathfield 1)
    Prod.: An account book for 1839-46 lists payments to Saunders for making bricks, roofing tiles and drain tiles
    Refs: TDE 133; OS 25in 29/13 (1874); KIR 28/85; census (1841-81); Kelly (1859-78).

10 Brickworks on the site now occupied by The Warren
    NGR: TQ 595 268
    Date: In operation in 1861 and marked on the map of 1875
    Op.: Probably James Saunders jun. in 1861 and Thomas Barden in 1881
    Cond.: Part of the firing-tunnel of the kiln runs underneath the house called Maylands
    Refs: OS 25in 29/5 (1875); census (1861, 1881); inf. Mrs Palmer (1991).

11 Brickworks on the south side of Lake Street
    NGR: TQ 596 293
    Date: Marked only on the map of 1898
    Refs: OS 25in 18/13 (1898).

12 Brickworks on the east side of the road north of Scotsford Bridge
    NGR: TQ 603 257
    Date: Marked on the maps of 1898 and 1909 and closed at the beginning of World War 1
    Op.: Scotsford Brick Yard, manager: George William Baldock
    Prod.: Bricks, tiles and drainpipes
    F.Inf.: For brickmaking, clay from a pit immediately to the south of the kiln was mixed with loam brought from an area closer to the river. Sand was dug from a pit at the entrance to Gilhope Farm. Mixing was done in a horse-driven pugmill and the kiln was built into the hillside, with its firing chambers facing south. A plan of the up-draught kiln, drawn c1894, shows the front elevation with two fireholes,

the hatchway at the rear and the floor, with 15 cross-flues and 14 benches, on which the bricks were stacked
    Cond.: The site was levelled in 1966
    Refs: OS 25in 29/6 (1898, 1909); A5767/6/38; Kelly (1899-1907); *Mayfield Parish Magazine*, Sept 1966 (ex inf. Mary Porter).

MOUNTFIELD

1   Brick and tile works on the north side of Vinehall Road
    NGR: TQ 757 206
    Date: Opened c1850 and marked on the map of 1875
    Op.: L. & H. Simes supplied drain tiles to the Ashburnham estate in 1852 and probably employed John Mills, who was living in Whatlington in 1851, as brickmaker. Mills himself supplied tiles between 1860 and 1870 and advertised in 1862 and 1867. By 1871 the brickmaker was Amos Elliott
    Refs: OS 6in 43 (1875); ASH 1749; census 1851-71; Kelly (1862-7).

2   Brickyard alongside the railway near Mountfield tunnel
    NGR: cTQ 732 204
    Date: In existence in 1851, when the railway was under construction
    Op.: The brickmaker in 1851 was William Warwick
    Ref.: Census (1851).

3   Brickyard south of Tunstall Farm
    NGR: TQ 724 210
    Date: In existence by 1871, marked on the map of 1874 but abandoned by 1898
    Op.: Thomas Dann in 1871 and 1881
    Refs: OS 6in 43 (1874); census (1871-81).

NEWHAVEN

1   Brickfield on Harbour Heights
    NGR: TQ 432 008
    Date: In use in 1846-7 for construction of the Newhaven branch of the London Brighton & South Coast Railway
    Ref.: Inf. Peter Wells/Geoffrey Mead (1993).

2   Brickfield north of Newhaven Fort
    NGR: TQ 446 003

Date: 7-8,000,000 bricks were made for the construction of the fort in 1865-70

F.Inf.: A steam engine was used, probably to power the pugmill. An old photograph in the Newhaven Museum collection shows the pond

Ref.: *East Sussex News*, 26 Oct 1866 (ex inf. J.E. Goodwin); *Sussex Express*, 30 Mar 2001.

3 Brickworks on present-day Valley Road
NGR: TQ 441 017
Date: Marked on the maps of 1875 and 1899
Op.: Edward Baker (cf Piddinghoe) advertised in the 1880s
Refs: OS 25in 78/3 (1875, 1899); Kelly (1882-7).

NINFIELD

1 Brickfield east of Ingrams Farm
NGR: TQ 717 121
Date: Little Brick Field and Lower Brick Field were listed on the tithe award of 1841
Ref.: TDE 107.

2 Brickyard at Lower Street
NGR: TQ 704 119
Date: In existence in 1841 and marked Brick & Tile Works on the map of 1873; not shown in 1899 but the brickmaker continued to advertise until 1907
Op.: Levi Lemmon (cf Hooe) was the tenant of Brickyard Field in 1841 and advertised in 1845. From the 1850s onwards the brickmakers were members of the Russell family: James Russell between 1851 and 1881 and Jesse Russell from 1890 to 1907
Refs: TDE 107; OS 25in 57/10 (1873); census (1851-1881); Kelly (1845, 1890-1907); *SIAS Newsletter* **46**, April 1985.

3 Brickworks at the corner of Marlpits Lane and Skinners Lane
NGR: TQ 709 134
Date: Opened c1866 when Normanhurst, in Catsfield, was under construction and closed c1914
Op.: Owned by the Normanhurst estate: the brickmakers in 1881 were George Mann and Samuel Hill
Prod.: Inventories of 1900-03 list kiln and

clamp bricks, tiles, fittings and land drains
Refs: OS 25in 57/6 (1874, 1899, 1909); census (1881); BMW A2/89; A5634/1/16, 30-31.

4 Brick kiln on the south side of Marlpits Lane
NGR: TQ 705 131
Date: In existence before 1813 but out of use by 1841
Op.: The tenant before 1760 was Thomas King, followed by three successive John Moons and Alex Coleman in 1813
Refs: TDE 107; Acc 165/1224.

NORTHIAM

1 Brickfield on the north side of the road from Horns Cross to Clayhill
NGR: TQ 834 231
Date: Brick Clamp Field was listed on a map of the Brickwall estate of 1627
Ref.: A 4050/38.

2 Brick kiln south of Brickwall House
NGR: TQ 831 236
Date: Brick Kiln Field was named on an estate survey of 1779; the kiln was in use in the mid-17th century when Jane, the third wife of Thomas Frewin, planted the garden and had bricks made to build the surrounding wall – hence the name. It may have been in use again when the house was altered by Sir Edward Frewen early in the 18th century
Refs: AMS 5881; FRE 7307; W.Mottram, 'Brickwall House, Northiam', *Downs Country,* July/Aug 1997.

3 Brick kiln west of Ockford Farm
NGR: TQ 816 232
Date: 18th century: marked only as Pit Shaw on the tithe award of 1840
Op.: Owned by the Tufton Place estate: the brickmaker may have been John Weekes, who agreed to supply bricks to the Earl of Thanet in 1754
Geol.: Wadhurst Clay: the pit lies to the north of the kiln site, close to the junction with the Ashdown Sand
Cond.: The base of the kiln was discovered when an orchard was being replanted

in 1991; two firing-tunnels and the slotted floor of the firing-chamber survive

Refs: TDE 96; Lloyd (1925) 18; observations made by members of HAARG and SIAS (1991).

4 Brick kiln to the east of Adams Lane
NGR: TQ 812 232
Date: Marked as Brick Kiln Shaw on a map of 1821
Op.: An alternative site for John Weekes' kiln in 1754 (cf site 3)
Cond.: There are signs of extensive clayworking in the shaw as well as quantities of brick and tile wasters, including valley tiles and coping bricks
F.Inf.: A lime-kiln on the western edge of the shaw was excavated in 1976
Refs: XA 16/1; inf. Gwen Jones (1977).

5 Brickyard on the Beckley boundary to the east of site 1
NGR: TQ 835 232
Date: In operation before 1837, when Brick Yard Land was added to a map of the Frewen estate; marked as Brick & Tile Works on the map of 1872 but disused by 1898
Op.: Described as 'late Gilbert's' in 1837; George Ranger was the tenant in 1840
Refs: AMS 5881; TDE 96; OS 25in 31/15 (1872, 1898).

6 Brickworks on the west side of Whitebread Lane
NGR: TQ 835 258
Date: Opened in the 1930s, re-opened after the war and closed in the late 1950s
Op.: M.P. Harris & Co. Ltd
Refs: Kelly (1934-8); inf. W.J. Haffenden (1991).

ORE

1 Several brickyards on land, formerly part of Fairlight Down, north of present-day Broadlands
NGR: TQ 836 120
Date: Called Kiln Field on a survey of 1816 and Bricklands on the map of 1873: three licences to dig earth and clay and burn bricks and tiles were granted

in this area in the 1830s
Op.: William Weller, the tenant in 1816, was a brickmaker (cf Guestling 1 & Hastings 3), as was Thomas Henbrey (cf site 2), the owner in 1843, when the land was described as 'meadow'. Licences to make bricks were granted in 1830 to Edward Martin and in 1835 to Henbrey and to William Gallop
Refs: XA 15/2; TDE 43; OS 25in 58/11 (1873); MIL F7/12, 13, 14.

2 Brickyard at Broomgrove NE of the railway station
NGR: TQ 826 108
Date: A brickyard was in existence on Bunger Hill Farm in the 1820s; it was listed on the tithe award of 1840 and marked as Brick Works on maps from 1873 to 1929
Op.: The tenant in 1828 was James Putland. Thomas Henbrey advertised in 1845 and from 1859 to 1867, the site probably having been used by the railway company in the interval. J.C. Parker, a builder, was working in Mount Pleasant Brickfields in 1879, followed by Stephen Message (cf Hastings 8) in the 1880s and 1890s and Percy Jackson from 1896 to 1903. Broomgrove Brick Co. Ltd advertised from 1910 to 1918
F.Inf.: In 1828 the site was said to contain an inexhaustible supply of brick earth and to produce the best bricks in the neighbourhood
Refs: TDE 43; OS 25in 58/15 (1873, 1899, 1909, 1929); *SWA*, 24 Apr 1826; HMAG ABS/D69; Kelly (1845, 1859-63, 1878-99, 1913-15); Pike/Hastings (1879, 1896 1903, 1910 18) (ex inf. D. Padgham).

3 Brickfield at the south end of Ore tunnel
NGR: cTQ 830 112
Date: In use when the railway was under construction from 1849
Op.: Messrs Hoof & Sons, railway contractors
Refs: HALSP, *Railways*, 17; census (1851).

4 Brickworks at Coghurst, above Ore tunnel
NGR: TQ 831 117
Date: First used when the railway was

under construction and still in operation in 1873

Op.: As site 3 in 1849

Refs: OS 25in 58/11 & 15 (1873); HALSP, loc. cit.

5 Brickworks on the corner of Winchelsea Road and Rock Lane

NGR: TQ 836 118

Date: Marked only on the map of 1873

Op.: Stephen Foster in 1882

Refs: OS 25in 58/11 (1873); Pike/Hastings (1882) (ex inf. D. Padgham).

6 Brickworks between Hoadswood Road and St Helens Down Road

NGR: TQ 823 112

Date: Marked on the map of 1873 but as Old Brick Kiln in 1899

Refs: OS 25in 58/15 (1873, 1899).

7 Brickworks on the east side of Beaney's Lane

NGR: TQ 811 128

Date: Marked on the map of 1873 but as Old Clay Pit in 1899

Refs: OS 25in 58/10 (1873, 1899).

8 Brick and tile works on the south side of the Ridge on the site of present-day Ranmore Close

NGR: TQ 812 125

Date: Marked on maps from 1873 to 1909

Refs: OS 25in 58/10 (1873, 1899, 1909).

9 Brickfield on the west side of Old London Road

NGR: TQ 835 113

Date: 1880s

Op.: William Rogers was the tenant in 1889

F.Inf.: The tenancy agreement was for a minimum of 400,000 bricks per year

Ref.: Sale catalogue in the possession of David Padgham.

10 Brickfield on the east side of Frederick Road

NGR: TQ 832 110

Date: In operation by 1887 and marked on the map of 1899

Op.: Frederick Head, a coal merchant, was also listed as a brickmaker from 1887 to 1897

Refs: OS 25in 58/15 (1899); Pike/Hastings (1887-97) (ex inf. D. Padgham)

11 Brickworks on the site of present-day Austen Way, off Rock Lane

NGR: TQ 838 123

Date: Opened in 1882 when John Austin was granted a 14-year lease of 4 acres of land; closed in the late 1950s

Op.: John Austin advertised from 1890 to 1903, the exors of J. Austin in 1907 and Ore (Hastings) Brickfields Ltd from 1930 to 1956. The foreman in the 1950s was Fred Benge

F.Inf.: The square kiln of 1910 had given place to three circular kilns by 1929

Refs: OS 25in 58/11 (1910, 1929, 1937); MIL D15; Kelly (1890-1907, 1930-38); Kelly/Hastings (1930-56) (ex inf. D. Padgham); *QMJ* (1933-44); J.M. Baines' notes in Hastings Ref. Lib.

PEACEHAVEN *see* PIDDINGHOE

PEASMARSH

1 Brick kiln on Stream Farm

NGR: TQ 894 229

Date: 17th century

Op.: Possibly Walter Carrew, who paid Hearth Tax 1665

F.Inf: The kiln was excavated in 1955

Refs: XA 5/2; V.F.M. Oliver, 'A 17th Century Brick Kiln' *SNQ* **14** (1955), 164-7.

2 Brickyard between Main Street and School Lane (now called Brickfield Estate)

NGR: TQ 888 226

Date: A brick kiln was in existence before 1717 and was still in operation in 1772. Described as Brickfield in 1831 and Brick Kiln Field in 1840, the yard was apparently not in use in 1872 but was revived in the 1880s and marked Brick Works on the maps of 1900 and 1909

Op.: The brick kiln, late Salmons, was occupied by John Holt in 1717 and his widow paid rent for it in 1733. Her lease was renewed in 1737 and another John Holt was declared bankrupt in 1760, when the kiln was offered for sale. James Jeakins of Rye (cf Rye 4) was the brickmaker in 1765 and 1772. Thomas Cavey advertised as a brickmaker in Peasmarsh in 1839. In 1887 the manager of Peasmarsh Brickworks was George Saunders

Refs: TDE 12; OS 6in 45 NW (1900) 25in 45/1 (1909); AMS 5735/53, 5887 &

6541/1/22; ASH 500; SAS/DE 237; *SWA*, 17 Nov 1760 & 21 Sept 1772; Robson (1839); Kelly (1887).

3   Brick kiln north of Flackley Ash
NGR: TQ 881 236
Date: 18th century or earlier
Op.:   Possibly John Petter, a farmer, whose probate inventory of 1755 mentioned a stock of bricks and 'the implements belonging to the brick kiln'
Cond.: Some heavily-glazed bricks in a hollowed-out bank mark the site of the kiln (1990)
Ref.:   W/INV 3081.

PENHURST

1   Brick kiln north of Hill Farm
NGR: TQ 702 169
Date: 19th century
Op.:   Probably Tilden Smith, who supplied bricks to the Ashburnham estate between 1851 and 1858
Cond.: The loam pit and traces of the kiln were visible at the corner of the shaw in 1980
Ref.:   ASH 1748.

PETT

1   Brickworks on the western edge of Pett Wood
NGR: TQ 866 145
Date: Marked on the map of 1873 only
Ref.:   OS 25in 58/8 (1873).

PEVENSEY

1   Brickfield east of the Castle Inn
NGR: TQ 657 041
Date: Marked 'C' on a sketch-map of 1805 and used to make bricks for the Martello towers in that year
Op.:   Mr Dalloway, contractor to the Board of Ordnance
Refs: PRO MFQ 307/16B; Beswick, 'Martello Towers', 23-4.

PIDDINGHOE

1   Brickyard north of the village between the Lewes road and the River Ouse
NGR: TQ 433 032
Date: In operation by 1805, marked on the map of 1874 but as Whiting Works only in 1899. However, the surviving kiln was said to have been last used in 1912
Op.:   Edward Baker first advertised in 1828 and members of the family continued to do so until 1903 although Thomas Don and Harry Breach were named as the tenants of the brickyard in 1893
Prod.: White bricks, red bricks, tiles, drainpipes, structural terracotta and brown-ware pottery; the adjacent chalk pit also supplied material for lime-burning
F.Inf.: The kiln was restored in 1981
Refs: TDE 57; QDP 218; OS 25in 67/14 (1874, 1899); CHR 17/17-18; *SWA*, 22 July 1805; *Brighton & Hove Gazette*, 28 Apr 1825 (ex inf. G. Mead); Pigot (1828-39); Kelly (1845-1903); O'Shea, 'Piddinghoe' 2-24; Osborne, 'Bakers', 24-7.

2   Brickfield south of site 1 on the west side of the road
NGR: TQ 433 030
Date: Marked only on the map of 1874
Op.:   Almost certainly Edward Baker, whose supply of brick earth on the narrow riverside site (No 1) was by this time running low
Ref.:   OS 25in 67/14 (1874).

3   Brickfield on the site of present-day Lake Drive Park, Peacehaven
NGR: TQ 408 016
Date: Early 1920s to cater for the post-war development
Geol.: Woolwich and Reading Beds
Ref.:   Postcard in the possession of Dr R.B.G. Williams.

PLAYDEN

1   Brick kiln on the east side of Iden Road
NGR: TQ 918 233
Date: The land was called Brockhoste in 1570 and Brickhose in 1631
Op.:   Possibly William Cromer, a brick maker who was living in Playden in 1590
Refs: AMS 4883-91; SAS/E 409; WSRO EpII/5/5 f269.

2   Brickyard on the high ground to the west of

Military Road

NGR: TQ 925 218

Date: A kiln was in existence in 1587, when 'the footway to the Brick Oast' was given as an abutment of property to the South-West; marked on a map of 1804 and listed on the tithe award of 1843

Op.: Lime Kiln Estate, including the brickyard, was owned by Samuel Reeves Esq. in 1804. William Aylward was the owner by 1843 when the yard probably supplied both bricks and lime for Thomas Aylward of Rye, who advertised as a brickmaker and limeburner between 1832 and 1855. In 1841 Trayton Foster was a brickmaker, living at Military Gate

Refs: AMS 4812; SAS/HC – Iden manorial records; TDE 11; Pigot (1832-9); census (1841); Kelly (1855).

PLUMPTON

1 Brickfield on the east side of Station Road north of the Sun Hotel

NGR: TQ 365 165

Date: Marked on the map of 1873 and as Old Clay Pit in 1897

Op.: Harry Stevens advertised from 1874 to 1882. The yard foreman William Lipscombe also advertised between 1878 and 1890. In 1881 he was employing 2 men and 2 boys

Refs: OS 25in 39/16 (1873, 1897); Kelly (1874-90); ed. B. Short, *Scarpfoot Parish: Plumpton 1830-1880* (1981), 32; inf. G. Mead (1988).

2 Brickfield on the west side of Station Road north of the Fountain Inn

NGR: TQ 363 172

Date: Said to have been in operation by 1872 but not shown on a map until 1897; marked Brick Works in 1910, when it had been extended westwards and closed in the early 1930s

Op.: Harry Stevens (cf site 1) followed by William Stevens in 1887 and E. & R. Norman (cf Chailey 1) from c1890 to 1930; Thomas Pratt was the yard foreman in 1895

Refs: OS 25in 39/16 (1897, 1910); Kelly

(1890-1930); Short, *op. cit.*, 32.

3 Brickfield on the east side of Station Road south of Plumpton Crossways

NGR: TQ 366 179

Date: 1870s and 1880s

Op.: Edwin Hemsley, a farmer/brick-maker, bought the land in 1872 and advertised in 1878 and 1882

Refs: Kelly (1878-82); Short, *op. cit.*, 32-33; inf. G. Mead.

4 Brickfield on the north side of Riddens Lane

NGR: TQ 363 165

Date: In operation by 1878 and marked on the maps of 1897 and 1910

Op.: William White & Son from 1878 to 1903; Henry White in 1907

Refs: OS 25in 39/16 (1897, 1910); Kelly (1878-1907); Short, *op. cit.*, 32.

5 Brickfield immediately to the north of site 4

NGR: TQ 362 166

Date: Marked on the maps of 1897 and 1910

Op.: Possibly Keymer Brick & Tile Co. (cf Keymer 15), who advertised in Plumpton in 1899 and 1903, and Thomas Carter in 1907

Refs: OS 25in 39/16 (1897, 1910); Kelly (1899-1907).

6 Brickyard on the west side of Wivelsfield Road opposite Heath Farm

NGR: TQ 362 188

Date: Marked on the maps of 1897 and 1910

Op.: Walder & Thomas in 1907 and 1915, James Thomas in 1918

Refs: OS 25in 39/8 (1897, 1910); Kelly (1907-18).

7 Brickfield east of Knowlands Farm on the East Chiltington boundary

NGR: TQ 367 167

Date: In operation by 1899 and marked on the map of 1910

Op.: Ebenezer Geall (cf Keymer 14) in 1899 and 1903, H. & E. Geall (cf South Bersted 7) in 1907

Refs: OS 25in 39/16 (1910); Kelly (1899-1907).

8 Brickworks on the east side of Station Road south of Lentridge Farm

NGR: TQ 366 172

Date: In operation by 1899; closed in 1960

Op.: A. Cox & Son, builders in Brighton,

advertised from 1899 to 1960

Prod.: Hand-made clamp-fired stocks: details of the methods used were given by Harold 'Darkie' Simmons in an interview in 1981

Refs: OS 25in 39/12 (1910); Kelly (1899-1938); *QMJ* (1927-1959); Short, *op. cit.*, 33; inf. G. Mead.

9 Brickworks on the west side of Station Road north of Letchmore Lodge
NGR: TQ 364 178
Date: In operation by 1907; closed c1940
Op.: George Norwood & Son from 1907 to 1918 followed by Tom & Harold Bartlett from 1922 to 1945
Refs: OS 25in 39/12 (1910); Kelly (1907-38): *QMJ* (1927-44).

10 Brickfield on the south side of Strawlands Lane on the East Chiltington boundary
NGR: TQ 366 168
Date: 1920s to 1940s
Op.: Honess & Thwaites
Refs: *QMJ* (1927-44); *SIAS Newsletter* **50**, Apr 1986.

POLEGATE *see* HAILSHAM, WESTHAM

PORTSLADE

1 Brickyard east of Copperas Gap
NGR: TQ 262 050
Date: In existence by c1830 and listed as Brickkiln Field on the tithe award of 1841; the northern half was in use as a brickfield in 1874 but had ceased operation by 1898
Op.: John Clayton (cf Hove 2) advertised as a brickmaker at Copperas Gap in 1832. John Blaker was probably working here in the 1860s and '70s and James Frederick Clayton, the son of John, gave his address as Courtney Terrace in 1882 and 1887
F.Inf.: A circular kiln is visible on a watercolour of Shoreham painted c1830 by J.M.W. Turner
Refs: TDE 69; OS 65/11 (1874); Pigot (1832); Kelly (1867-87); watercolour in Blackburn Museum.

2 Brickfield on the west side of Station Road

NGR: TQ 263 054
Date: In existence by 1862 and closed in the 1880s
Op.: James Holes (Holis) was stated to be an established brickmaker when he applied for a spirit licence for his beer-shop, called the Half Brick, in Windmill St in 1862. He advertised from 1867 to 1882
Refs: OS 65/11 (1874); *Brighton Herald*, 30 Aug 1862; Kelly (1867-82).

3 Brickfield between sites 1 and 2
NGR: TQ 263 052
Date: In existence by 1867 and closed in the 1880s
Op.: T. Stringer advertised in 1867, followed by James Stringer from 1874 to 1882
Refs: OS 65/11 (1974); Kelly (1867-82).

4 Brickfield between Old Shoreham Road and Victoria Road
NGR: TQ 257 057
Date: In existence by 1867 and closed c1910
Op.: Austin & Lee advertised in 1867, Austin & Lynn from 1874 to 1887 and Burtenshaw & Saville from 1890 to 1910.
F.Inf.: By 1897 the claypit had reached a depth of over 20ft
Geol.: Woolwich and Reading Beds
Cond.: Now a recreation ground
Refs: OS 6in 65 (1874) 65/7 (1898); Kelly (1867-1907); Pike/Brighton (1902-10); Foster, *Mines* (1897-1901); White, *Brighton & Worthing*, 15; Young & Lake, *Brighton & Worthing*, 73.

RINGMER

1 Brick kiln alongside Delves House
NGR: TQ 447 126
Date: The brick-kiln was mentioned in a document of 1651 and marked as Brick Place on a map of 1704. It probably went out of operation shortly after this date
Op.: Possibly John Bristow, mentioned as a brickmaker between 1700 and 1722
F.Inf.: Several large ponds in the grounds of Delves House mark the site of clay extraction
Refs: AMS 5799/2; SAS/FA 806; ADA 19; inf. John Kay.

2 Brick kiln at Rushey Green
NGR: TQ 452 123
Date: Probably erected in the 1680s but first specifically mentioned in 1695, the kiln continued in operation until c1740
Op.: Richard Garrett, followed by his son Thomas
Prod.: Bricks and roofing tiles
F.Inf.: Garrett was also a lime-burner
Refs: ADA 19 & 44; SM D5/234; inf. John Kay.

3 Brick kiln(s) on Arches Farm south of the Broyle
NGR: TQ 463 126
Date: From before 1689 until at least 1727; Kiln Pond was marked on a map of 1767
Op.: Thomas Wakerell until 1695, followed by John Foord until 1722, when he supplied bricks for the building of Stanmer House. His successors were his brother Edward and his nephew Charles Tasker, who also supplied bricks and tiles for Stanmer House in 1723 and 1726
Refs: A2551; ADA 19; A4600/7; inf. John Kay.

4 Brick kiln on the north side of the Broyle near Munkin Gate
NGR: TQ 471 154
Date: c1690 to c1770; marked on a map of 1765
Op.: James Ticehurst from c1690, followed by Nicholas Clark (cf Framfield 2)
Refs: AMS 5915/2; PAR 461/31/1/1; inf. John Kay.

5 Brick kiln on the Broyle west of Lower Lodge
NGR: TQ 462 129
Date: In operation by 1754, when 2,000 bricks were taken from the Broyle to Glynde Place; marked on the map of 1765 with adjacent clay pits and broken ground
Op.: Thomas Crowhurst supplied bricks for Glynde Place stables in 1754 and was still brickmaking in Ringmer in 1767
Refs: AMS 5915/2; GLY 2772; Lusted, 'Glynde', 48.

6 Brick kiln on the west side of the Broyle near Fingerpost Farm
NGR: TQ 459 133
Date: Marked on the map of 1765
Op.: John Elphick, a farmer, took clay from the Broyle for his kiln
Refs: AMS 5915/2; ADA unlisted box (ex inf. John Kay).

7 Brickyard in Plashett Park
NGR: TQ 460 147
Date: Early 19th century; Brick Clamp Plot and Field were named on the tithe award of 1840
Op.: Richard Devonish advertised for a brick- and tilemaker in 1819
Ref.: TDE 137; SWA, 8 Mar 1819.

8 Brick kiln (?) NE of Clayhill House
NGR: TQ 447 144
Date: Probably 18th century; wasters were found during excavation of a pipeline in 1992
Ref.: Inf. Mark Gardiner (1992).

9 Brickyard adjoining Middle Broyle Farm
NGR: TQ 476 141
Date: Opened c1820, enlarged in 1890 and closed in 1971
Op.: Walter Guy was granted a lease of the brickyard in 1828. His successor, from the 1830s until his death in 1872, was Henry Turner. A new lease to James, Edwin and Benjamin White jun. was granted in 1874 and surrendered in 1889. The land was then bought by W.L. Christie of Glyndebourne and the yard managed by the estate foreman. The last brickmaker in the 1960s was a Mr Divall
Prod.: Bricks, tiles and drainpipes, as shown by inventories of the yard taken in 1872, 1891 and 1920. Both kiln- and clamp-fired bricks were made prior to 1920 but only clamp-fired ones thereafter
F.Inf.: A 300yd industrial light railway, used to transport clay from the pit, was included in the 1920 inventory. The only machinery in the yard at the end of its life was a pugmill driven by an oil engine
Geol.: Weald Clay
Refs: TDE 137; OS 6in 54 NE (1875, 1898, 1910); BUR 2/1/216; GBN 16/1 & 3;

BMW A2/44 & 316; *Brighton Gazette*, 15 Sept 1825 (ex inf. G. Mead), Robson (1839); Kelly (1851-1915); White, *Lewes*, 29; Lake et al, *Lewes*, 33.

10 Brickyard at Black Gate, now known as Brickyard Farm
- NGR: TQ 461 144
- Date: Mid-19th century
- Op.: Thomas Guy and Reuben Ellis were brickmaker's labourers here in 1851, probably working for Henry Turner (cf site 9)
- Ref.: Census (1851).

11 Brickyard near Ringmer Green
- NGR: TQ 450 128
- Date: Known as Potters Field, the site yielded clay for brickmaking in the 1890s
- Op.: William Frederick Martin, a building contractor
- Refs: Kelly (1895); W. Martin, 'A Forgotten Industry: Pottery at Ringmer' *SAC* **45** (1902), 128.

RIPE

1 Brick kiln on the east side of Ripe Lane
- NGR: TQ 516 108
- Date: The earth pits and land called Brykhost were mentioned in a mortgage of 1560; the name had become Brickhoys by 1822
- Refs: SAS/A 681; BL Add Ch 30780 (ex inf. C. Whittick).

2 Brickfield to the west of Ripe Lane
- NGR: TQ 514 108
- Date: The field names Brickfield and Brick Croft (511 103) were mentioned in the Manor of Laughton Court Book in 1767 and marked on an early 19th-century survey
- Refs: A 2327/1/4/31 map 12; SAS/A 664.

ROBERTSBRIDGE *see* EWHURST, SALEHURST

ROTHERFIELD

1 Brick kiln on the southern edge of Castle Wood
- NGR: TQ 553 273
- Date: A lease of 1587 relating to 28a of Le

Heise (Little Ease Farm) included the Brickhost Field, listed as Brick Field on the tithe award of 1839
- Refs: TDE 156; C. Pullein, *Rotherfield* (1928), 166.

2 Brickfield on present-day Kingsbury Farm
- NGR: TQ 555 279
- Date: Six acres called Brickfield, on the NE side of Castle Wood, were mentioned in a deed of 1591; still called Brick Field in 1839
- Refs: TDE 156; Pullein, *op. cit.*, 160.

3 Brick kiln on Rotherfield Hall estate
- NGR: cTQ 543 290
- Date: Brick Croft was mentioned in a sale document of 1645
- Ref.: Pullein, *op. cit.*, 330.

4 Brick kiln south of Bletchinglye Lane, Town Row
- NGR: TQ 573 300
- Date: Brick Kiln Farm was mentioned in the will of Humphrey Fowle in 1756 and on the land tax assessment of 1785
- Refs: TDE 156; Pullein, *op. cit.*, 396; *SRS* **77**, 181.

5 Brickfield on Walsh Manor
- NGR: TQ 525 287
- Date: Brick Field was listed on the tithe award of 1839
- Ref.: TDE 156.

6 Brick kiln on the edge of Orphanage Wood west of Catt's Hill
- NGR: TQ 573 307
- Date: Brick Kiln Field was listed on the tithe award of 1839
- Ref.: TDE 156.

7 Brickyard on the Abergavenny estate near Danegate
- NGR: TQ 559 338
- Date: Brickyard Field was listed on the tithe award of 1839
- Ref.: TDE 156.

8 Brickyard on the west side of Eridge Road at Boarshead
- NGR: TQ 532 324
- Date: Possibly in existence by 1774; Upper Brick Yard, Lower Brick Field and Brick Field Pit were all listed in 1839
- Op.: George Hoadly of Rotherfield, brickmaker, married Mary Wickens in

1774. In 1839 the tenant was Thomas Wickens

Refs: TDE 156; *SRS* **25**, 213.

9 Brickyard opposite the end of Treblers Road near Castle Hill

NGR: TQ 548 278

Date: Probably in existence by 1829 and marked on the tithe map of 1839; the brickyard was listed in a conveyance of 1872 and was abandoned in the 1890s

Op.: Samuel Walter in 1829; William Walter, the owner/occupier in 1839, was employing a man and 2 boys in 1851 and Charles Walter advertised from 1874 to 1890

Refs: TDE 156; OS 6in 28 (1875); AMS 5430/260; census (1851); Kelly (1874-90); *SRS* **26**, 446.

10 Brickyard at the corner of Rotherfield Road and Old Forest Lane

NGR: TQ 545 298

Date: Called Gilbert Brick Yard on the tithe award of 1839

Ref.: TDE 156.

11 Brickyard at the corner of Brickyard Lane, Mark Cross

NGR: TQ 583 317

Date: Established by 1839 and closed in 1937

Op.: Edward Walter (cf Wadhurst 3) was the owner/occupier in 1839. John Manser was a brickmaker and local preacher at Mark Cross in 1851 and advertised in 1859. Henry Callow was in charge between 1861 and 1874, probably as the tenant of Edward Joseph Walter, who advertised in 1878. In 1879 the yard was leased to Thomas Pollington (cf Withyham 2), whose family ran it until 1937

Prod.: Kiln-fired bricks, tiles and drainpipes

Refs: TDE 156; OS 25in 18/9 (1875, 1898, 1910); census (1861-81); Kelly (1859-1934); *SRS* **75**, 52; inf. David Pollington, 'Kilnside', Mark Cross (1978).

12 Brickyard south of Steep Hill Farm, Jarvis Brook

NGR: TQ 534 282

Date: In operation by 1861, called Sandhill Brickyard in a conveyance of 1872 and

marked on the maps of 1875 and 1898

Op.: Thomas Barden was the brickmaker here in 1861 and 1871 and N. Blackford in 1881. John Paine, a builder, advertised in 1895 followed by James Blackford in 1899 and Luck Bros in 1903

Refs: OS 25in 28/3 (1875, 1898); AMS 5430/260; census (1861-81); Kelly (1895-1903).

13 Brick kiln on the east side of the former railway west of Trull's Hatch

NGR: TQ 572 292

Date: Marked on railway plans of 1874

Ref.: QDP 409.

14 Brickworks on the north side of Yew Tree Lane, Trull's Hatch

NGR: TQ 574 297

Date: In operation by 1881 and marked on the map of 1898

Op.: Henry Callow, the son of the brickmaker at Mark Cross (site 11) was working here in 1881 with Ambrose Earl as his assistant. Earl himself advertised in the following year but by 1887 the yard appears to have been in the hands of Edgar Bassett of Town Row

Geol.: Ashdown beds, yielding both clay and sand

Refs: OS 25in 17/16 & 18/13 (1898); census (1881); Kelly (1882-7); Bristow & Bazley, *Tunbridge Wells*, 55.

15 Brickfield on Lews Farm on the west side of Sheriff's Lane

NGR: TQ 563 288

Date: In operation by 1881 and marked on the maps of 1898 and 1910

Op.: Jabez Nicholson, foreman brick maker, and William Fry, brick and tilemaker, were both living in this area in 1881. Fuller & Thornback advertised in 1899 and William Fuller jun. in 1903 and 1907

Refs: OS 25in 17/16 (1898, 1910); census (1881); Kelly (1899-1907).

16 Brickworks alongside the railway at Jarvis Brook station

NGR: TQ 532 296

Date: Opened c1880 and closed in 1980

Op.: In 1881 George Booth, a

Yorkshireman, was managing the yard for Joseph Firth & Sons, who advertised in 1882. By 1890 the firm was called Crowborough Brick & Terra Cotta Co. with Joseph J. Rook as manager. The name was changed to Crowborough Brick Co. in 1903 and the company was acquired by Redland Brick in 1961

Prod.: Principally purple-grey kiln-fired stock facing bricks but for a short period at the outset tiles and terra cotta ornaments were also made. Bricks from this works were used to build Victoria Station and, more recently, City University in London

Geol.: Ashdown Beds, consisting here of grey and white silts with thin clay seams. In 1960 the company was disposing of material unsuitable for brickmaking as 'landscape garden rock'

F.Inf.: Bricks were burnt in three continuous kilns and a 2ft-gauge railway was used for transport within the works

Refs: OS 25in 17/15 (1898, 1910, 1931); census (1881); Kelly (1882-1938); *QMJ* (1927-60); Bristow & Bazley, *Tunbridge Wells*, 56, 114; *Kent & East Sussex Courier*, 7 Mar 1980; *SIAS Newsletter* **26**, Apr 1980; *BBS Information* **25** (1981); J. de Havilland, 'Crowborough Brickworks' *Great Bush Telegraph* **4** (1982); Chalkpits Mus., *Industrial Railways*.

17 Brickfield east of New Road, Crowborough Cross
NGR: TQ 519 312
Date: In operation by 1887, marked on the map of 1899
Op.: William Pratt advertised as a baker and brickmaker from 1887 to 1899 followed by T. Pratt until 1907
Geol.: A clay seam within the Ashdown Beds
Refs: OS 6in 17 SW (1899); Kelly (1887-1907); Bristow & Bazley, *Tunbridge Wells*, 54.

18 Brickworks on the Horsegrove estate at the corner of Mayfield Lane
NGR: cTQ 556 292
Date: Early 20th century
Op.: William Edmund Fuller advertised in

1903 and 1907
Refs: Kelly (1903-7); Pullein, *op. cit.*, 322.

19 Brickworks on Alderbrook Farm, Crowborough
NGR: TQ 520 292
Date: Marked on the map of 1911 only
Op.: Connor Bros, builders, advertised in 1927
Refs: OS 6in 17 SW (1911); *Brighton & Sussex Trades Dir.* (1927).

RYE

1 Pottery and tile kilns on the west side of Rye Hill
NGR: TQ 921 211
Date: 14th or 15th century
Prod.: Some roofing tiles, as well as floor tiles and pottery were produced
Refs: L.A. Vidler, 'Floor Tiles and Kilns, St Bartholomew's Hospital, Rye' *SAC* **73** (1932), 84-94; Vidler, 'Kilns Found at Rye' *SAC* **74** (1933), 46; Vidler, 'Final Report' *SAC* **77** (1936), 106-9.

2 Brick kiln on the south side of Leasam Lane
NGR: TQ 915 215
Date: The 'brick kiln lane' was referred to in a lease of 1737 and Brick Kiln Field was marked on a map of c1805
Ref.: DAP Norton; ASH 500.

3 Brick kiln between Iden Road and Tighe's Wood
NGR: TQ 915 229
Date: Marked as Brick Kiln Field on a map of c1770
Ref.: DAP Norton.

4 Brickyard at Cadborough on the north side of Udimore Road
NGR: TQ 912 203
Date: In existence from at least the mid-18th century and in operation until c1918
Op.: James Jeakins, a local builder, owned the yard in 1763 followed by James Smith, a limeburner and brickmaker, at the end of the 18th century. Jeremiah Smith advertised as a potter and brickmaker in the 1830s and William Mitchell took over as his manager in the 1840s. By 1859 S. Catt was the manager of the brickyard, which was now separate from the

pottery. He advertised until 1874 but by 1878 George Russell was running the business, which was sold to him in 1885. By 1916 the yard had been bought by Frank Ashenden, a local builder, who was killed in World War 1

Prod.: Bricks, roofing tiles and ornamental fittings, chimney pots and agricultural drainpipes; in the 19th century earthenware and glazed pottery were also produced

Refs: TDE 1; OS 25in 45/6 (1875, 1898, 1911); *SWA*, 28 Nov 1763; Pigot (1834-9); Kelly (1859-87); Baines, *Pottery*, 46; Deacon's *Almanac and Directory of Rye* (1916) (ex inf. Tarquin Cole).

RYE HARBOUR *see* ICKLESHAM

ST LEONARDS

1 Brickyard north of present-day West St Leonards station
NGR: TQ 789 091
Date: Opened by 1805 and in operation for most of the 19th century: marked Old Brick Yard on the map of 1898
Op.: Farncombe & Breeds in 1805 and Edward Farncombe in 1839; William Skinner advertised as a brickmaker in the 1830s and later operators were members of the Hughes family (cf site 4)
F.Inf.: Some of the bricks for the Martello towers and for Bo-peep tunnel were made on this site
Refs: OS 1 in 5 (1813) 6in 71 (1873) 71 NW (1898); QDP/E171/3; Pigot (1832-9); HALSP, *Railways*, 15; T.B. Brett, mss *History of Hastings* & J.M. Baines' mss notes in Hastings Library.

2 Pottery and brickyard at Silverhill
NGR: TQ 801 110
Date: A brickyard was associated with the pottery between 1839 and the early 1850s
Op.: Solomon Stubberfield was the brickmaker in 1851, employing two men, one of whom was Aaron Foord (cf Hastings 5)
Refs: Census (1851); Baines, *Pottery*, 74-6.

3 Brickworks near the junction of Harley Shute Road and Bexhill Road
NGR: TQ 782 089
Date: There was a brickyard in this area in 1855. The brickworks was marked on the map of 1900, was no longer active in 1909 but was revived in the 1920s
Op.: C. & E. Farncombe advertised as brick-makers on Filsham Farm in 1855; Charles Hughes (cf site 4) was working on the Filsham estate between 1890 and 1903
Prod.: Sand-lime bricks in the 1920s: a large quarry in the Ashdown Sand, which was already in existence in 1897, was utilised for this purpose
Ref.: OS 25in 71/1 (1900, 1909); Kelly (1855, 1900-1903); Foster, *Mines* (1898-1901); White, *Hastings and Dungeness*, 92.

4 Brickworks on the east side of London Road South of Silverhill
NGR: TQ 800 106
Date: In existence in 1861, marked on the map of 1874 and closed c1890
Op.: In 1861 the owners were Messrs Hughes, builders and brickmakers, of Mercatoria. The foreman, who hanged himself in the yard in that year, was Edward Barnes. Henry Hughes advertised in 1862 and 1867 and Charles Hughes from 1878 to 1887
Refs: OS 25in 58/14 (1874); SHE 2/7/702; Kelly (1862-87).

5 Brickworks on present-day Windmill Road west of Silverhill
NGR: TQ 796 107
Date: In operation from the 1870s and marked on the map of 1899
Op.: William Draper, of St Leonards Mill, from 1874 to 1887 and the Hard Brick Co. Ltd (cf Hollington 10) from 1900 to 1906
Refs: OS 25in 58/13 (1899); Kelly (1874-87); Pike/Hastings (1900-06) (ex inf. D. Padgham).

6 Brickworks on the site of present-day Haven Road
NGR: TQ 778 090
Date: Marked on the map of 1900 only
Op.: Probably Peter Jenkins (cf Hastings 9), a builder, who offered a choice of bricks from six different yards in 1899

Refs: OS 25in 71/1 (1900); Kelly (1882-99); Pike/Hastings (1890-1902) (ex inf. D. Padgham).

SALEHURST

1 Brick kiln south of Park Farm
NGR: TQ 751 228
Date: Brick Kiln Field and nearby Tile Croft, marked on a survey of 1811, may have been the site of brickmaking for the Robertsbridge ironworks in the mid-16th century. In 1717 a lease of the furnace included the brick kiln and liberty to dig clay to make bricks and tiles
Op.: William Ovenden was the principal brick- and tilemaker in 1549 (an alternative site for his operations is Ewhurst 1 iii) Thomas Snepp of Battle and his son Thomas were the lessees in 1707
Refs: BAT 4437; CKS U1475 B8/2 (ex inf. G. Jones); HEH BA71/15.

2 Brick kiln north of the road from Hurst Green to Bodiam
NGR: TQ 749 260
Date: Land called Tyllerst was mentioned in a will of 1567; Brick Kiln Field and Tylers Field to the north were marked on a map of Boarsney Farm in 1770
Refs: AMS 5368; *SRS* **53**, 83.

3 Brick and tile kiln south of Great Wigsell
NGR: TQ 760 272
Date: Tyle Croft was marked on a map of 1685 and bricks and tiles were being made c1720
Op.: In 1720 the stock of William Clarke, grazier, included bricks and tiles
Refs: AMS 5765; W/INV 1249.

4 Brick kiln SE of Iridge Place
NGR: TQ 740 268
Date: Listed on the tithe award of 1841; possibly in use when alterations, were made to the house in 1717
Refs: TDE 86; *VCH* **9**, 221.

5 Brick kiln west of London Road at Silverhill
NGR: TQ 733 263
Date: Brick Kiln Mead on Grove Hill Farm was listed in 1841
Ref.: TDE 86.

6 Brick kiln west of Rocks Hill
NGR: TQ 751 249
Date: Brick Kiln Shaw was listed in 1841 and brick and tile debris found there in 1969
Refs: TDE 86; Draper & Martin, 'Local Industry', 58.

7 Brickyard on Starrs Farm on the east side of the London road
NGR: TQ 739 251
Date: In existence by 1808 and in use until 1844
Op.: William Weller from 1816 to c1835 followed by his son William
Refs: SAS/HC 345/3; TDE 6; ALF 7/1-32.

8 Brickyard south of the road from Hurst Green to Hawkhurst
NGR: TQ 736 278
Date: In existence by 1841; closed during World War 1
Op.: William Weller jun. (cf site 7) in 1841 followed by Thomas Catt, who was formerly employed at site 7. Daniel Austin (cf Etchingham 5) was the tenant for a period until 1865, when Charles Pankhurst took over. From 1871 onwards the brickmakers were members of the Saunders family
Prod.: Bricks, tiles and drainpipes: a pipe machine and dies were purchased from the Hurst Green Foundry in 1907
F.Inf.: The brickmaker's house was included in a valuation of 1865
Cond.: The depression where the kiln stood was still visible in 1969
Refs: TDE 86; OS 25in 30/3 (1873, 1897, 1909); ALF 7/17; AMS 6214; A2232/162; census (1871); Draper & Martin, 'Local Industry', 57.

9 Brickyard on Bugsell Farm
NGR: cTQ 726 243
Date: 1870s and 1880s
Op.: Francis Bourne in 1878 and 1882; Richard Willard advertised as a farmer and brickmaker at Robertsbridge in the 1890s
Refs: Kelly (1878-82, 1895-99).

10 Brickworks east of Robertsbridge station
NGR: TQ 734 235
Date: Opened in the early 1870s and closed in 1915
Op.: Robertsbridge Brick Co. Ltd: the

manager in the early 20th century was J. Pankhurst

Prod.: Bricks, tiles and drainpipes: fire bars and a pipe machine were purchased from the Hurst Green Foundry in 1905

F.Inf.: The plant and fixtures were valued at £50 in 1915

Refs: OS 25in 30/15 (1873, 1898, 1909); AMS 6214; BMW A2/268; Kelly (1903-15); Draper & Martin, 'Local Industry', 58.

11 Brick kiln on Browns Farm

NGR: TQ 735 225

Date: Brickkiln Field and Brickearth Field were included in a lease of the farm in 1723 and Kilnfield was marked on a map of 1811

Refs: BAT 4435; HEH BA 71/19.

SEAFORD

1 Brickworks on the site of present-day Lions Place

NGR: TV 489 987

Date: Uncertain

Ref.: Seaford Museum card index No 1600 (ex inf. G. Mead).

2 Brickworks on the north side of Blatchington Road

NGR: TV 482 993

Date: Before 1875, when only a pond remained SW of the gas works and a claypit was shown to the south (482 992)

Refs: OS 25in 78/12 (1875); Seaford Museum (as site 1).

see also: EAST BLATCHINGTON

SEDLESCOMBE

1 Brickyard on the west side of Footland Wood

NGR: TQ 763 198

Date: Marked on the tithe map of 1843

Op.: The tenant in 1843 was John Adams

Ref.: TDE 20.

2 Brickyard on Castlemans Farm on the west side of Hurst Lane

NGR: TQ 783 194

Date: Marked on the tithe map of 1843

Op.: Spencer Crisford, a farmer and bricklayer, was the tenant in 1843. George Apps, the brickmaker, lived in one of the adjacent Brickyard Cottages (the site now occupied by Littlehurst)

Refs: TDE 20; B. Lucey, *Twenty Centuries in Sedlescombe* (1978), 244.

see also: BATTLE, WESTFIELD

SELMESTON

1 Brickfield NE of Sherrington Manor

NGR: TQ 509 078

Date: Brick Field was listed on the tithe award of 1840

Ref.: TDE 125.

TICEHURST

1 Brick kiln on the edge of Boarzell Wood

NGR: TQ 711 297

Date: Probably in use when Pashley Furnace was in operation in the 16th and early 17th centuries: Brickhouse Field was marked on a map of 1689

Ref.: A 4683.

2 Brickyard (now Brick Kiln Farm) on the south side of High Street

NGR: TQ 677 302

Date: In existence by 1785 and still in operation in 1847

Op.: Owned by the Ticehurst House estate; the tenant of the brick kiln and land was Thomas Perron in 1785 and William Noakes in 1840. In 1847 the outgoing tenant of the brickyard was Thomas Barden

Prod.: Kiln-fired bricks and tiles

Refs: TDE 2; A2232/32, 60; *SRS* **77**, 199.

3 Brickfield on the north side of Tinkers Lane

NGR: TQ 693 311

Date: Brick Field was listed on the tithe award of 1840

Op.: The tenant in 1840 was John Buckland

Ref.: TDE 2.

4 Brickyards on the Whiligh estate

NGR: TQ 660 311, 655 307

Date: i. Brickfield Pond and Shaw on the eastern edge of the park, listed on the tithe award of 1840, probably the site of an earlier estate brickyard
ii. Brick Yard and Brick-kiln Coppice and Plantation, on the north side of the road at Shover's Green, listed in 1840

Ref.: TDE 2.

5 Brickyard on the south side of High Street east of Shovers Green
NGR: TQ 657 305
Date: 1840s and 1850s
Op.: Owned by the Whiligh estate; the tenant in 1840 was Stephen Stevenson and the brickmaker in 1841 and 1851 was Joel Oliver
Refs: TDE 21; census (1841-51).

6 Brickworks on the east side of Churchsettle Lane
NGR: TQ 654 299
Date: In operation by the 1870s and closed c1939
Op.: George Oliver and Stephen Luck were brickmakers here in 1871, followed by George Bines in 1881 and 1891. W.O. Carter advertised at Maplesden in 1885 and William Piper bought a tile machine and had a pipe machine repaired at Hurst Green foundry in 1889 and 1892 respectively
Refs: OS 25in 18/16 (1875-1932); census (1871-91); AMS 6214; Pike/Hastings (1885).

7 Brickworks on the south side of High Street west of Wallcrouch
NGR: TQ 662 303
Date: Early 20th century
Op.: Owned by the Whiligh estate, the yard was operated by the estate with members of the Butcher family as brickmakers
F.Inf.: In the 1930s, bricks were burnt in circular downdraught kilns
Ref.: Inf. Harold Wells (1992).

UCKFIELD

1 Brickyard on the west side of Ridgewood Common
Exact location not known
Date: 1740s
Op.: Richard Teeling had encroached on the common in 1745 and in the following year his encroachment was described as 'a kiln and a brickplace'
Ref.: ADA 117.

2 Brickyard on Ridgewood Common near Horsted Pond
NGR: TQ 475 194
Date: In existence from before 1745 until c1830

Op.: John Whatford was presented for encroachment in 1745 and in 1756 his grant of copyhold included a brick kiln and two 'workhouses'. In 1761 the premises were sold to Richard Paine whose nephew Joseph Paine, a brickmaker, inherited the property in 1776. The yard was offered for sale in 1787 and was bought by the occupier, George Taylor. In 1810 he sold the business to John Kenward, a miller. His brickmaker was probably Thomas Ware, who was living nearby in Framfield from at least 1826
Refs: ADA 117-123; QRE 793; *SWA*, 15 Oct 1787 & 28 Jan 1788; ELT Uckfield.

3 Brickyard at Bates Hole east of Union Point
NGR: TQ 476 201
Date: In operation from c1832, listed on the tithe award of 1838 and marked on maps from 1875 to 1957
Op.: John Kenward (cf site 2), with Thomas Ware as brickmaker, until 1845 when the yard was sold to the Earl of Liverpool. In 1855 stock from the yard was sold by Goldsmith and Ware and in 1859 the tenants were Benjamin Ware and another. Henry Tyhurst (later Tyhurst & Son) was the lessee from c1867 to 1905, when a new lease was granted to Amos & William Ware (cf site 6)
Prod.: An inventory of 1905 lists the kiln, pugmill and implements for making bricks, plain and ornamental tiles and drainpipes
Refs: TDE 33; OS 25in 40/8 (1874, 1899, 1910) 1:25,000 TQ 42 (1957); ADA 124, 126; PAR 286/12/1; LT Uckfield; BUR 2/1/40; BMW A2/136; census (1841-61); Kelly (1845, 1859-1938); docs. held by Messrs Dawson Hart & Co.

4 Brickworks on the north side of New Road, Ridgewood
NGR: TQ 478 197
Date: c1867 to c1890
Op.: Benjamin Ware (cf site 3); George Best, who advertised as a brickmaker at Ridgewood in 1887, was probably managing the yard for Ware

Refs: OS 25in 40/8 (1874); ADA 129; Kelly (1874-1887).

5 Brickfield south of Framfield Road
NGR: TQ 476 206
Date: Opened in the late 1890s and closed in the late 1930s
Op.: Tyhurst & Son (cf site 3 & Buxted 2), who traded until 2000 as builders' merchants, built offices in Framfield Road in 1881 and advertised as brickmakers until 1938
Refs: OS 25in 40/4 (1898, 1910); Kelly (1882-1907); *QMJ* (1933); *DBC* (1938); *Friday Ad* (Uckfield), 5 Aug 1983.

6 Brickworks and pottery at the junction of New Road and Eastbourne Road
NGR: TQ 481 197
Date: Opened in 1883 and closed in 1970
Op.: Benjamin Ware (cf sites 3 & 4), incorporated as Benjamin Ware & Sons Ltd in 1908
Prod.: Bricks, roofing tiles and ornamental fittings, drainpipes, flower pots and earthenware
F.Inf.: Some clay was brought from Whitesmith, in Chiddingly
Refs: OS 25in 41/5 (1899, 1910); Kelly (1887-1938); *QMJ* (1927-59); *Southern Weekly News*, 15 July 1955; *SIH* **1** (1970/1), 42; docs. held by Messrs Dawson Hart & Co.; inf. H. McCurdy.

7 Brick kiln on the Uckfield to Shortbridge road west of Copwood Farm
NGR: TQ 456 212
Date: 18th century: probably in use when Copwood House was built in the 1720s, marked on a map of 1766 but not shown on the map attached to a highway diversion order of 1790
Refs: Acc 6497/21.2; QD 643 m45; inf. Christopher Whittick.

WADHURST

1 Tile kiln on the east side of present-day Riseden Road at Snape
NGR: TQ 623 303
Date: Tiles were made at Snape in the 1350s, the most likely site being Kell Field, listed on the tithe award of 1839
Refs: TDE 132; SAS/G 44/6 (ex inf. C. Whittick).

2 Brick kiln west of the road from Buckland Hill to Bartley Mill
NGR: TQ 633 348
Date: Upper and Lower Brick Kiln Fields and Brick Kiln Shaw were listed on the tithe award of 1839
Ref.: TDE 132.

3 Brickyard on the site of present-day Sandyden House, Mark Cross
NGR: TQ 587 313
Date: In existence from c1800, listed in 1839 and closed in 1863
Op.: The owner/occupier in 1839 was George Wickens but the brickmakers were members of the Walter family: Joseph Walter c1800 and his grandson Edward Joseph Walter in 1863 (cf Rotherfield 11)
Refs: TDE 132; H.S. Eeles, *Mark Cross Past and Present* (1970), 31, 48.

4 Brickyard at Best Beech between Mayfield Lane and Fairglen Road
NGR: TQ 616 314
Date: In existence in 1839, marked on the map of 1875 and to the east (617 314) in 1899
Op.: Edward Walter (cf Rotherfield 11) was the owner/occupier in 1839; by 1867 the yard was in the hands of John Fairbrother (cf site 5); Thomas Pollington (cf Rotherfield 11) advertised in the 1890s
Refs: TDE 132; OS 6in 18 (1875) 18 SW (1899); A2232/171; Kelly (1895-99).

5 Brickyard at Pell Green at the junction of Cousley Wood Road and Balaclava Lane
NGR: TQ 642 329
Date: In existence in 1839 and marked on the maps of 1880 and 1898
Op.: John Fairbrother was the tenant in 1839 and advertised from 1851 to 1867, followed by Horace and Samuel Fairbrother from 1874 to 1895
Prod.: Bricks, tiles and drainpipes
F.Inf.: In 1867 two pugmills and a pipe machine were included in a probate valuation of the yard, which amounted to £19 17s 5d. Repairs were made to the tile machine in 1889 and to the pipe machine in 1891

Refs: TDE 132; OS 25in 18/7 (1880, 1898);
        A2232/171; AMS 6214; Kelly (1851-95).

6   Brickworks on the north side of Station Road
    west of the railway
    NGR: TQ 611 337
    Date: Marked only on the map of 1874
    Ref.:   OS 25in 18/6 (1874).

7   Brick and tile works in Wadhurst Park
    NGR: TQ 631 288
    Date: Marked only on the map of 1875
    Op.:   Edward Bishop was probably the
            brickmaker here in 1871
    Refs: OS 6in 29 (1875); census (1871).

8   Brick(?) kiln on the east side of Partridges
    Lane north of Beggars Bush
    NGR: TQ 608 317
    Date: Old Kiln on the map of 1909, an
            overgrown pit at the edge of the wood
            has the appearance of an abandoned
            brickyard
    Ref.:   OS 25in 18/10 (1909).

9   Brickworks at Woods Green on the west side
    of Osmers Hill
    NGR: TQ 638 333
    Date: Marked on the map of 1909 and in use
            until the 1920s
    Op.:   George T. Kemp advertised from 1913
            to 1924
    Refs: OS 25in 18/7 (1909); Kelly (1913-24).

10 Brickyard at Walland Farm
    NGR: cTQ 645 300
    Date: Late 1890s to late 1930s
    Op.:   Samuel Fairbrother jun. advertised in
            1899, 1903 and again in 1938
    Refs: Kelly (1899-1903); DBC (1938).

11 Brickworks on the south side of Gloucester
    Road, Sparrows Green
    NGR: TQ 635 325
    Date: Marked only on the map of 1909
    Op.:   George Lavender was the manager in
            1907
    Refs: OS 25in 18/7 (1909); Kelly (1907).

12 Brickworks at Pennybridge Farm, Tidebrook
    NGR: cTQ 613 309
    Date: 1920s to 1940s
    Op.:   Industrial Silica Ltd c1923, Wadhurst
            Silica Ltd in 1927 and Sussex Brick Co.
            (cf Horsham 15) in the 1930s
    Prod.: Silica bricks and allied products
    Geol.: Tunbridge Wells Sand

Refs: Kelly (1927-34); QMJ (1933-44); inf.
        Charles Bocking (1983).

WALDRON

1   Brick clamp south of Manor Farm, Horam
    NGR: TQ 576 172
    Date: Possibly in use when the manor house
            (now demolished) was built in the
            early 17th century; Brick Clumps Field
            was listed on the tithe award of 1841
    Ref.:   TDE 150.

2   Brickyard on Easons Farm, Sharps Corner
    NGR: TQ 572 182
    Date: In operation by 1861 and closed c1914
    Op.:   Owned by the Fuller estate: the
            brickmakers were William Barden
            from 1861 to 1869, John Benge from
            1869 to 1882, then W & T Barden in
            1886 and John Benge again from 1890
            to 1899
    Prod.: Kiln-fired bricks, tiles and agricultural
            drainpipes
    Refs: OS 25in 41/12 (1875, 1898, 1910);
            SAS/RF/F/2/1; RAF A 2300 (Fuller
            estate schedule); census (1861); Kelly
            (1862-99); Pike/Eastbourne (1886).

3   Brickfield on the east side of Waldron Thorns,
    Heathfield
    NGR: TQ 582 210
    Date: Marked only on the map of 1910
    Ref.:   OS 25in 42/1 (1910).

4   Brickworks at Great Easterfields on the north
    side of the road from Horam to Chiddingly
    NGR: TQ 570 163
    Date: Opened c1930 and closed c1960
    Op.:   Horeham Road Brickworks Ltd until
            the 1950s, when it came under the
            control of the Lunsford Co. (cf Bexhill
            10) and subsequently of Sussex &
            Dorking United Brick Cos Ltd
    Prod.: Kiln-fired, wire-cut bricks
    F.Inf.: A diesel engine was used to operate
            the grinding machinery and also the
            buckets which brought the clay up
            from the pit. These were chained
            together and ran along an inclined rail
    Refs: Kelly (1930-4); QMJ (1933-59); inf. Mr
            Morgan, of Kingston Villas, which
            were built to house the brickyard
            workers (1978).

5 Brickyard near Heatherden House, Cross-in-Hand
  NGR: cTQ 565 214
  Date: Mid-19th century
  Op.: The owner in 1857 was W.B. Gains and in 1863 J.G. Boucher
  Prod.: The full range of bricks, tiles and drainpipes
  Refs: BUR 2/1/59, 123.

WARBLETON

1 Brick and tile kilns south of Warbleton church
  NGR: TQ 609 182, 612 181
  Date: Brickhost Field, mentioned in a deed of 1649, had become Brickhurst Mead in 1838. The tilehouse to the SE was first mentioned in a rental of 1552
  Op.: The owner of the tilehouse in 1552 was Thomas Langredge
  Refs: TDE 50; RAF A2300; ASH B652.

2 Brick kiln on the east side of the stream NE of Bucksteep Mill
  NGR: TQ 655 157
  Date: Brick Croft, mentioned in a deed of 1717, can be identified with Brick Bank on the tithe award of 1838
  Cond.: An area of burnt earth and brick debris was noted in 1982
  Refs: TDE 50; D 1651; inf. Colin Rose (1982).

3 Brick kiln SE of Cralle Place
  NGR: TQ 612 158
  Date: Brick House Field, listed on the tithe award of 1838, was probably the site of brickmaking when the house was enlarged in 1724
  Ref.: TDE 50.

4 Brickyard on the east side of Middle Lane south of Turners Green
  NGR: TQ 634 195
  Date: In existence by 1796; closed in 1918
  Op.: Samuel Cornford in 1796 followed by several generations of the Cornford family, ending with John from 1890 to 1918
  Prod.: Kiln-fired bricks, tiles and agricultural drainpipes
  Refs: TDE 50; OS 25in 42/7 (1874, 1896, 1909); Beswick, *Bricks and Tiles*, 7-8.

5 Brickyard on the east side of Middle Lane south of Foords Farm
  NGR: TQ 633 193
  Date: In operation by 1824; abandoned c1840
  Op.: Jesse Goldsmith (cf Wartling 2)
  Refs: TDE 50; ASH 1720; Beswick, *Bricks and Tiles*, 8.

6 Brickyard on the west side of the road south of Three Cups
  NGR: TQ 635 199
  Date: In operation by 1825; closed in 1940
  Op.: James Goldsmith until 1850, followed by Henry Goldsmith. Pennington Martin leased the yard from 1863 to 1870 and was succeeded by Charles Message and John White, his neighbour at Coppice Farm, who were in partnership between 1870 and 1879. After this, Message ran the business on his own, followed by his sons, who traded as Message Bros from 1913 to 1934. W.J. (Bill) Message advertised on his own in 1938
  Prod.: Kiln and clamp bricks, tiles and drainpipes
  Geol.: Ashdown Sand
  Refs: TDE 50; OS 25in 42/7 (1874, 1896, 1909); ASH 1722, 1750-54 & L2724-41; BUR 2/1/164; White, *Lewes*, 18; Beswick, *Bricks and Tiles*, 8-13.

7 Brick(?) kiln at the corner of Furnace Lane
  NGR: TQ 611 189
  Date: Kiln Plot was marked on a map of 1827 but by 1838 there was a lime kiln only on the site
  Op.: Joseph Errey, the lessee in 1827, was a brickmaker
  Refs: TDE 50; SRO Acc 2840.

8 Brickyard SE of Rushlake Green
  NGR: TQ 628 183
  Date: 1930s
  Op.: H. Funnell advertised in 1936
  Refs: *Brighton & Tunbridge Wells Telephone Directory* (1936); inf. W. Funnell (1987).

WARTLING

1 Brickyard on Dann's Farm SE of Cowbeech
  NGR: TQ 619 132
  Date: Opened in 1691, still in operation in

1785 but listed only as Kiln Pit Shaw in 1839

Op.: A licence to dig earth and clay was granted to Edward Calverly and William Dan in 1691 and renewed for a further 21 years in 1703. William Dan, brickmaker, was married by licence in 1711 and John Dan was the tenant of the farm and kiln in 1785

Prod.: Bricks and tiles

Refs: TDE 88; SAS Box 17; A 2797; AMS 4459; *SRS* **6**, 202 & **77**, 216.

2 Brickyard and pottery on the east side of Tilley Lane, Boreham Street

NGR: TQ 663 127

Date: In existence by the 1820s, the yard ceased production c1879 and was re-opened briefly in the 1930s

Op.: Jesse Goldsmith (cf Warbleton 5) from at least 1819 until the 1850s. By 1861 he had been succeeded by Henry Goldsmith, who was followed by James Message (cf site 3). The London group which re-opened the works in the 1930s advertised as Herstmonceux Brick & Tile Co.

Prod.: Bricks, tiles, drainpipes, chimney pots and earthenware in the 19th century

Refs: TDE 88; OS 25in 56/12 (1874); *SWA*, 18 Jan 1819, 9 Jan 1826 & 26 Feb 1827; census (1841-71); *Brighton & Tun. Wells Telephone Directory* (1936); Kelly (1938); Lieut-Col John Curteis, mss notes on Wartling (1938) in Hastings Library (ex inf. Philippa Heal).

3 Brickyard(s) at Trolliloes NE of Cowbeech

NGR: TQ 629 149

Date: In operation in the 1840s and 1850s, revived after World War 1, offered for sale in 1925 and closed in the late 1930s

Op.: James Message, assisted by various members of his family in the 19th century; Trolliloes Brick, Tile & Pipe Co. Ltd advertised in 1933

Refs: TDE 88; census (1841-51); sale catalogue in the possession of P. Heal; *QMJ* (1933).

4 Brickyard behind the Bull Inn at Boreham Street

NGR: TQ 666 112

Date: Mid-19th century

Op.: The yard was owned by Alfred Dawes, a builder. The brickmaker in 1851 was Henry French

Refs: Census (1851); inf. P. Heal.

WESTFIELD

1 Brickyard(s) on Southings Farm

NGR: TQ 824 162

Date: Brick Kiln Field was marked between Southings and Pattletons Farms on a map of 1748 and brickmaking was taking place in the same area in the early 1900s

Op.: Members of the Pelling family were brickmakers in the latter period

Cond.: Brick and tile debris was found close to a large pit in 1985

Refs: HMAG MA8; inf. G. Jones (1985) & D. Padgham (1991).

2 Brickyard at the entrance to Oaklands Park (now in par. of Sedlescombe)

NGR: TQ 784 175

Date: Late 18th and early 19th centuries: listed as Brick Yard Field on the tithe award of 1840 when a small enclosure to the NW was called Old Brickyard Field

Op.: In 1773 a cottage and 1½ acres adjoining this site were leased to William Weller, brickmaker. The lease was renewed for a further 21 years in 1796

Refs: TDE 154; A4426/6.

3 Brickyard in Share Wood south of New England Lane (now in par. of Sedlescombe)

NGR: TQ 789 164

Date: In existence by 1840 and closed in 1936

Op.: In 1840 the owner was John Weller, the son of William (cf site 2) and the tenant was George Booth. From 1847 the tenant was George Carrick followed by Charles and Thomas Carrick by 1890, Charles Carrick from 1913 to 1922 and Carlos Carrick from 1924 onwards

Prod.: Bricks, roofing tiles and drainpipes

Cond.: The remains of the double kiln were still visible in 1985

Refs: TDE 154; OS 25in 58/1 (1873, 1899, 1909, 1929); A 4426/6; census (1851-

81); Kelly (1890-1930); B. Lucey, *Sedlescombe* (1978), 384-5; inf. J. Haselfoot (1978) & G. Jones (1985).

4 Brickyard on the east side of the road south of Brede Bridge

NGR: TQ 828 174

Date: In existence in 1840, marked as Brick & Tile Works on the map of 1872 and, slightly to the south, in 1899 and 1909

Op.: The owner/occupier in 1840 was Henry Smith of Little Knights Farm. The brickmaker in 1851 was George Streeten. A coal merchant and hop grower called Glazier occupied the new site between 1887 and 1918

F.Inf.: Products were probably shipped from Brede Wharf adjacent to the site

Refs: TDE 154; OS 25in 44/15 (1872, 1899, 1909); census (1851); inf. D. Padgham.

5 Brick and tile works on Cockmartins Farm

NGR: TQ 807 144

Date: 1859 to c1900

Op.: The farm was part of the Beauport Park estate of Sir Charles Lamb; William Ward (cf Westham 4 ii) was responsible for equipping the yard in 1859

Refs: OS 25in 58/6 (1873, 1897); Acc 5046; BUR 2/1/83.

WESTHAM

1 Brick kiln east of Sheepsham (Shepham) Lane

NGR: TQ 599 054

Date: Brick Plot was listed on the tithe award of 1838

Cond.: A pond and a brick bridge are the only remaining evidence; the bricks measure 9in x 2½in x 4½in

Ref.: TDE 84; inf. D.W. Brook (1991).

2 Brickfield on the west side of Friday Street

NGR: TQ 619 037

Date: The yard was established some time before 1864, when it was offered for sale together with a large quantity of bricks; marked Old Brick Field on the map of 1875

Op.: The owner in 1864 was a Mr Backhurst; George Goldsmith and his three sons were brickmakers at Friday Street in 1871

Refs: OS 25in 69/14 (1875); BUR 2/1/136; census (1871).

3 Brickyard at Red Dyke, south of Dittons Road

NGR: TQ 606 043

Date: Opened in the 1850s and closed in the 1930s. Kiln Field marked on the tithe map on the opposite side of Dittons Road (607 046) may indicate earlier brickmaking in this area

Op.: William Oliver was the master brickmaker in 1861, employing 10 men. James Funnell was the senior brickmaker by 1871, George Funnell advertised from 1899 to 1918 and Harry Funnell from 1922 to 1938

Prod.: Some kiln-fired bricks in the 19th century; hand-made clamp bricks in the 20th century

Geol.: Weald Clay

Cond.: A pond, some of the brickyard buildings and three cottages, dated 1857, were noted in 1991

Refs: TDE 84; OS 25in 69/14 (1875, 1899, 1910, 1928); census (1861-71); Kelly (1899-1934); *DBC* (1938); Lake et al, *Lewes*, 35; inf. D.W. Brook (1991) & G. Funnell (1992).

4 Two brickfields north of the railway near Pevensey & Westham station

NGR: TQ 639 045 & 640 045

Date: One was in existence before 1850 and both were marked in 1875

Op.: i. The brickmaker in 1850 was a Mr Bassett. J. Fisher advertised in 1855 followed by Henry Fisher in 1866 and 1870 and John Fisher in 1874 and 1878
ii. W. Ward advertised in 1859 and 1862, followed by Jesse Dann from 1867

Prod.: Tiles were manufactured prior to 1851 but subsequently the output on both sites was of clamp bricks only

F.Inf.: The wind pump, once used to drain the claypit, has been re-erected at the Weald and Downland Open Air Museum, Singleton

Refs: OS 25in 69/15 (1875); BUR 2/1/1B; RAF 37/23; PEV 390; Kelly (1855-87); Pike/ Eastbourne (1886) (ex inf. D.W. Brook).

5 Brickfield on the site now occupied by Langney cemetery
NGR: TQ 628 030
Date: Before 1882, when the site was sold to the Eastbourne Burial Board
Op.: James Hayward was the owner in 1882
Ref.: Inf. Vera Hodsoll.

6 Brickworks at Hide Hollow
NGR: TQ 630 034
Date: Marked on the maps of 1899 and 1910
Op.: Possibly Jesse Dann after clay reserves were exhausted at site 4
Cond.: The site has been redeveloped but a small pond remains in the garden of a bungalow opposite the Crematorium
Refs: OS 25in 69/15 (1899, 1910); Kelly (1890-1907); inf. D. Brook (1991).

7 Brickworks on the east side of Friday Street south of the railway
NGR: TQ 619 039
Date: Opened in the 1890s and closed c1939
Op.: William Kemp advertised from 1895 to 1907 and again in 1938
Geol.: Red-mottled grey silty clay (Weald Clay)
Refs: OS 25in 69/14 (1899, 1910, 1929, 1937); Kelly (1895-1907); *DBC* (1938); White, *Lewes*, 32; Lake et al, *Lewes*, 35.

8 Three brickfields at Langney
NGR: TQ 625 027, 625 028 & 625 029
Date: Marked on the map of 1898; the two southern ones had been amalgamated by 1908 and only this one remained in 1932
Op.: i. Various members of the Gearing family: Albert Gearing in 1890 and 1895, Edwin Gearing in 1895 and 1899, A.L. Gearing from 1899 to 1907 and A. Gearing between 1913 and 1922
ii. James Wood & Son, builders of Eastbourne, advertised as brickmakers in 1903 and had their bricks made in Langney
iii. P.J. Jackson & Son advertised from 1913 to 1934 followed by Charles Jackson in 1938
Cond.: Two ponds remain to the south of the shopping centre
Refs: OS 25in 80/2 (1898, 1908, 1932); Kelly (1890-1938); inf. J. Kinnison Bourke & D. Brook.

9 Brickfield south of Willingdon Drove
NGR: TQ 622 029
Date: Marked on the map of 1908 only
Op.: Probably Fred Vine, who advertised between 1907 and 1922
Refs: OS 25in 80/2 (1908); Kelly (1907-22).

10 Brickworks between Pevensey Road and the railway at Polegate
NGR: TQ 591 048
Date: Marked on the map of 1909 only
Refs: OS 25in 69/9 (1909).

WHATLINGTON

1 Brick and tile kiln ½ mile NW of Whatlington church
NGR: TQ 754 189
Date: Possibly 17th century: brick and tile wasters and burnt earth were found during excavations in 1984
Op.: William Row was a brickmaker in Whatlington in 1638
Refs: *SRS* **1**, 248; G. Jones 'Archaeological Observations of the Mountfield to Hastings Water Pumping Main Pipeline' *SAC* **123** (1985), 243.

WILLINGDON

1 Brickfield SE of St Anthony's Hill
NGR: TQ 631 015
Date: Marked 'B' on a sketch-map of 1805; used to make bricks for the Martello towers in that year
Op.: The Board of Ordnance
Refs: PRO MFQ 307/16B; Beswick, 'Martello Towers', 23.

2 Brickfield on Lottbridge Drove near the former Eastbourne gasworks
NGR: TQ 625 011
Date: Marked on maps from 1899 to 1932
Geol.: Gault clay
Refs: OS 80/6 (1899, 1908, 1932); C. Reid, *Geology of the Country around Eastbourne* (1898), 14.

3 Brickfield on Willingdon Levels east of Hampden Park station
NGR: TQ 612 023
Date: Marked on the maps of 1908 and 1932
Op.: Members of the Goldsmith family, some of whom were still living in Brickyard Cottage in 1983

Refs: OS 6in 80 NW (1911, 1932); inf. V.
Hodsoll (1983).

WILMINGTON

1   Tile kiln at Wilmington Green
NGR: TQ 547 050
Date: In existence in 1530 when the Dean
and Chapter of Chichester Cathedral,
who   owned   the   manor   of
Wilmington, allowed their tenants
tiles for repairs. Land called the 'tile
host' in 1673, when the kiln was no
longer in use, can be identified on a
map of 1725
Refs: AMS 5879/4; SAS/CP 218-23; *SRS* **52**,
80-1.

2   Brickyard and pottery in Bayley's Lane
NGR: cTQ 555 069
Date: c1733 to at least 1763
Op.: John Crowhurst supplied bricks for
the Arlington poorhouse in 1733.
James Crowhurst was selling pottery
by 1756. The yard, including a brick
kiln and a pot kiln, was offered for
sale in 1759 but John Crowhurst was
still a brickmaker here in 1764
Refs: PAR/232/9/1 (ex inf. E. Doff); *SWA*,
26 Feb 1759; Vaisey, *Turner*, 42, 103,
275; *SRS* **25**, 107.

3   Brickyard at Thornwell
NGR: cTQ 555 063
Date: Opened c1895
Op.: The owner's name was Vinall and the
brickmakers were William and Jesse
Drewett of Polegate
Ref.: 'Wootton footpath case' *Sussex Express*
4 Feb 1899 (inf. S. Harcourt Smith).

WINCHELSEA *see* ICKLESHAM

WITHYHAM

1   Tile kiln between London Road and
Royalmires Wood
NGR: TQ 511 333
Date: The name Tilehouse, on the map of
1813, suggests tilemaking in the 16th
century or earlier, as do Tylers Field,
Tylers Wood and Tylers Mead to the
SE, listed on the tithe award of 1843
Refs: OS 1in (1813); TDE 138.

2   Brick and tile works north of Cooks Corner,
Crowborough
NGR: TQ 514 323
Date: Marked on the map of 1874: only
Brickfield Cottages remained in 1899
Op.: Members of the Pollington family,
who later moved to Mark Cross (cf
Rotherfield 11)
Refs: OS 6in 17 (1874, 1899); inf. D.
Pollington (1978).

3   Brick and tile works on the south side of St
John's Road, Crowborough
NGR: TQ 509 315
Date: Marked only on the map of 1874
Ref.: OS 6in 17 (1874).

4   Brick and tile works on the south bank of the
river Grom at Groombridge
NGR: TQ 529 374
Date: Marked only on the map of 1874
Ref.: OS 25in 6/11 (1874).

5   Brick and tileworks west of All Saint's
Church, Blackham.
NGR: TQ 496 401
Date: Marked on maps from 1874 to 1910
Op.: William Divall advertised from 1890
to 1899 and Day & Co. in 1907
F.Inf.: A photograph of a stack of tiles at
Withyham was published in 1938
Refs: OS 25in 6/1 (1874, 1898, 1910); Kelly
(1890-1907); *SCM* **12** (1938), 796.

6   Brickyard on Lyewood Common
NGR: TQ 498 373
Date: Marked on the maps of 1898 and 1910
Op.: H. & E. Waters, builders, of Forest
Row (cf Hartfield 6)
Refs: OS 6in 6 SW (1898, 1910); inf. Ralph
Muggeridge (1980).

7   Brickyard in the Hamsell area
NGR: cTQ 54 34
Date: 1880s
Op.: William Barden, who was born in
Waldron (cf Waldron site 2) was a
brickmaker here in 1881
Ref.: Inf. Mrs P.M. Dyson (great-grand-
daughter)

WIVELSFIELD

1 Brickyard NE of More House
  NGR: TQ 344 208
  Date: Listed as Brick Mead on a survey of 1792 and as Brick Plot on the tithe award of 1838
  Refs: AMS 6145; TDE 23.

2 Brickyard on Hurst House Farm
  NGR: cTQ 338 224
  Date: Mid-17th to mid-18th centuries
  Op.: Thomas Hurst, who built the brick house (dated 1660), supplied bricks to Giles Moore in 1664 and 1666. Two of his descendants, Henry (d. 1708) and John (d. 1748), called themselves bricklayers but were probably also brickmakers
  Refs: *SRS* **68**, 44-6, 52; inf. Margaret Goodare (1992).

3 Brickyard on Lywood (Lyoth) Common
  NGR: cTQ 351236
  Date: 1850s
  Op.: John Napper, a brickmaker employing 4 men, was living here in 1851
  Ref.: Census (1851).

47. West Sussex: parishes with brickyards listed in the gazetteer

APU APULDRAM   FIS FISHBOURNE
ASH ASHINGTON   FIT FITTLEWORTH
BAL BARLAVINGTON   GRA GRAFFHAM
BAR BARNHAM   GRE GREATHAM
BIG BIGNOR   HAR HARDHAM
BIN BINSTED   HUN HUNSTON
CHT CHITHURST   LOD LODSWORTH
COL COLDWALTHAM   LYM LYMINSTER
EAS EASTERGATE   MID MIDHURST
                       N.MU NORTH MUNDHAM
                       RUM RUMBOLDSWYKE
                       STO STOPHAM
                       TAN TANGMERE
                       TOR TORTINGTON
                       WAL WALBERTON
                       WAR WARNINGCAMP
                       WAS WASHINGTON
                       WIG WIGGONHOLT
                       WOO WOOLAVINGTON

0   km   10

GAZETTEER FOR WEST SUSSEX

Documents listed under 'References' in this section are lodged at the West Sussex Record Office, Chichester, unless otherwise stated.

ALBOURNE

1   Brick kiln NW of Bishop's Place
    NGR: TQ 263 158
    Date: Brickell Field was marked on a map of 1679. This was called Brick Field in 1840
    Refs: CAP/1/29/18; TDE 104.

2   Brick kiln near the boundary with Newtimber parish
    NGR: TQ 265 151
    Date: Listed as Brick Kiln Shaw in 1840
    Refs: TDE 104.

ALDINGBOURNE

1   Brickfield at Woodgate
    NGR: SU 941 040
    Date: Late 1930s
    Op.: Woodgate Brick Co. advertised in 1938
    Refs: OS 6in 62 SW (1937); Kelly (1938).

AMBERLEY

1   Brickyard at Rackham
    Exact location not known
    Date: Late 17th century
    Op.: John Campion, whose probate inventory was taken in 1690
    Prod.: Kiln-fired bricks and tiles
    Ref.: EpI/29/3/68.

2   Brick kiln on the south side of a lane across Amberley Wild Brooks
    NGR: TQ 033 142
    Date: Brick Kiln Plot was listed on the tithe award of 1846
    Op.: The tenant in 1846 was Lewis Rossiter
    Ref.: TDW 2.

NORTH AMBERSHAM

1   Brick and tile kiln on Surney Farm SE of Verdley Place
    NGR: SU 914 267
    Date: 2nd or 3rd century: the site was surveyed in 1987
    F.Inf.: A collection of tile from the site is retained by the Haslemere Archaeological Society

Ref.: West Sussex Sites and Monuments Record No 1810.

2   Brick kiln east of Lower House Farm
    NGR: SU 912 280
    Date: Brick Kiln Field was listed on the tithe award of 1847
    Op.: The tenant in 1847 was Thomas Chalcraft
    Ref.: TDW 88.

ANGMERING

1   Brickyard in Hammerpot Field north of Arundel Road
    NGR: TQ 065 058
    Date: Not known: evidence of brickmaking activity was uncovered by ploughing in 1987
    Ref.: West Sussex Sites and Monuments Record No 4487.

APULDRAM

1   Tilery SW of Dell Quay
    NGR: SU 832 019
    Date: Between 1st and 4th centuries: possibly the source of tiles for Roman buildings in Chichester and Fishbourne
    Ref.: Rudling, 'Dell Quay', 81-90; West Sussex Sites and Monuments Record No 0631.

2   Brickfield on the south side of Birdham Road
    NGR: SU 849 031
    Date: Late 1920s and 1930s
    Op.: The owner was William Leggatt
    F.Inf.: A photograph of Edward Beaumont setting bricks on the hacks in the late 1920s is in the possession of his great-nephew John Roberts
    Refs: OS 61 SW (1933); inf. J. Roberts (1991).

ARDINGLY

1   Brickfield on the south edge of Rivers Wood
    NGR: TQ 332 277
    Date: Brickfield Shaw was listed on the tithe award of 1840
    Ref.: TDE 32.

2   Brickyard on the north bank of the river Ouse north of Rivers Wood
    NGR: TQ 333 284

Date: Brick Plot and Brickyard Wood were listed in 1840
Op.: The tenant in 1840 was John Bannister
Ref.: TDE 32.

3 Brick kiln in Kiln Wood north of the abandoned Ouse Valley railway
NGR: TQ 337 268
Date: In use when the proposed line was under construction in 1865 and for some time thereafter
Op.: Finches, builders, of Haywards Heath (cf Cuckfield 16)
Ref.: Inf. C. Anscombe & G. Thomerson (1986).

4 Brickyard and pottery on the west side of College Road
NGR: TQ 345 294
Date: c1880 until c1914; a brickfield in the same area was opened in the 1930s and closed in the 1950s
Op.: George Box, who was also a contractor and timber merchant, first advertised in 1882. By 1895 the proprietors were Box & Turner. E.H. Munnion Ltd, builders, were the operators in the later period
Prod.: Bricks, tiles, drainpipes and flowerpots in the 19th century; Sussex purple stocks in 1951
Refs: OS 6in 14 SE (1899, 1907); Kelly (1882-1907); R.W. Pepper, *East Grinstead and its Environs* (1885); *QMJ* (1933-51).

ARUNDEL

1 Brickyard NE of Park Farm
NGR: TQ 004 075
Date: A brick kiln and 'brickhouses' were mentioned in a lease of 1732 and Arundel Park brick kiln was included in the estate accounts until at least 1776. The site was listed as Brick Yard Platt on the tithe award of 1840
Refs: TDW 5; Arundel Castle MSS. MD6266 & A442 (ex inf. T.P. Hudson).

2 Brickyard on the north side of the Chichester road
NGR: SU 996 075
Date: The kiln was shown on a map of 1772 but the yard appeared to have been abandoned by 1840 when it was listed as West Brick Kiln Field

Ref.: Arundel Castle MS. H1/3 (ex inf. T.P. Hudson); TDW 5.

3 Brickyard near the gasworks on Ford Road
NGR: TQ 023 065
Date: 1890s and early 1900s
Op.: Arthur Burrell, builder and contractor (cf Tortington), from 1895 to 1903
Geol.: Reading Beds
Refs: Kelly (1895-1903); Reid, *Chichester*, 34.

ASHINGTON

1 Brickyard north of Brownhill in a detached part of the parish
NGR: TQ 145 165
Date: The brick kilns were listed on the tithe award of 1847 but had been abandoned by the 1870s when only the name Brickyard Copse survived
Op.: W.W. Richardson Esq. was the owner/occupier in 1847
Refs: TDW 6; OS 6in 37 (1875).

2 Brickworks on the east side of London Road
NGR: TQ 133 163
Date: 1930s
Op.: Frederick Day & Son advertised in 1934 and A.D. Reith in 1936
Refs: Kelly (1934); *Brighton & Tun. Wells Telephone Directory* (1936).

ASHURST

1 Brickyard on the south side of Spithandle Lane
NGR: TQ 178 148
Date: Opened c1733, still in existence in 1830 but described as Old Brickyard c1835
Op.: John Hills leased the yard from 1733 until his death in 1736 and his widow carried on the business until 1743, with John Pollard as brickmaker. John Peto of Steyning, a bricklayer, became the owner in 1757 and Henry Elliott was a brickmaker in Ashurst in 1763
Prod.: Kiln-fired bricks and tiles; fragments of pink roof tile were found in the field to the east of the clay pit in 1985
F.Inf.: There was also a limekiln in the yard in 1736
Refs: Wiston MS. 5615; EpI/29/11/65 & 73; *SRS* **32**, 1; *VCH* **6** (2), 80; inf. E. Holden (1985).

BALCOMBE

1 Brickfield on Yewtree Farm
   NGR: TQ 313 318
   Date: Brick Field was listed on an estate survey of c1800
   Ref.: MF 673.

2 Brickyard behind Monks Forest Cottage on the west side of Balcombe Lane (London Road)
   NGR: TQ 309 326
   Date: In existence in 1867, the yard was used in the 1880s to make bricks for Highley Manor and other estate buildings and closed c1910
   Op.: The owner was Henry Faure Walker of the Highley estate
   Refs: L. Fairweather, *Balcombe: the story of a Sussex village* (1981); inf. Joan Dutton (1991).

3 Brickfield north of Holt Cottages on the west side of Haywards Heath Road
   NGR: TQ 315 296
   Date: Marked on the map of 1875 and as disused in 1898
   Op.: The yard belonged to the Balcombe Place estate
   Prod.: Building and paving bricks; in 1881 the latter were used for paving the market in Haywards Heath
   Refs: OS 6in 15 (1875) 15 SW (1898); D.L. Secretan, *Balcombe* (1937), 69.

4 Brickfield at the NE corner of Great Wood
   NGR: TQ 324 319
   Date: Marked only on the map of 1898
   Ref.: OS 6in 15 NW (1898).

5 Brickfield at the northern end of Balcombe tunnel
   NGR: TQ 291 325
   Date: 1839-40 during the construction of the tunnel
   Prod.: Clamp-burnt bricks: the bases of the clamps and of two pugmill sites, as well as extensive areas of brick debris, were uncovered by excavations in 1997.
   Refs: Pat Millward, 'The Building of Balcombe Tunnel' *SIH* **30** (2000), 14; Southern Archaeology, *Turners Hill to Buchan Hill Trunk Main Watching Brief* (1997).

BARLAVINGTON

1 Brickyard on the east side of the road SW of Crouch Farm
   NGR: SU 975 169
   Date: Listed on the tithe award of 1839; marked as Brick Field in 1875 but disused by 1896
   Op.: The yard was owned by the Barlavington Estate
   F.Inf.: The pugmill is now at the Weald and Downland Open Air Museum, Singleton
   Refs: TDW 9; OS 6in 35 (1875) 35 SE (1896); F.G. Aldsworth, 'A 19th-century brickyard pugmill from Barlavington' *SAC* **127** (1989), 263-6.

BARNHAM

1 Brickfield on the south side of Yapton Road at Saxby
   NGR: SU 965 040
   Date: Marked only on the map of 1910
   Op.: Sparks (cf Yapton) had a brickfield at Barnham in the early 1920s
   F.Inf.: The clay-mill was powered by a Lister engine
   Refs: OS 6in 62 SE (1910); inf. B. Foreman (1988).

see also: EASTERGATE

BARNS GREEN *see* ITCHINGFIELD

LOWER BEEDING

1 Brick clamp in St Leonard's Forest
   Exact location not known
   Date: 1584
   Ref.: *VCH* **2**, 253.

2 Brickyard at Plummers Plain on the east side of Leechpond Hill
   NGR: TQ 221 272
   Date: In operation in 1803 and marked on the map of 1875; the yard went out of use shortly after 1882
   Op.: The site belonged to the Leonardslee estate. Richard Morley was granted a seven year lease in 1848 and advertised in 1855 and 1859. In 1882 the tenant was John Dearing
   Prod.: Kiln-fired bricks and tiles
   Refs: OS 6in 25 (1875); Kelly (1855-59, 1882);

ESRO SAY 2831; *VCH* **6** (3), 25.

3   Brickyard at Crabtree
NGR: cTQ 220 252
Date: In operation in 1816
Op.:   William and Philip Kensett in 1816, thereafter Philip Kensett (cf West Grinstead 3)
Ref.:   *SWA*, 18 Mar 1816.

4   Brickworks and pottery on the south side of Crawley Road east of Hopper Farm
NGR: TQ 233 344
Date: In existence by 1845, called Hopper Brickyard and Pottery in 1851 and marked on maps from 1874 onwards; it was still in operation in 1959
Op.:   Thomas Broadwood advertised as a farmer and brickmaker at Holmbush in 1845 and Thomas Shaw was a tilemaker here in 1851. By 1855 Thomas Norman from Clayton (qv) was established as a brickmaker and was later joined by his brother Jesse. By 1890 the business, now called Holmbush Pottery Works, was in the hands of Gent & Linfield who advertised until 1927 and Charles Gent was the manager until 1938
Prod.:   Bricks, tiles, chimney pots, water pipes and brown-ware pottery were listed in 1856 (see illus. 32)
Refs: OS 6in 3 (1874) 3 SW (1899, 1913); Kelly (1845-1938); *QMJ* (1927-59); Baines, *Pottery*, 169; *VCH* **6** (3), 25.

5   Brickfield on the south side of Forest Road west of Colgate
NGR: TQ 223 327
Date: Marked on the map of 1874, Colgate Brickyard was offered for sale in 1878 and again in 1881. The yard was revived c1910 and finally closed in 1940
Op.:   Reuben Dearing advertised in 1874, E. Stoner was the tenant in 1881 and E. Linfield advertised from 1910 to 1939
Refs: OS 6in 14 (1874); Kelly (1874); Pike/Horsham (1910-39); sale particulars in the possession of G.H.W. Coomber.

6   Brickworks on the south side of Sandygate Lane
NGR: TQ 223 274
Date: The successor to site 2, the yard was opened in the early 1890s and closed c1930

Op.:   Jas. Brewer was the manager for Sir E.G. Loder bart in 1895; E. Winfield was a brickmaker in Lower Beeding in 1927
Refs: OS 6in 23 NW (1913); Kelly (1895, 1927).

UPPER BEEDING

1   Brick kiln at Horton in the north of the parish
NGR: cTQ 210 313
Date: Brick Kiln Field was mentioned in a deed of 1762
Ref.:   SAS/ND 34 (ex inf . T.P. Hudson).

BEPTON

1   Brickyard on Bepton Common east of Severals Road
NGR: SU 867 204
Date: In existence by 1751 and shown on maps and plans of 1834, 1838 and 1860; the yard was not marked on the map of 1880 but nevertheless appears to have continued in operation until c1890
Op.:   Richard Pearson in 1751 and John Pearson in 1783. John Percy (? Pearson) was the tenant in 1838. John Pearson, the tenant in 1860, was followed by Peter Pearson from 1874 to 1878 and Mrs Fanny Pearson in 1882. Job Sherwood advertised in 1887 and 1890
Refs: QR/W 477 f 95; TDW 11; QDP/W 126; *SRS* **32**, 118 & **35**, 346; Kelly (1874-90); inf. J.C.V. Mitchell.

see also: WOOLBEDING

SOUTH BERSTED

1   Brickyard in North Bersted on the north side of Loats Lane
NGR: SU 916 013
Date: Brick Croft was listed on the tithe award of 1842
Op.:   The tenant in 1842 was Henry Sparkes
Ref.:   TDW 115.

2   Brickyard at the north end of present-day Argyle Road, Steyne Street and Chapel Street
NGR: SZ 932 991
Date: In existence in 1839 and listed as Brick Field and Brick Kiln Field East on the tithe award of 1842; not marked in

1875 but a brickfield was shown south of the gas works in 1898

Op.: James Tomsett advertised in 1839 and Mrs Nancy Tomsett was the owner/occupier in 1842. Reuben Marner advertised in Chapel Street in 1851 and 1855 and Richard Caplin gave his address as Steyne in 1874 and Market Street in 1882

Refs: TDW 115; OS 6in 74 NW & SW (1898); Pigot (1839); Kelly (1851-55, 1874-82).

3 Brickfield on the west side of present-day Argyle Road

NGR: SZ 932 990

Date: In operation by 1842 and shown, together with site 4, on a mid-19th century plan of Bognor

Op.: John Boiling was the tenant in 1842

Refs: TDW 115; PM 56.

4 Brickfield on the east side of present-day Victoria Road

NGR: SZ 930 990

Date: In operation by 1842, shown on a mid-19th century plan of Bognor and still in use in the 1880s

Op.: Reuben Marner (cf site 2) was the tenant in 1842; Richard Allen gave his address as Victoria Park in 1882 and as West Bognor in 1887

Refs: TDW 115; PM 56; Kelly (1882-7).

5 Brickfield north of the gas works

NGR: SZ 932 993

Date: Marked only on the map of 1898

Op.: Possibly Henry Woods, who advertised in West Bognor in the 1880s but in Longford Road in 1890 and Station Road in 1895

Refs: OS 6in 74 NW & SW (1898); Kelly (1882-95).

6 Brickfield between London Road and Upper Bognor Road

NGR: SZ 937 997

Date: Marked only on the map of 1898

Ref.: OS 6in 74 NW & SW (1898).

7 Brickfield between present-day Collyer Avenue and Mons Avenue

NGR: SU 927 000

Date: In existence by 1895 and marked on the map of 1910

Op.: H. & E. Geall (cf Keymer 14 & Plumpton 7) advertised from 1895 to 1907, followed by Henry Geall from 1913 to 1918. The foreman and manager was Thomas Hawes, son-in-law of Ebenezer Geall

Refs: OS 6in 74 NW & SW (1910); Kelly (1895-1918); James Cartland, *Byegone Bognor* (1979), photograph No 147; inf. David Hawes (1992).

8 Brickfield on Chichester Road SE of Holy Cross Church

NGR: SU 923 008

Date: In existence by 1907 and marked on the map of 1910

Op.: Tate Bros advertised with works in Chichester Road in 1907 and in North Bersted from 1913 to 1922. H.N. Booker (cf site 9) also used this site

Refs: OS 6in 74 NW & SW (1910); Kelly (1907-22); inf. D. Hawes.

9 Brickfield on the south side of Barton's Lane, North Bersted

NGR: SU 924 010

Date: Marked on the maps of 1910 and 1932; closed c1940

Op.: Harold Nutcombe Booker advertised in North Bersted from 1913 to 1938

Refs: OS 6in 74 NW & SW (1910, 1932); Kelly (1913-38).

10 Brickfields on the west side of present-day Sherwood Road

NGR: SU 925 005

Date: Marked on the map of 1910 and one field to the north in 1932; closed c1936

Op.: i. Harris Harry Gibbs advertised in North Bersted from 1913 to 1918
ii. Seymours, builders, in the 1930s

F.Inf.: Machine-made concrete bricks were said to have been produced in the 1930s

Refs: OS 6in 74 NW & SW (1910, 1932); *Bognor Post*, 31 Oct 1970; Venables & Outen, *Bognor*, 19.

11 Brickfield on the north side of Chichester Road east of site 10

NGR: SU 926 004

Date: Opened in the 1920s as the successor to site 10(i), marked on the map of 1932 and called Big Tree Works in 1933

Op.: P.N. Gibbs

Refs: OS 6in 74 NW & SW (1932); *QMJ* (1933); inf. D. Hawes.

12 Brickfield on the west side of Westloats Lane
NGR: SU 924 003
Date: Opened in the early 1920s and closed in the late 1930s
Op.: Thomas Hawes (cf site 7) and his son Alfred
F.Inf.: A horse-driven pugmill was used and bricks, as elsewhere in the district, were clamp-burnt
Refs: OS 6in 74 NW & SW (1932);. *DBC* (1938); Venables & Outen, *Bognor*, 19; inf. D. Hawes.

13 Brickfield on the site of present-day Frith Road
NGR: SU 923 000
Date: Marked only on the map of 1932
Ref.: OS 6in 74 NW & SW (1932).

14 Brickfield on the west side of Chalcraft Lane, North Bersted
NGR: SU 920 008
Date: Opened in 1928, extended to the SW and closed c1940
Op.: Alfred Hawes (cf site 12), G.E. Carter & Sons and Herbert W. Seymour (cf site 10) all worked on this site
Refs: OS 6in 74 NW & SW (1932); Kelly (1934-38); *DBC* (1938); inf. D.Hawes.

15 Brickfield on the south side of Chichester Road, on the site of present-day Winston Close, North Bersted
NGR: SU 919 010
Date: Marked only on the map of 1932
Op.: Possibly G.A. Neal & Sons, builders, who developed Newtown estate and advertised as brickmakers in Chichester Road in the 1930s
Refs: OS 6in 74 NW & SW (1932); Kelly (1934-38); inf. D. Hawes.

BIGNOR

1 Brickyard on the west side of the pond in Bignor Park
NGR: SU 989 159
Date: Listed as Brick Kiln Field on the tithe award of 1844; marked as Old Brick Kiln on the map of 1896
F. Inf.: Bricks for the pump house on the estate are said to have been made here in the 19th century
Refs: TDW 12; OS 6in 35 SE (1896); inf . M. Palmer (1989).

BILLINGSHURST

1 Brick kiln on the south side of Horsham Road
NGR: TQ 105 286
Date: Brick Kiln Field was listed on the tithe award of 1841
Ref.: TDW 13.

2 Brickyard north of Rosier Farm
NGR: TQ 097 255
Date: Called Wildans Brickyard, it was in operation by 1858 and marked on the map of 1879
Op.: E. Breething in 1858
Prod.: Kiln and clamp bricks, plain tiles and drainpipes
Geol.: The Weald Clay was described in 1858 as strong red and yellow clay and in 1968 as pale greyish-brown and buff silty clay
Refs: OS 6in 24 (1879); Hunt, *Mining Records*, 40; Thurrell et al, *Haslemere*, 40.

3 Brickfield on the east side of Station Road
NGR: TQ 088 254
Date: Marked only on the map of 1875
Ref.: OS 6in 23 (1875).

4 Brickyard at Spurland on the south edge of Bignor Wood
NGR: TQ 074 285
Date: A brick kiln was shown on the map of 1895 and the site was marked as Brick Field in 1910
Op.: W.H. Puttock advertised in 1899 and 1903
Refs: OS 6in 12 SE (1895, 1910); Kelly (1899); Pike/Horsham (1903).

5 Brickyard on Marringdean Road north of Little Gillmans Farm
NGR: TQ 086 248
Date: In existence by 1890, marked on the map of 1896 as Station Brick Yard but known as Gillmans Brickyard from the 1930s onwards. It shut down during World War 2 but was later revived and finally closed in the late 1960s
Op.: Ephraim Wadey advertised as a brickmaker at Parbrook from 1890 to 1913. The yard was operated by W. Burchell & Sons from 1930 to 1934 and by Gillmans Bricks (Billingshurst) Ltd from 1936

Geol.: Weald Clay

Refs: OS 6in 23 NE (1896, 1909) 1:25,000 TQ 02 (1959); Kelly (1890-1913, 1930-38); *QMJ* (1944); Thurrell et al, *Haslemere*, 29, 41, 140.

BINSTED

1 Tile kiln on the east side of Binsted Lane
NGR: SU 979 065
Date: 14th century
Prod: Roof and decorated floor tiles
F.Inf.: There was also a pottery kiln on the site, which was excavated in 1965-7
Ref.: K.J. Barton, *Medieval Sussex Pottery* (1979), 170-1.

2 Tile kiln at West Stubbs pit north of Arundel Road
NGR: SU 978 073
Date: Probably 17th century
F.Inf.: A lime kiln was also found on the site
Ref.: West Sussex Sites and Monuments Record No 1338.

3 Brick kiln on Arundel Road in the NE corner of the parish
NGR: SU 989 074
Date: Brick Kiln Piece was listed on a survey of 1825
Op.: Possibly Thomas Fowler of Binsted, who had a brick kiln in 1738
Refs: Add. MS. 9248; inf. Heather Warne.

4 Brick kiln east of the junction of Binsted Lane and Arundel Road
NGR: SU 984 072
Date: Brick Kiln Copse was listed on the tithe award of 1838
Ref.: TDW 15.

BOGNOR REGIS *see* SOUTH BERSTED

BOLNEY

1 Brick kiln north of Bolney Park Farm
NGR: TQ 268 243
Date: Brick Mead was listed on the tithe award of 1842; a pond and shaw on the north side of the field probably mark the site of the yard
Ref.: TDE 10.

2 Brickfield on the west side of Spronketts Lane
NGR: TQ 242 239
Date: Listed as Brick Field Coppice in 1842

Ref.: TDE 10.

3 Brickyard on the north side of Jeremy's Lane
NGR: TQ 262 248
Date: Opened c1864, marked as Wykehurst Brick Yard on maps from 1874 onwards and advertised for sale in 1923, after which date it appears to have gone out of use
Op.: Owned by the Wykehurst Park estate
F.Inf.: Kiln Cottage adjoining the road was originally the brickyard office
Refs: OS 6in 25 NE (1874, 1899, 1913); SP 1538; inf. T.E. Evans (1980).

4 Brickfield west of Crosspost
NGR: TQ 256 224
Date: Marked only on the map of 1898
Op.: Possibly Stephen Knight, a joiner and brickmaker, who advertised in Cuckfield and Bolney in 1895
Refs: OS 6in 25 SE (1898); Kelly (1895).

BOSHAM

1 Brick kiln and tilehouse on Bosham Hoe
NGR: SU 807 016
Date: Mentioned in a lease of 1759, marked on maps from 1813 to 1879 and as Old Brick Kiln in 1898
Op.: John Twine was the lessee in 1759 and Henry Fogden the tenant in 1841
Cond.: The shore is still littered with broken bricks
F.Inf.: Furze to fire the kiln was cut in neighbouring Furzefield. There was no road from Bosham, so workmen were brought over every morning by boat from Itchenor
Refs: OS 1in 5 (1813) 6in 60 (1879) 60 SE (1898); *SRS* **72**, 174; TDW 17; Maurice Hall, *Bosham and its Berkeley Barons* (1985), 114; inf. Angela Bromley-Martin (1985).

2 Brickworks and pottery at the junction of Portsmouth Road and Chequer Lane
NGR: SU 819 049
Date: In existence by 1867; closed during World War 1
Op.: In 1867 the owner was Alfred Cheeseman and the manager George Hounson. The latter had been succeeded by Robert Hounson in 1895

F.Inf.: The buildings are now used by Brinkmans Nurseries and the tiles on the office roof are said to represent the different types of tile produced at the works

Refs: OS 6in 61 (1875) 61 NW (1898,1910); Kelly (1867-1915); inf. A. Bromley-Martin (1985).

3 Brickfield south of Colner Farm
NGR: SU 801 053
Date: In existence by 1896; closed c1918
Op.: John Wyman Teed Heaver advertised here from 1913 to 1918
Refs: OS 6in 60 NE (1896, 1910); Kelly (1913-18).

4 Brickfield on the west side of Brooks Lane at Broadbridge
NGR: SU 814 053
Date: Marked on maps from 1910 to 1938
Op.: J.W.T. Heaver (cf site 3) advertised from 1913 to 1918 and his executors continued in business until 1930
Refs: OS 6in 61 NW (1910, 1932, 1938); Kelly (1913-30).

BROADWATER

1 Brickyard near the 'Half Brick' on Brighton Road
NGR: TQ 163 029
Date: First recorded in c1792; abandoned by 1875
Op.: Newland's brick kiln was mentioned in 1829 and Harry Newland was the owner/occupier in 1847. William Coppard advertised as a brickmaker at Navarino in 1845 and J. Howell was a brick- and tilemaker there in 1867
Refs: TDW 21; Pigot (1839); Kelly (1845, 1867); H. Smail, *Warwick House* (1952) & *Worthing Map Story* (1949), 117 (ex inf. K. Cosway).

2 Brickyard at the north end of Gloucester Place
NGR: TQ 146 025
Date: Pre-1847, when it was described as Old Brickyard
Op.: The owner/occupiers in 1847 were Charles Hide, a builder, and William Patching
Ref.: TDW 21.

3 Brickyard west of Crescent Road
NGR: TQ 143 024
Date: In existence by 1838 and described as Smith's Brickyard in 1847, when Old Brickyard (143 023) and Brickyard (144 025) were also listed
Op.: John Weller Smith was the owner and one of the occupiers in 1847
Refs: Par. 29/13/1; TDW 21.

4 Brickfield on the corner of Brighton Road and Brougham Road
NGR: TQ 168 031
Date: c1855 to c1910
Op.: J. Venn advertised in 1855 and 1859, followed by W. Longhurst in 1867 and Samuel Walker from 1887 to 1907
Refs: OS 25in 64/15 (1875, 1898); Kelly (1855-1907).

5 Brickfield on the site of present-day Meadow Close
NGR: TQ 167 033
Date: Marked only on the map of 1875
Op.: Possibly William Wenban Smith, who advertised as a timber merchant and brickmaker from 1878 to 1895
Refs: OS 25in 64/15 (1875); Kelly (1878-95).

6 Brickworks on the corner of Ham Road and Meadow Road
NGR: TQ 162 034
Date: In operation by 1878 and marked on the map of 1898
Op.: Robert Henry West, who advertised from 1878 to 1899, gave his address as Ham Lane in 1882
Refs: OS 25in 64/15 (1898); Kelly (1878-99).

7 Brickfield on the north side of Brougham Road west of site 5
NGR: TQ 164 033
Date: Probably the successor to site 5; marked on the map of 1898
Op.: As site 5; William Wenban Smith & Son advertised in 1899
Refs: OS 25in 64/15 (1898); Kelly (1899).

8 Brickfield east of present-day Chatham Road
NGR: TQ 163 031
Date: Marked only on the map of 1898
Op.: Probably Charles C. Cook who advertised from 1890 to 1907
Refs: OS 25in 64/15 (1898); Kelly (1890-1907).

186

9 Brickfield north of the railway on the east side of Angola (formerly Ladydell) Road
NGR: TQ 157 038
Date: In existence by 1907 and marked on the map of 1913
Op.: Alfred Gill advertised in 1907 in Ladydell Road
Refs: OS 6in 64 SE (1913); Kelly (1907)

10 Two brickyards north and south of the railway at Ham Bridge halt (East Worthing station)
NGR: TQ 160 038 and 160 037
Date: c1910 to the 1930s
Op.: Alfred Gill (cf site 9) advertised from 1913 to 1933 in Ham Road
Refs: Kelly (1913-27); *QMJ* (1927-33); *DBC* (1938); White, *Brighton & Worthing*, 86.

BURGESS HILL *see* CLAYTON, KEYMER

BURY

1 Brickfield and pottery west of West Burton Road
NGR: TQ 001 150
Date: 2nd or 3rd century
Ref.: P.J. Martin, 'Some recollections of a part of the Stane Street Causeway in its passage through West Sussex' *SAC* **11** (1859), 127 (map), 137.

2 Brick kilns SW of Triphill Farm
NGR: TQ 004 175
Date: In operation in 1780 but out of use by the early 1800s (the name Triphill appears to be a corruption of Brickkiln)
Op: Thomas Knight was the tenant from 1780 to 1804
Refs: TDW 25; LT Bury.

CHICHESTER

1 Tile kilns at the northern end of Southgate
NGR: SU 860 045
Date: Medieval: elements of four kilns were found during construction of a supermarket in 1979
Ref.: West Sussex Sites and Monuments Record No 4773.

2 Brick kilns in North and East Pallant
NGR: SU 862 047
Date: Remains of kilns found during excavations at East Pallant House and

the City Club in 1981 were thought to be of early 18th century date
Op.: Several brickmakers were known to be living in Chichester around this time e.g. Andrew Price and William Styant in 1715 and John and Thomas Hammond in the 1720s
Prod.: Bricks measuring 8½in x 4in x 2in and plain roofing tiles
Refs: Report of Chichester Excavation Committee for 1981; *SRS* **9**, 319 & **12**, 149, 168, 238.

3 Brick kiln in the parish of St Bartholomew
NGR: cSU 853 045
Date: Early-18th century: listed as Brickkiln Field in 1780
Op.: Richard Gates was a brickmaker in the parish in 1731
Ref.: William Gardner's Town Plan (1769); LT Chichester St Bartholomew (1780); *SRS* **32**.

CHIDHAM

1 Brick kiln west of New Barn SW of Chidham village
NGR: SU 782 027
Date: Brick Kiln Marsh on Chidham Farm was listed on an estate survey of 1785
Ref.: Add. MS. 2158.

2 Brick kiln in the area of Scant Road
NGR: SU 797 069
Date: Pre-1847 when two Brick Kiln Fields were listed on opposite sides of the road
Ref.: TDW 30.

3 Brickfield north of the railway at Nutbourne Halt
NGR: SU 789 059
Date: Marked only on the map of 1909
Ref.: OS 6in 60 NE (1909).

see also: WESTBOURNE

CHITHURST

1 Brickfield north of Pennels Bridge at Milland
NGR: SU 837 268
Date: Marked on maps of 1874 and 1896, as Brick Works in 1910 and closed c1940
Op.: George Trigg advertised in the 1870s followed by Robert Rapley from 1882

to 1895. H. Booker & Son were running the works in the 1930s
Geol.: Predominantly red Weald Clay
Refs: OS 6in 21 (1874) 21 NE (1898, 1910); Kelly (1874-95, 1934-8); Thurrell et al, *Haslemere*, 32, 140.

see also: TROTTON

CLAPHAM

1 Brickyard on Clapham Common
NGR: TQ 093 059
Date: 18th to 20th centuries: closed in 1978
Op.: John Clarke was a brickmaker in Clapham in 1704. Thomas Colebrooke was granted a licence to dig clay in 1731 and Stephen Baker was the lessee of the yard from 1766. John Bishop was in charge by 1832, was the owner/occupier in 1843 and advertised from 1855 to 1867. E.C. Patching was the owner in 1887 and became the secretary of Clapham Common Brick & Tile Co. which advertised from 1899. From 1922 the manager was J.F. Jordan, whose descendants ran the business until 1978
Prod.: Clay bricks, building bricks, tiles, paving tiles and hollowware in 1742: paving bricks were a speciality in the 1930s and hand-made bricks were still produced for special orders up to 1958
F.Inf.: An open-topped kiln with a capacity of 20,000 bricks was mentioned in 1869. This was later replaced by three circular down-draught kilns, which were still in existence in 1974
Geol.: The brickyard is situated at the junction of the London Clay and the Reading Beds
Refs: TDW 32; OS 6in 63 (1875) 63 NE (1898 et seq.); EpI/29/50/44; Pigot (1832); Kelly (1855-1938); *SRS* **9**; White, *Brighton & Worthing*, 64, 68; *QMJ* (1927, 1959); *VCH* **6** (1), 10, 16.

CLAYTON

1 Brickyard on Westend Farm
NGR: TQ 300 197
Date: c1578 to c1650

Op.: Possibly Robert Edsaw
Ref.: H. Warne, *Heart of Burgess Hill: the History of its Brick and Tile Trade 1578-1855* (forthcoming).

2 Brickyard (?) on the north bank of the river SW of Clayton Priory
NGR: TQ 299 177
Date: The field name Brick Mead on the tithe award of 1838 suggests brickmaking in the 16th or 17th centuries
Ref.: TDE 72.

3 Brickyard north of present-day Victoria Way
NGR: TQ 307 188
Date: c1636 to 1716
Op.: Henry Marten, probably followed by his son-in-law Thomas Parker until 1678
Ref.: Warne (forthcoming).

4 Brickyards on Dunstalls Farm
NGR: TQ 306 198
Date: A yard was in existence by 1659 but went out of use c1752. There were brick kilns on an adjacent site in the second half of the 18th century and a brick kiln in the same area was referred to in the enclosure award of 1857. A Brick Works was in operation from 1895 until the 1930s
Op.: i. James Saunders from c1659 to 1667; Thomas Giles from c1682 to 1694; Richard Jordan from 1694 to 1706; John Parker (cf Keymer 1) from 1708 to 1713; George Taylor from 1713 to 1744; James Parker (cf site 5) from 1745 to 1751; John(?) Billinghurst (cf Ditchling 2) from 1751 to 1754; William(?) Haslegrove from 1754 to 1756; William Marchant from 1756 to 1794
ii. William Bryant (cf site 8) advertised from 1895 to 1915 followed by Bryant and Barstow from 1922 to 1927 and the Dunstall Brick Co. from 1933 to 1938
Refs: OS 6in 39 NW (1899, 1912); ESRO ADA 1; QDD/6/E8; *SRS* **77**, 57; Kelly (1895-1927); *QMJ* (1927-33); *DBC* (1938); Warne (forthcoming).

5 Brickyard to the east of site 1
NGR: TQ 304 197
Date: c1670 to c1750

Op.: James Parker was fined for digging brick earth on the common in 1713 and supplied bricks and tiles for the building of Stanmer House in 1726

Refs: ESRO ADA 1 & A 4600/7; Warne (forthcoming).

6 Brickyard on the west side of London Road
NGR: TQ 307 191
Date: 1850s to 1870s
Op.: Charles Tulley and his father-in-law Thomas Avery advertised as brick-makers in 1855, followed by Tulley alone from 1859 to 1866
Refs: OS 25in 39/5 (1877); Kelly (1855-66); Avery, *Burgess Hill*, 6.

7 Brickworks on the north side of Royal George Road
NGR: TQ 306 193
Date: In operation by 1878 and marked on the map of 1899
Op.: Richard Berry advertised from 1878 to 1895 and the exors of R. Berry in 1899
Refs: OS 6in 39 NW (1899); Kelly (1855-99); Avery, *Burgess Hill*, 6.

8 Brickfield on the south side of West Street
NGR: TQ 305 196
Date: Marked on the map of 1877, by 1898 the brickfield occupied a much larger site to the west (303 195), where it remained in operation until after 1912
Op.: William Bryant and his son Ernest
Refs: OS 25in 39/5 (1877) 6in 39 NW (1899, 1912); Avery, *Burgess Hill*, 6.

9 Brickworks south of Poveys Farm
NGR: TQ 299 192
Date: Marked on the map of 1912
Op.: Wm. Meeds & Son (cf Keymer 3) used the area, which later became the Victoria Pleasure Gardens, for clay-digging and exploited the land to the west, as the clay in the area of their works became exhausted
Refs: OS 6in 39 NW (1912); Avery, *Burgess Hill*, 6.

COCKING

1 Brick kiln on the east side of the Midhurst road north of the junction with Bex Lane
NGR: SU 880 191
Date: In operation in 1780 but went out of use not long after this: marked Old Brick Kiln on a map of 1830
Op: Christopher Croucher (cf Woolbeding 1) paid tax for the brick kiln in 1780 and was succeeded as occupier by Nicholas Philp
Refs: Cowdray MS. 1723; LT Cocking (1780-91).

2 Brickfield near the site of Cocking station
NGR: SU 874 162
Date: Lower Brick Field was listed on the tithe award of 1842
Op.: The tenant in 1842 was Benjamin Challen (cf Trotton 2)
Ref.: TDW 35.

3 Brickyard on the north side of Bex Lane
NGR: SU 883 189
Date: Called Beck's Kiln Field on a map of 1830, the yard was in operation in 1842, marked as Brick Field in 1880 but disused by 1898
Op.: Major Newland was the tenant in 1842; Alfred Lewis advertised from 1874 to 1882
Refs: Cowdray MS. 1723; TDW 35; OS 6in 34 (1880) 34 NE (1898); Kelly (1874-82).

4 Brickfield between the Midhurst road and the former railway near Holmingwood
NGR: SU 880 193
Date: Late 1860s and early 1870s when the line was under construction
Geol.: Gault clay
Ref.: Inf. J.C.V. Mitchell (1985).

5 Brickyard NW of Pitsham Farm
NGR: SU 877 199
Date: In existence by 1869 and still in operation (2001)
Op.: Owned by the Cowdray estate: Maurice Henry Tallant advertised in 1882, Tallant Bros (cf Fernhurst 2) from 1887 and F.A. Tallant in 1903, followed by Ernest William Stevens in 1913. The yard then came under the control of George English of the Nyewood Co. (cf Harting 3) which operated the works until c1960, when it was taken over by W.T. Lamb & Sons
Prod.: In addition to a wide range of hand-moulded bricks including ash-glazed headers, architectural terracotta and some mathematical tiles are also produced

189

F.Inf.: The old downdraught kiln (built c1972), though still in existence, went out of use in 1998 and has been replaced by a fibre-lined computer-controlled kiln. Stock bricks are still clamp-fired.

Refs: OS 6in 34 NE (1898) 1:25,000 SU 81 (1958); Kelly (1882-1913); *QMJ* (1927-59); *SIAS Newsletter* **20**, Oct 1978; film in the possession of J.C.V. Mitchell; inf. A. Merritt (1992); inf. Jonathan Lamb (2001).

COLDWALTHAM

1 Brick kiln on the western boundary of the parish
NGR: TQ 007 164
Date: Listed as Brick Kiln Field on the tithe award of 1841
Ref.: TDW 36.

COWFOLD

1 Brickfield on the east side of the road north of Crabtree Gate
NGR: TQ 217 243
Date: In operation by 1875 and closed c1915
Op.: Edward Brewer, manager to R. Hoper Esq., advertised from 1890 to 1915
Cond.: Brick Kiln Cottages north of the site are still in existence
Refs: OS 6in 25 (1875) 25 SW (1898, 1912); Kelly (1890-1915).

2 Brickfield near Potters Farm west of Cowfold
NGR: TQ 209 225
Date: Possibly in operation from 1882 but marked only on the map of 1912
Op.: Holloway & Fieldus, who had a depot in Brighton, advertised in 1882 and George Wassell in 1890
Refs: OS 6in 25 SW (1912); Kelly (1882, 1890).

CRAWLEY *see* IFIELD, WORTH

CRAWLEY DOWN *see* WORTH

CUCKFIELD

1 Brickyard NE of Handcross
NGR: TQ 266 301
Date: Bricks were advertised for sale at

Bigse's kiln in 1794. The yard was listed on the tithe award of 1843 but closed by 1874 when only Brickyard Wood remained
Op.: Joseph Biggs & Co. were the tenants in 1843
Refs: TDE 91; OS 6in 14 (1874); *SWA*, 18 Aug 1794.

2 Brickfield on the south bank of the river Ouse ½ mile north of Bigges Farm
NGR: TQ 291 279
Date: Brick Field was listed on the tithe award of 1843: a possible alternative site for Bigse's kiln (cf site 1)
Ref.: TDE 91.

3 Brickfield on Tyes Farm east of Staplefield
NGR: TQ 286 280
Date: Listed as Brick Field in 1843
Ref.: TDE 91.

4 Brickfield on Pains Place Farm SE of Ansty
NGR: TQ 299 215
Date: Listed as Brick Field in 1843
Ref.: TDE 91.

5 Brick kiln SE of Hatchgate Farm east of Cuckfield village
NGR: TQ 315 246
Date: Listed as Brick Kiln Pit in 1843
Ref.: TDE 91.

6 Brickyard on the east side of Ardingly Road
NGR: TQ 308 254
Date: Marked on maps of 1843 and 1874; called Longacre Brickyard in 1882 and closed shortly after this date
Op.: Joseph Jeffery from at least 1843 to 1859 and Joseph Bacon Jeffery from 1862 to 1882
Refs: TDE 91; OS 6in 26 (1874); Kelly (1845, 1859-78); *SWA*, 28 Feb 1882.

7 Brickfield on the west side of Sussex Road, Haywards Heath
NGR: TQ 333 234
Date: In existence by 1849 and closed in the 1890s
Op.: Sergison's new brickyard in Haywards Heath was mentioned in 1849, presumably on this site. William Ashdown was the manager of Haywards Heath Brickworks in 1862. Jacob Grist advertised from 1878 to 1887 followed by John Gaston in 1890

Refs: OS 25in 16/10 (1875); Kelly (1862-90); W.K. Ford & A.C. Gabe, *The Metropolis of Mid-Sussex: a History of Haywards Heath* (1981), 49.

8 Brickfield on the west edge of Gores Wood north of Cuckfield Hospital
NGR: TQ 309 259
Date: Marked only on the map of 1874
Ref.: OS 6in 26 (1874).

9 Brickfield on the east side of London Road
NGR: TQ 307 253
Date: Marked only on the map of 1874
Op.: Possibly Stephen Knight, a builder and contractor at Whitemans Green, who advertised as a brickmaker in 1895
Refs: OS 6in 26 (1874); Kelly (1895).

10 Brickfield on the west side of Hazelgrove Road, Haywards Heath
NGR: TQ 333 237
Date: Marked only on the map of 1875
Ref.: OS 25in 26/10 (1875).

11 Brickfield on the south side of Franklynn Road opposite the end of present-day Western Road, Haywards Heath
NGR: TQ 336 233
Date: Marked only on the map of 1875
Ref.: OS 25in 26/11 (1875).

12 Brickfield on the north side of Ashenground Road, Haywards Heath
NGR: TQ 332 232
Date: Marked on the maps of 1874 and 1899
Op.: Thomas Gower advertised from 1874 to 1882
Refs: OS 6in 26 (1874) 26 SW (1899); Kelly (1874-82).

13 Brickfield at Broadstreet west of the former gasworks
NGR: TQ 311 249
Date: In existence by 1882 and closed c1904
Op.: John Norris advertised in 1882 followed by E. Norris & Sons in 1887 and Edward Norris in 1903
Prod.: Clamp bricks
Refs: OS 6in SW (1899); Kelly (1882-1903).

14 Two brickfields on the south side of New England Road, Haywards Heath
NGR: TQ 335 238 & 338 239
Date: One was in existence by 1882, both were marked on the map of 1899, the eastern one had been redeveloped by 1912 but the other continued until the beginning of World War 2
Op.: Richard King advertised in 1882 and 1887. The brickfields were later owned by Pannetts, builders, of Haywards Heath
Refs: OS 6in 26 SE (1899, 1912, 1938); Kelly (1882-7); inf. C. Anscombe/G. Thomerson (1986).

15 Brickfield between Eastern and Western Roads, Haywards Heath
NGR: TQ 339 235
Date: Marked on the map of 1910 and closed in the 1930s
Op.: Thomas White, a builder who had his offices in Franklynn Road, advertised from 1882 to 1938, evidently making bricks on another site before this one was opened
Prod.: Hand-moulded, clamp-burnt bricks
Refs: OS 25in 26/11 (1910, 1937); Kelly (1882-1922); *QMJ* (1927-33); *DBC* (1938); inf. Sydney Redman (1984).

16 Brickfield on the site of present-day Dellney Avenue, Haywards Heath
NGR: TQ 339 233
Date: 1890s to 1930s
Op.: Jesse Finch, builder, of Perrymount Road, advertised in 1895 followed by Horace Finch from 1907 to 1933. In 1934 the business was in the hands of Ross Bros Ltd who had a depot in Burgess Hill
Prod.: Clamp bricks
Refs: OS 25in 26/10 (1910); Kelly (1895-1934); *QMJ* (1933); *DBC* (1938); inf. C. Anscombe/G. Thomerson (1986).

WEST DEAN

1 Brick kiln on the west side of Hylter's Lane
NGR: SU 837 132
Date: Brick House (836 127), now called Brick Kiln Farm, was marked on the map of 1825 and Brick Kiln Plantation was listed on the tithe award of 1845. Brick Kiln Cottages were first named on the map of 1898 and a small pit to the north can be seen on the 1958 map
Refs: *SRS* **72**, 174; TDW 141; OS 6in 68 NW (1898) 1:25,000 SU 81 (1958).

DUNCTON

1 Brickyard, probably on the common
Exact location not known
Date: Late 17th and early 18th centuries:
bricks were available for use at
Petworth in 1702
Op.: Thomas Boad's brick-kiln was
mentioned in his probate inventory of
1696
Refs: EpI/29/69/40; PHA 6324 No 49.

DURRINGTON

1 Brickyard west of Cote Street
NGR: TQ 113 059
Date: In operation in 1768 but described
only as Kiln Field in 1839
Op.: James Blunden in 1768 and William
Blunden in 1778
Refs: TDW 42; Arundel Castle MS. HC5 (ex
inf. T.P. Hudson); *SRS* **35**, 308.

2 Brickworks on the west side of Durrington
Lane
NGR: TQ 118 048
Date: Marked on the map of 1898 and in
operation until c1918
Op.: Durrington Brick Co. advertised from
1899 to 1918. In 1899 the managing
director was W.W. Smith (cf
Broadwater 5 & 7)
F.Inf: Brickfield House and Brickfield
Cottages are still standing (1985)
Refs: OS 6in 64 SW (1898); Kelly (1899-
1918); inf. B. Glaisyer (1985).

EARNLEY

1 Brick kiln on the south side of Earnley Road
at the junction with Bookers Lane
NGR: SZ 815 972
Date: Called Brick Kiln and Nortons on the
tithe award of 1845
Op.: The tenant in 1845 was William Tribe
Ref.: TDW 43.

EASTERGATE

1 Brickfield in Eastergate
Exact location not known
Date: Mid-19th century
Op.: R.W. Field
Ref.: Hunt, *Mining Records*, 39.

2 Brickfield at the west end of Elm Grove
South, West Barnham
NGR: SU 953 048
Date: Opened c1929 and closed in 1950
Op.: G. & C.H. Stevens
F.Inf: Parts of two barrows found on the site
are at Amberley Museum
Refs: Deeds of No. 101 Barnham Road (ex
inf. B. Hopkins).

EDBURTON

1 Brickfield NW of Badger Wood Farm
NGR: TQ 245 135
Date: Listed on the tithe award of 1841
Op: In 1841 the tenant was James Hills
Ref.: TDW 168.

ELSTED

1 Brickyard between the former railway and
Elsted Road east of the station
NGR: SU 835 206
Date: In existence by 1878 and closed c1930
Op.: Edward Eames advertised in 1878
followed by James Heighes from 1887
to 1895. From 1899 onwards the yard
was in the hands of William Russell,
later Russell & Son
Cond.: Part of the kiln is incorporated in the
buildings now used by a haulage
company
F.Inf.: Brick moulds from this yard are (1992)
in the Mallison Craft Collection,
Selbourne, Hants.
Refs: OS 6in 21 SW (1898, 1910); Kelly (1874-
1922); *QMJ* (1927); inf. V. Mitchell
(1985).

FAYGATE *see* RUSPER

FELPHAM

1 Brickyard on the south side of Limmer Lane
on the site of present-day Halliwick Gardens
NGR: SZ 957 997
Date: Brick Croft was listed on the tithe
award of 1844 and was possibly the
site of a brickworks in the early 1900s
The tenants in 1844 were the Misses
Sparks and James Boiling; C. Boyling
advertised in 1907 followed by Mrs
Ellen Boyling in 1913 and 1915
Refs: TDW 54; Kelly (1907-15).

2 Brickfields in Sundale Lane (now in the par. of Middleton-on-Sea)
NGR: SU 972 005
Date: In operation from c1899 until the 1940s
Op.: i. George Shaw, of Middleton Brickfields, advertised from 1899 to 1907 and from 1933 to 1944
ii. Edward Lunn, of Middleton Brickyard, advertised from 1913 to 1938, his manager being a Mr. Merritt
iii. John Tulley (Brickmakers) Ltd of Sundale Lane and F. Luff Valentine, of Middleton Brickworks, were also in business in 1936
Prod.: Kiln-fired bricks at Middleton Brickyard in the 1930s
Refs: OS 6in 74 NE (1910, 1932); Kelly (1899-1930); *QMJ* (1927-44); *Brighton & Tun. Wells Tel. Dir.* (1936); *DBC* (1938); inf. G. Hardwell of Bognor (1990).

3 Brickworks on the west side of Flansham Lane (now the Hurstwood Estate)
NGR: SU 961 004
Date: 1926 to 1939
Op.: Felpham Brick & Estates Co. managed by S.W. Cole
Prod.: Clamp bricks
Refs: Add. MS. 20288-90; Kelly (1930-38); inf. G. Hardwell.

4 Brickfield between Flansham Lane and Middleton Road
NGR: SU 963 004
Date: c1927 to c1960
Op.: Flansham Brickworks, owned by Bailey, Hartley & Watton, builders, of Felpham
Prod.: Sussex clamp bricks, facing bricks and breeze slabs (1959)
F.Inf.: Before World War 2 a horse-driven pugmill was used, ashes came from Portsmouth power station, bricks were hand moulded and dried on hacks and one clamp, containing c700,000 bricks, was burnt per season
Refs: *QMJ* (1927-59); Kelly (1934-38); inf. G. Hardwell.

5 Brickworks at the junction of Hoe Lane and Stanover Lane, Flansham (now in the par. of Yapton)
NGR: SU 956 013
Date: 1930s
Op.: The Felpham Brick & Estates Co. (cf site 3) advertised in Hoes Lane in 1934 and 1938
Refs: OS 6in 74 NE (1932, 1939); Kelly (1934-38); inf. supplied by Felpham & Middleton Local History Workshop.

FERNHURST

1 Brick kiln on the east side of Midhurst Road
NGR: SU 896 279
Date: Brick Kiln Field was listed on the tithe award of 1846
Op.: The tenant in 1846 was Richard Luff
Ref.: TDW 55.

2 Brickyard on Henley Common SW of Dawes Farm
NGR: SU 890 264
Date: In operation before 1846; closed in the 1930s
Op.: The yard belonged to the Petworth estate. Henry Williams was the tenant until 1846, when a new lease was granted to James Madgwick, who advertised from 1851 to 1874. F.A. Tallant of Easebourne was running the business by 1878, followed by Tallant Bros (cf Cocking 5) from 1887 to 1895. It was under direct estate management until c1927 when George English (cf Harting 2) took over
Prod.: Bricks, roofing tiles, drain tiles and pipes
F.Inf.: Hand-propelled waggons were in use on the narrow-gauge railway across the main road in the 1920s
Refs: TDW 55; OS 6in 21 (1879) 21 NE (1896, 1910); Cowdray MS. 1813; Kelly (1851-1930); inf. J.C.V. Mitchell (1985).

3 Brickyard east of Bell Road north of Kingsley Green
NGR: SU 897 310
Date: In existence by 1878 but abandoned by 1898
Op.: Edmund Roe advertised from 1878 to 1895
Refs: OS 6in 10 NE (1898); Kelly (1878-95).

see also: NORTH AMBERSHAM

FISHBOURNE

1 Brickyard north of Clay Lane
   NGR: SU 843 052
   Date: Marked on maps of 1839 and 1844 and still in existence in 1858
   Op.: The tenant in 1839 was William Styles Goodeve
   Refs: TDW 87; QDP/W89; Hunt, *Mining Records*, 39.

FITTLEWORTH

1 Brickyard near the hamlet of Bedham
   Exact location not known
   Date: 17th and 18th centuries: bricks were available for use at Petworth in 1702
   Op.: John Roberts was a brickmaker in Fittleworth in 1642. Sarah Thear supplied bricks to the Petworth estate in 1784 and Thomas Thear, brickmaker, was living here in 1794
   Refs: PHA 6324 No 49 (ex inf. A. McCann); *SRS* **54**, 7 & **35**, 422; inf. R. Titttensor (1985).

2 Brickfield on the west side of the lane between Fittleworth and Churchwood
   NGR: TQ 014 195
   Date: Marked on plans of 1903; the outline of the pit is shown on the map of 1910
   Geol.: Fittleworh Beds (base of Sandgate Beds)
   Refs: QDP/W 218; OS 6in 36 NW (1910); Reid, *Chichester*, 11; inf. Roger Bristow (1981).

FORD

1 Brickworks on the site of Ford aerodrome
   NGR: cSU 998 025
   Date: 1920s
   Op.: Zachariah Peskett of Angmering (cf Rustington 3)
   Ref.: Inf. Ben Foreman, who had worked there (1989).

FUNTINGTON

1 Brickyard on the east side of Newells Lane
   NGR: SU 798 063
   Date: Marked on maps from 1778 to 1909
   Op.: Richard Yalden was a brickmaker in Funtington in 1796. In 1806 Mr Gruggen was the occupier of a brick and tile yard on Hambrook Common which was for sale. Joseph Hoar, the tenant in 1838, advertised as a potter in Nutbourne (cf Westbourne 1) in 1845
   Refs: *SRS* **72**, 91, 108; PM 4; TDW 60; OS 1 in 5 (1813) 6in 60 (1879) 60 NE (1896, 1909); *SRS* **35**, 437; *SWA* 24 Feb 1806.

2 Brick kiln north of Clay Lane on the line of the Fishbourne by-pass
   NGR: SU 833 059
   Date: Brick Kiln Field was listed on the tithe award of 1838
   Op.: The owner/occupier in 1838 was Willis Hardman and W. Hardham advertised as a brickmaker in Chichester in 1851, his supplies probably coming from this yard
   Refs: TDW 60; Kelly (1851).

3 Brickworks north of the railway at Nutbourne Halt
   NGR: SU 789 059
   Date: Marked on the map of 1909, gone by 1932
   Ref.: OS 60 NE (1909, 1932).

GORING

1 Brickyard on the south side of present-day Amberley Drive
   NGR: TQ 108 021
   Date: Brick Croft was listed on the tithe award of 1843
   Ref.: TDW 61.

2 Brickyard on the south side of Arundel Road east of Castle Goring
   NGR: TQ 106 056
   Date: Opened c1780 and closed in the late 1850s
   Op.: William Blunden (cf Durrington 1) had moved to Goring by 1781 and advertised in 1798. Another William was the owner/occupier in 1843 and advertised in the 1850s

Refs: TDW 61; OS 6in 64 (1879); *SRS* **35**, 329; *Universal British Directory* (1798); Kelly (1851-55).

3   Brickworks between the gas works and the railway
NGR: TQ 115 031
Date: Referred to as Courtlands Brickyard in 1907, marked as Worthing West End Brickworks on the map of 1909 and still in operation in the 1930s
Op.:   Goring Brick Co. Ltd advertised in 1930 and 1938
Refs: OS 25in 64/13 (1909); QDP/W 247; *SAC* **105** (1967), 56; Kelly (1930); *DBC* (1938).

GRAFFHAM

1   Tile kiln (?) east of the road from Graffham to Wiblings Farm
NGR: SU 930 184
Date: 2nd or 3rd century: Roman tiles and pottery were found in the brook in 1932 and much larger quantities observed in 1972
Ref.:   West Sussex Sites and Monuments Record No 1491.

see also: WOOLAVINGTON

GREATHAM

1   Brickworks on Batchelor's Farm
NGR: cTQ 040 152
Date: 1930s
Op.:   Greatham Brick & Tile Co. Ltd advertised in 1936 and Greatham Brick & Sand Co. in 1938
Refs: *Brighton & Tun. Wells Tel. Dir.* (1936); Kelly (1938).

EAST GRINSTEAD

1   Brickfield NE of Tablehurst Farm, Forest Row
NGR: TQ 435 354
Date: Mentioned in a lease of 1580 possibly in use when the farmhouse was rebuilt in the late 16th century
Refs: ESRO SAS/RF 12/24 (ex inf. M.J. Leppard); inf. E.C. Byford.

2   Brick kiln NW of Court Inholmes, Forest Row
NGR: TQ 415 349
Date: Listed as Brickhurst Field on the tithe award of 1840, this had been the site of the hammer pond of Brambletye Forge in the late 16th century and may have been used for brickmaking when Brambletye House was built c1630
Cond.:   A low mound in the corner of the field containing brick debris and burnt clay was found in 1981
Refs: TDE 45; inf. C.F. Tebbutt (1981).

3   Brickyard(s) on the south side of London Road (formerly the common)
NGR: TQ 388 385
Date: The first reference to brickmaking on the common was in 1670 and a brick-kiln, possibly on this site, was mentioned in 1679. The yard was marked on maps from 1817 to 1873. From 1875 onwards only pottery was made
Op.:   John Butching in 1670 and John Mathew in 1679. William Avery was rated for a brick kiln in 1811 and Elphick and Avery paid rent from 1829 to 1851, followed by George Lynn, a builder, from 1852 to 1875
Prod.:   In the 1850s pottery and terracotta were added to the range: examples can be seen in East Grinstead Museum
Refs: QDP/W371; TDE 45; OS 6in 5 (1873); Pigot (1832-9); Kelly (1855-74); Hunt, *Mining Records*, 39; M.J. Leppard, 'Brickmaking in East Grinstead' *BEGS* **27** (1979); 'Addenda and Corrigenda' *BEGS* **44** (1988); Baines, *Pottery*, 151.

4   Brickyard on Moats Farm near the present-day gas works
NGR: TQ 391 387
Date: Called Brick Kiln Field in 1776, the yard was in use until c1881 when the Oxted railway line was built
Op.:   William Avery (cf site 3) was rated for the brick kiln in 1824 but it appears to have been operated by John Turley until c1856. He was followed by Samuel Relf, who was succeeded by his nephew Charles Waters from c1867
Refs: OS 6in 5 (1873); Pigot (1832-39); Kelly (1851-78); census (1851); Leppard, *op.cit.* (1979) and 'Brickmaking in East Grinstead: Additional Notes' *BEGS* **30** (1981).

5 Brickyard on the south side of Imberhorne Lane (now Park Road)
NGR: TQ 386 383
Date: Possibly in existence by 1803; marked as Brick Works on the map of 1873
Op.: Robert Norman, listed as a brickmaker in East Grinstead in 1803, was working in this area in 1811. A later operator was a Mr Silvester of Three Bridges
Prod.: Clamp-fired stock bricks in the mid-19th century
Refs: OS 6in 5 (1873); ESRO LPL/1/E1; Leppard (1979, 1981).

6 Brickworks on the south side of Holtye Road north of Shovelstrode
NGR: TQ 424 393
Date: In operation from the late 1850s until at least 1885
Op.: Henry Barnett advertised in 1859 and 1862
Refs: OS 6in 5 (1873); Kelly (1859-62); Leppard (1979, 1981).

7 Brickyard at Pock Hill east of Ashurst Wood
NGR: TQ 437 364
Date: 1860s
Op.: Steven Jeffrey was a brickmaker here in 1861; Sydney Patience was paid £2 10s for making bricks for the Ashdown Park estate in 1869, probably on this site
Refs: Census (1861); E.C. Byford, *Ashdown Park* (1994); inf. M.J. Leppard.

8 Brickfield on the west side of Lewes Road NW of Forest Row
NGR: TQ 417 360
Date: Listed on sale particulars of 1865
Op.: Owned by the Brambletye estate: the tenant in 1865 was a Mr Divall (cf Hartfield 4)
Ref.: Sale particulars (ex inf. M. Tighe).

9 Brickfield at the southern edge of Holden Wood NE of Ashurst Wood
NGR: TQ 443 374
Date: Marked only on the map of 1873
Ref.: OS 6in 5 (1873).

10 Brickworks on the south side of Durkins Road
NGR: TQ 389 390

Date: Opened in the early 1880s and closed c1914
Op.: Charles Waters (cf site 4) followed by A.C. Waters from 1895
Refs: OS 25in 5/5 (1899, 1910); Kelly (1882-1913); Leppard (1979) and 'Addenda and Corrigenda: Brickmaking' *BEGS* **41** (1987).

11 Brickworks on the east side of Dunnings Road
NGR: TQ 395 371
Date: Opened in the late 1890s and closed c1913
Op.: Clement and Henry Gasson, builders, made bricks here for the Sunnyside estate in the late 1890s and advertised as brickmakers from 1907 to 1913
F.Inf.: Broken bricks and dust from the yard were used to surface Coombe Hill Road which was known locally as Red Road
Refs: OS 25in 5/9 (1899); Kelly (1907-13); Leppard (1979, 1987, 1988).

12 Brickworks on Hackenden Lane
NGR: TQ 394 393
Date: In operation by 1899; closed in 1956
Op.: Harwood & Young in 1899 and the early 1900s, followed by Harold Barter Harwood from 1915 and the Hackenden Brick Co. Ltd from 1922. Four generations of the Furminger family were foremen of the yard
Prod.: Clamp bricks
F.Inf.: The pugmill was powered by a woodburning steam engine until c1910 and later by a gas engine. Bricks were hand-moulded at first but later a Berry machine was installed
Geol.: Grinstead Clay
Refs: OS 25in 5/5 (1910, 1936); Kelly (1915-1938); Foster, *Mines* (1900-01); *QMJ* (1927-51); Bristow & Bazley, *Tunbridge Wells*, 92; R.H. Wood, 'Some Notes on Hackenden Brickyard' *BEGS* **26** (1979).

WEST GRINSTEAD

1 Brickyard on the north side of Cowfold Road near the junction with Worthing Road
NGR: TQ 168 227
Date: Listed as Old Brickyard Field in 1837

on land belonging to the West Grinstead Park estate, it was probably in use when a brick mansion was built there c1600

Refs: TDW 142; *VCH* **6** (2), 91.

2 Brick kiln east of Littleworth
NGR: TQ 196 203
Date: Brick Kiln Field was listed on the tithe award of 1837
Ref.: TDW 142.

3 Brickyard and pottery on Jolesfield Common
NGR: TQ 188 204
Date: In operation by the 1770s and closed c1900
Op.: Michael Burgess was a brickmaker here in 1782 and Noah and Thomas Billinghurst were both working here in 1784. The latter was granted the copyhold of the brick kilns and land in 1791 but in 1794 he handed over to William Evershed, who was succeeded in 1801 by Phillip Kensett, followed by other members of the Kensett family. Alfred Richardson advertised in the 1870s and thereafter advertisements were for Jolesfield Brick, Tile and Pottery Works, manager: J.T. Magwire
Prod.: Bricks, tiles and earthenware
Cond.: Brick buildings on the site are now used as dwellings and a garage
Refs: TDW 142; OS 6in 37 (1875) 37 NE (1898); LT West Grinstead (1791-1832); Kelly (1859-87); *SRS* **35**, 351; Baines, *Pottery*, 174; *VCH* **6** (2), 98.

4 Brickyard on the east side of Worthing Road north of Green Lane
NGR: TQ 166 223
Date: Marked on the tithe map of 1837, called Waterloo Brick Works in 1875 and 1898 and still in use in the 1920s
Op.: Owned by the West Grinstead Park estate
Prod.: Bricks, tiles and drainpipes
Cond.: Site destroyed when the A24 was widened in the 1960s
Refs: TDW 142; OS 6in 14 (1875) 14 SE (1898, 1914); *VCH* **6** (2), 98.

5 Brickyard and pottery south of High Street, Partridge Green
NGR: TQ 193 191

Date: Called Westland Brick Yard on the map of 1874, described as Brick, Tile & Pottery Works from 1887 and closed c1952
Op.: Charles Kempshall advertised from 1882 to 1903, followed by Edwin Kempshall until 1930. The yard had been sold c1925 to Allfreys of Pulborough, who operated it until its closure
Prod.: Red kiln-fired facing bricks, tiles, ornamental fittings, flower pots and earthenware
Cond.: Now a housing and trading estate
Refs: OS 6in 14 (1875) 14 NW (1898, 1912); Kelly (1882-1930); Paris, 'Partridge Green', 32; *VCH* **6** (2), 98; inf D. Cox (1988).

6 Brickfield west of the former railway NW of Partridge Green
NGR: TQ 187 193
Date: Marked on maps of 1898 and 1914; closed in the 1930s
Op.: David Kensett, who had been working at Jolesfield Common until 1867, established a new brickyard at Partridge Green in the 1870s, either on this site or site 7, both of which were used by the Kensett family. Frederick Kensett was running the business by 1907 and advertised until 1938
Prod.: Clamp-burnt bricks
Cond.: Later used as a poultry farm, so few traces of brickmaking remain
Refs: OS 6in 37 NE (1898, 1914); Kelly (1878-1930); Pike/Horsham (1903-33); *DBC* (1938); Paris, 'Partridge Green', 32; *VCH* **6** (2), 98; inf. D. Cox.

7 Brickworks in South Street, Partridge Green
NGR: TQ 194 192
Date: Marked only on the map of 1898
Op.: The Kensett family (cf site 6)
Prod: Bricks and tiles: David Kensett advertised as a brick- and tilemaker and as shopkeeper, cattle dealer and coach builder as well
Cond.: Site redeveloped for housing
Refs: OS 6in 38 NW (1898); Kelly (1882-1903); Paris, 'Partridge Green', 32; inf. D. Cox.

8 Brickworks east of the former Partridge Green station

NGR: TQ 192 189

Date: Opened c1890 and closed in the 1930s

Op.: William John Norman advertised in 1895 and 1899 and Walter Hillman from 1903 to 1927. Hillman was a building contractor, his brickyard being managed by Mr Paris for nearly 30 years until its closure

Prod.: Clamp-burnt stock bricks

F.Inf.: The yard had its own railway siding

Cond.: Site redeveloped as a trading estate

Refs: OS 6in 38 NW (1898, 1912); Kelly (1890-1907); *QMJ* (1927); Paris, 'Partridge Green', 31-2; inf. D. Cox.

9 Brickworks NW of the former West Grinstead station

NGR: TQ 183 227

Date: In operation in 1890, marked as Works on the map of 1958; now derelict (1988)

Op.: Owned by the West Grinstead estate; Geo. Wassell (cf Cowfold 2) was brickmaking here in 1890

Refs: OS 1:25,000 TQ 12 (1958); Kelly (1890); inf. Don Cox.

10 Brickyard east of Pinlands Farm

NGR: TQ 187 180

Date: Mentioned in railway plans of 1836

Op.: The tenant in 1836 was William Harding

Ref.: QDP/W69.

HANDCROSS *see* CUCKFIELD, SLAUGHAM

HARDHAM

1 Brickworks on the north side of the railway at Hardham junction

NGR: TQ 033 175

Date: In existence in 1903; new kilns and a brick-drying shed were built in 1926

Geol.: Gault Clay

F.Inf.: The works was served by a siding on the Midhurst line; in 1926 the average number of wagons dealt with daily was two inward and two outward

Refs: Reid, *Chichester*, 15; S.E. Winbolt, 'Excavations at Hardham Camp' *SAC* **68** (1926), 91; inf. A Hemans (1987).

HARTING

1 Brickyard on the edge of Brick Kiln Copse west of Down Park Farm

NGR: SU 783 221

Date: Probably the site of brickmaking for Uppark House in the 1690s, in irregular use from at least 1789 and marked on maps from 1813 to 1910

Op.: Owned by the Uppark estate

Cond.: Traces of the kiln remain and the pugmill was excavated and surveyed in the 1970s

Refs: OS 1in 5 (1813) 6in 20 (1873) 20 SE (1896, 1910); TDW 65; cat. of Uppark estate docs; inf. J.C.V. Mitchell (1985).

2 Brickyard on the west side of the road at Nyewood

NGR: SU 799 215

Date: In existence by 1873 and closed c1900

Op.: W. Pannell advertised in the 1870s followed by Charles Gay Roberts from 1882 to 1899

Refs: OS 6in 20 (1873); Kelly (1874-1899).

3 Brick and tile works on the south side of the former railway at Nyewood

NGR: SU 801 218

Date: This works replaced the old brickyard (site 2) c1900 and continued until the 1960s

Op.: Nyewood Brickworks Co., owner: Herbert Hutchinson Esq. in 1903. This became Nyewood Brick & Tile Works Ltd, with George English as its manager, from 1907 to 1930. In the early 1960s it was taken over by W.T. Lamb & Sons (cf Pulborough 4 & Cocking 5)

Prod.: Orange and dark red facings, wire-cut and clamp bricks and hand-made sand-faced tiles were advertised in 1906. Nyewood interlocking soundproof partition bricks were added in 1908

Cond.: The site was surveyed in 1983 prior to the demolition of the chimney and kilns

F.Inf.: There was a siding from Rogate station into the brickworks and bricks were said to have been exported to Europe and America. A photo survives of a steam delivery truck marked 'Nyewood'

Refs: OS 6in 20 SE (1896, 1910); Kelly (1903-38); *Sussex County Handbook* (1906-8); *QMJ* (1933-44); M. Hutchinson, *Childhood in Edwardian Sussex* (1981), 81-3; inf. J.C.V. Mitchell (1985).

HAYWARDS HEATH *see* CUCKFIELD, LINDFIELD, WIVELSFIELD

HEENE

1 Brickfield on the corner of Boundary Road and Grand Avenue
NGR: TQ 134 024
Date: Marked on the map of 1875 and still in use in 1890
Op.: The land was sold by the Heene Estate Co. to James Webb in 1878 and was subsequently let to Hobbs & Co. on a lease expiring on 1 Feb 1894
F.Inf.: Approximately 1,000,000 bricks were made in 1889
Refs: OS 6in 64 (1875); ESRO A 4982/42.

HENFIELD

1 Brickyard on Broadmare Common
NGR: TQ 214 151
Date: The yard was in existence by 1735 and still in operation in 1875. Brick Kiln Field (213 150), listed under separate ownership in 1844, may at one time have been part of this operation
Op.: Possibly Richard Bound, who died in 1749 and his son Thomas, who died in 1773. R. Pattenden sen. advertised for a tenant for the house and brick kilns in 1816. George Morley advertised as a brickmaker in 1867 and 1874
Refs: TDW 157; OS 6in 38 (1875); Ep VI/42/2 p65 (ex inf. T.P. Hudson); ESRO W/A58.74 & W/A65.787; *SWA*, 18 Mar 1816; Kelly (1867-74).

2 Brickfield south of Eastout
NGR: TQ 226 147
Date: Brick Field was listed on the tithe award of 1844
Op.: The tenant in 1844 was James Hoadley
Ref.: TDW 157.

3 Brick kiln on the west side of Newham Lane
NGR: TQ 215 146
Date: Brick Kiln Field in 1844 and Brickfield in 1914

Op.: Thomas Wisden was the owner/occupier in 1844 and Wisden's exors were still the tenants in 1914
Refs: TDW 157; Par. 100/30/3 f34.

4 Brickworks on the west side of the Steyning road
NGR: TQ 218 143
Date: Opened in 1934 and closed in 1969
Op.: Henfield Bricks Ltd
Prod.: In the 1930s around 50 men were employed making c100,000 pressed bricks and semi-rustic facings. By 1958, the workforce was down to 40 but weekly production was up to 175,000-240,000 and products included glazed tiles and fireplaces as well as hand-made stocks, sand-faced and rustic wire-cut facings and plain and slotted wire-cuts
Geol.: Weald Clay
Refs: OS 1:25,000 TQ 21/31 (1975); MP 159; Kelly (1938); *QMJ* (1944-59); *VCH* **6** (3), 152.

WEST HOATHLY

1 Brickfield east of Dalingridge Place
NGR: TQ 390 320
Date: Brick Field was listed on the tithe award of 1841
Op.: The tenant in 1841 was Stephen Knight
Ref.: TDE 41.

2 Brick kiln on the edge of Duckells Wood south of Vowels Lane
NGR: TQ 352 343
Date: Brick Kiln Field was listed on the tithe award of 1841
Op.: The tenant in 1841 was John Riddle, a name connected with brickmaking in Lindfield and Worth (qv)
Ref.: TDE 41.

3 Brickworks on the east side of the former railway north of Sharpethorne
NGR: TQ 373 330
Date: Opened c1880 when the Lewes to East Grinstead railway was under construction, marked as Coombe Brick Field on the maps of 1898 and 1910 and still in production (2001)
Op.: Alan Herbert Stenning advertised in the 1880s and Trayton Stevens (cf

Hamsey 2) in 1895. By 1899 W. Hudson had taken over. The firm was known as Hudsons Ltd from 1913 until 1976 when it became Ibstock Brick Hudsons: now Ibstock Brick Ltd

Geol.: Wadhurst clay

Prod.: Clamp-fired multi-coloured stocks and some hand-moulded kiln-fired specials

Refs: OS 6in 15 NE (1898, 1910); Kelly (1882-1938); *QMJ* (1927-59); Bristow & Bazley, *Tunbridge Wells*, 32; inf. G. Taylor (1992).

4 Brickworks on Shagswell Lane NW of the former station at Sharpethorne

NGR: TQ 369 329

Date: Marked only on the map of 1898

Op.: William S. Colman advertised in the 1890s followed by his executors in 1903

Refs: OS 6in 15 NE (1898); Kelly (1895-1903).

HORSHAM

1 Brick kiln north of Roffey

NGR: TQ 19 33

Date: Brick Coppice was listed on the tithe award of 1844

Ref.: TDW 68.

2 Brickfield on the east side of Hard's Hill

NGR: TQ 177 282

Date: Great Brick Field was listed on the tithe award of 1844

Ref.: TDW 68.

3 Brickyard on the east side of Hurst Road

NGR: TQ 178 313

Date: A brickyard, probably on this site, was in existence in 1777. It was marked on a map of 1831 and by 1844 had extended northwards. Known as Lambsbottom Brickworks, it continued in operation until c1900

Op.: Edward Griffith and Henry Mitchell advertised for brick-moulders in 1777 and in 1831 the tenant's name was Mitchell. Nightingale and Butcher had taken over by 1839, the tenant in 1844 being Moses Nightingale, followed by other members of the Nightingale family who advertised from 1855 to 1903

Refs: Add. MS. 37085; TDW 68; OS 25in 13/8 (1875) 6in 13 NE (1896); Pigot (1839); Kelly (1855-1903); inf. C. Whittick.

4 Brickyard on the north side of Depot Road

NGR: TQ 183 310

Date: In existence in 1787 and still in operation in 1831

Op.: Charles Sayers was involved in brickmaking pre-1787 and in 1831 the tenant was Miss Sayer

Refs: Add. MS. 37085; inf. T.P. Hudson.

5 Brickfield on the east side of the railway on the site of the former gaol

NGR: TQ 177 305

Date: Opened in 1850 and marked on the map of 1875

Op.: Owned and managed by Henry Michell, the brewer, who advertised as a brickmaker in 1859

Prod.: Half a million bricks were supplied when the Crystal Palace was re-sited at Sydenham in 1852

Refs: OS 6in 13 (1875); Kelly (1859); Neale, *Horsham*, 49, 52.

6 Brickfields on Foundry Lane

NGR: TQ 181 313 & 181 316

Date: The first was marked on the map of 1875; by 1896 this site was occupied by the foundry and a new brickfield had been opened to the north; this was abandoned by 1909

F.Inf.: The original site was bought by W. & H.J. Lintott, who advertised as Brick & Tile Machinery makers in 1899 and 1903. They continued to make pugmills until the foundry closed in the mid-1950s

Refs: OS 25in 13/8 (1875) 6in 13 NE (1896, 1909); Kelly (1899-1903); inf. D. Cox (1991).

7 Brickfield between Depot Road and Harwood Road

NGR: TQ 186 310

Date: Marked on the map of 1875, enlarged eastwards and called Depot Brick Field by 1896; closed in 1939

Op.: Owned by the Horsham Park estate: the tenants were members of the Nightingale family (cf site 3), James from 1887, Peter from 1903 and Leonard in 1938

Prod.: Royalty was paid at the rate of 1s 6d per thousand on clamp bricks and £2 per kiln on kiln-fired bricks and other ware, a total of £62 12s 6d being paid in 1910

Refs: OS 25in 13/8 (1875) 6in 13 NE (1896, 1909); SP 500; sale particulars of 1911 and 1948 in the possession of G.H.W. Coomber; Kelly (1887-1938); Pike/Horsham (1903-39); *QMJ* (1927); *DBC* (1938).

8 Brickfield on the east side of the railway south of Queen Street

NGR: TQ 175 302

Date: Marked on maps from 1875 to 1909; closed c1915

Op.: S. Lock advertised from 1890 to 1899 followed by F. Sendall from 1903 to 1915

Refs: OS 6in 13 (1875) 13 SE (1896, 1909); Kelly (1890-9); Pike/Horsham (1903-15).

9 Brickworks south of Depot Road on the site of present-day Potters Croft

NGR: TQ 184 308

Date: In existence in 1874 but disused by 1896

Op.: John M. Putney advertised at Oakhill in 1874

Refs: OS 6in 13 SE (1896); Kelly (1874).

10 Brickfield on the NE side of the railway at Southwater

NGR: TQ 161 260

Date: In operation by 1874 and marked on maps of 1879 and 1898

Op.: Thomas & Jesse Norman (cf Lower Beeding) advertised in 1874 and 1882 followed by Charles Weller from 1887 to 1903

Prod.: Bricks, tiles and drainpipes

Refs: OS 6in 24 (1879) 24 NE (1898); Kelly (1874-1903).

11 Brickfield on the common north of Spencer Road

NGR: TQ 168 314

Date: In existence by 1878 and closed c1960

Op.: Peters & Redford advertised in 1878 followed by Peters & Parker (cf Slinfold) in 1882. William Potter gave his address as Victory Road in 1907 and 1910 followed by J. & S. Agate

from 1915 to 1959

Refs: OS 6in 13 NE (1909, 1948); Kelly (1878-82, 1907); Pike/Horsham (1910-39); *QMJ* (1927-59).

12 Brickfields to the south of King's Road

NGR: TQ 185 314 - 187 317

Date: Brick House Mead north of Harwood House, named on the tithe award of 1844 suggests that this was the site of brickmaking at an earlier date. By 1882 a brickfield was in existence on the NE part of the site and was named as Crossways Brick Field on the map of 1932. This yard closed in 1940 but the southern part of the area was still shown as a brickfield on the map of 1965

Op.: i. G. Sharp advertised as a brickmaker in Crawley Road in 1882 followed by William Liley from 1890 to 1918
ii. Frank Potter advertised in Crawley Road from 1895 to 1903
iii. James Dinnage, of Crossways Brickfield, advertised from 1903 to 1944

Refs: TDW 68; OS 6in 13 NE (1896, 1909, 1948) 1:25,000 TQ 13 (1965); Kelly (1882-1938); Pike/Horsham (1903-39); *QMJ* (1927-44).

13 Brickworks on the east side of Rusper Road at Roffey

NGR: TQ 187 319

Date: Probably in existence by 1882, marked as Milthorpe Brick Works in 1898 and as Brick Field in 1911

Op.: C.H. Davies advertised in Star Lane, Roffey in 1882

Refs: OS 6in 14 NW (1898, 1911); Kelly (1882).

14 Brickyard on the south side of Two Mile Ash Road west of Southwater

NGR: TQ 138 265

Date: Marked on the maps of 1896 and 1913

Op.: Henry Bennett advertised from 1895 to 1910

Refs: OS 6in 24 NW (1896, 1913); Kelly (1895-1907); Pike/Horsham (1910).

15 Brickworks north of Warnham Station

NGR: TQ 172 343

Date: Established c1888 on a site to the west of the railway (168 341); by 1909 the main site of operations had moved to the east side of the line. Subsequently the buildings and claypit have been extended northwards and the works is still in operation (2001)

Op.: Robert Peters, a builder, bought the site in 1888 and Peter Peters advertised in 1890 and 1895. In 1899 he sold to a London builder, William Belcher, who established the Sussex Brick Co. Ltd, which, in 1903, became the Sussex Brick and Estates Co. Ltd. A merger of 1935 resulted in the formation of the Sussex and Dorking United Brick Companies which in turn merged with the Redland group in 1958/9. Now owned by Ambion Brick Co. Ltd

Prod.: Stock bricks at the outset, to which pressed bricks were added in 1899; in 1992 kiln stocks were produced at the Wealden works and perforated wire-cuts at the Holbrook works. The latter has now been replaced by a new works, known as Warnham, in which robots are use to produce kiln-fired stocks, the entire process being completed in one week

Refs: OS 6in 13 NE (1896 et seq.); MP 1274; Kelly (1890-1938); *QMJ* (1927-59); Whitehouse, *Warnham*, passim; records of the Sussex Brick Co. in Horsham Museum.

16 Brick and tile works on the SW side of the railway at Southwater
NGR: TQ 158 260
Date: Opened in 1867, enlarged in 1890 and again in 1896 to supply the bricks for the building of Christ's Hospital: closed in 1982
Op.: Peter Peters (cf site 15) from 1890 to 1899 when the works was taken over by another Horsham builder called Mills and William Wenban Smith, a builders' merchant from Worthing (cf Broadwater 5), who formed the Southwater Brick Tile Terra Cotta Pipe & Clay Co. In 1907 this was merged with the Sussex Brick & Estates Co. Ltd (cf site 15).
Prod.: A wide range of bricks, including pressed engineering bricks, tiles,

drainpipes and ornamental terracotta fittings
Refs: OS 6in 24 NE (1909) 1:25,000 TQ 12 (1958); Kelly (1890-1938); Pike/ Horsham (1903-39); *QMJ* (1927-59); *Pictorial Trade Record* new series iv, 18 (19 Aug 1912); Whitehouse, *Warnham*, 6-7; *VCH* **6** (2), 179; inf D. Mariner, Christ's Hospital Museum (2001).

17 Brickworks on Bonfire Hill, Southwater
NGR: cTQ 150 265
Date: 1920s to 1950s
Op.: Charles Gent (cf Lower Beeding 4) followed by John Brown & Son (Shoreham Ltd)
Prod: Clamp-fired bricks
Refs: Kelly/Horsham (1938-55); inf. Mrs M. Cramp.

HORSTED KEYNES

1 Brickyard east of Broadhurst Manor
NGR: TQ 389 300
Date: Uncertain: the names Great and Little Brickhurst Fields may be linked to the discovery of 'many bricks of a very ancient type' when one of the adjacent lakes was drained
Ref.: F. Stenton Eardley, *Horsted Keynes: the Church and Parish of St Giles* (1939).

2 Brickyard on the east side of the road south of Cinderhill
NGR: TQ 378 296
Date: In existence in 1839 and closed c1915
Op.: The tenant in 1839 was John Norman. Thomas and Charles Briggs advertised from 1887 to 1903. William Smith advertised at Cinder Hill in 1913
Refs: TDE 301; OS 6in 15 (1874) 25in 15/16 (1897, 1910); Kelly (1887-1903, 1913).

3 Brick and tile works on the west side of Horsted Lane south of Sharpethorne
NGR: TQ 377 318
Date: First marked on the map of 1875 and in operation until World War 2
Op.: Thomas & Charles Briggs (cf site 2) gave their address as Horsted Lane from 1907 and as Courtlands Brick & Tile Works in the 1930s
Cond.: Largely overgrown, a modern

bungalow on the site of the brickyard buildings is called 'The Kiln'

Refs: OS 6in 15 (1875) 15 NE (1898, 1912, 1938); Kelly (1907-38); *QMJ* (1927-44); inf. M. Tighe (1988).

4 Brickfield at Leamlands SE of Horsted Keynes station

NGR: TQ 373 291

Date: In existence by 1897 and closed c1915

Op.: William Tester advertised from 1899 to 1915

Refs: OS 25in 15/16 (1897, 1910); Kelly (1899-1915).

5 Brickworks on the west side of Freshfield Lane

NGR: TQ 385 262

Date: Started in 1899 and still in operation (2001)

Op.: Owned by the Hardy family: John and Alfred Setford (cf Fletching 2) advertised in 1907; from 1927 onwards the company traded as Freshfield Lane Brickworks

Prod.: Sand-faced, clamp-fired stock bricks: moulding is now fully automatic

Geol.: Wadhurst Clay and Grinstead Clay

Refs: OS 25in 27/5 (1910) 1:25,000 TQ 22/23 (1971); Kelly (1907, 1930-8); *Brighton & Sussex Trades Dir.* (1927); *QMJ* (1959); Bristow & Bazley, *Tunbridge Wells*, 32, 35, 88; *SIAS Newsletter* **23**, July 1979.

HUNSTON

1 Brickfield behind Brickfield Cottages on the West side of Selsey Road

NGR: SU 867 029

Date: Brick Field was listed on the tithe award of 1847; Brick Kiln Field two fields to the south probably also took its name from this operation

Op.: The owner/occupiers in 1847 were the trustees of William Field (cf North Mundham)

Ref.: TDW 70.

2 Brickfield on Foxbridge Farm south of Poyntz Bridge

NGR: SU 865 021

Date: Marked on the maps of 1896 and 1913

Refs: OS 6in 61 SE (1896, 1913).

3 Brickfield on the south side of the disused canal east of Poyntz Bridge

NGR: SU 867 022

Date: Marked on the map of 1896, by 1913 the brickfield had been moved to the east (868 022)

Refs: OS 6in 61 SE (1896, 1913).

4 Brickworks on the east side of the former Selsey tramway north of the station

NGR: SU 860 017

Date: In existence by 1899 and marked on the map of 1913

Op.: West Sussex Brick Co. Ltd advertised from 1899 to 1907 and John Ogburn Holt in 1913

F.Inf.: A railway loop was provided for the brickworks

Refs: OS 6in 61 SE (1913); Kelly (1899-1913); V. Mitchell & K. Smith, *Branch Line to Selsey* (1983).

HURSTPIERPOINT

1 Tile kiln north of Danny

NGR: TQ 286 154

Date: 2nd century

Ref.: J.E. Couchman, 'A Roman Cemetery at Hassocks' *SAC* **66** (1925), 34-61 & map facing p34

2 Brickyard at Sayers Common on the boundary with Alboume

NGR: TQ 264 183

Date: In existence in 1808, marked on maps from 1842 and in use until c1955

Op.: Richard King was the tenant in 1842. William Ashdown (cf Keymer 9 & Cuckfield 7) advertised in 1845 and 1851, followed by Dearing & Page in 1855 and Thomas Page from 1859 to 1890. His widow carried on the business until 1907 and was succeeded by Edwin Page who advertised until 1924, when Walter Wm. Lynn took over. W. Allfrey & Sons (cf West Grinstead 5) advertised from 1930 to 1938

Prod.: High-quality multi-coloured facing stocks, roofing tiles and land drains, according to sale particulars of 1955

Refs: TDE 29; OS 6in 38 (1874) 38 SE (1898, 1912, 1938, 1947); PHA 899 (ex inf. T.P.

Hudson); SP 1716; Kelly (1845-1938); *QMJ* (1927).

3   Brickyard north of Little Park Farm
    NGR: TQ 282 171
    Date: 1850s to c1900
    Op.: Stephen Gander advertised from 1855 to 1874
    Prod.: Bricks, tiles and some pottery
    Refs: OS 6in 38 (1874); Kelly (1855-74); Baines, *Pottery*, 168.

4   Brick and tile works at Goddard's Green
    NGR: cTQ 285 201
    Date: Late 1930s
    Op.: Hurst Brick & Tile Co. Ltd
    Refs: *Brighton & Tun. Wells Telephone Dir.* (1936); Kelly (1938).

IFIELD

1   Brickyard on the west side of the London road south of Lowfield Heath
    NGR: TQ 269 383
    Date: Marked on a map of 1855
    Ref.: Par. 109/20/2.

2   Two brickfields at Gossops Green south of the railway
    NGR: TQ 256 366 & 254 365
    Date: Marked on the map of 1874 only
    Refs: OS 6in 3 (1874).

3   Brickfields south of Crawley station
    NGR: TQ 270 362 & 270 360
    Date: The first went out of use in 1881 when the site was bought by James Longley, builder. The second, which replaced it, was marked only on the map of 1895
    Op.: Wm. Sumner jun. advertised in 1882
    Refs: OS 6in 3 SE (1895); Kelly (1882); inf. Peter Longley (1984).

4   Brick and tile works on the site of present-day Perryfield Road
    NGR: TQ 264 361
    Date: In existence from 1882, called New Town Brick, Tile, Pipe & Pottery Works in 1895 and closed in the late 1920s
    Op.: Richard Cook & Sons, builders, advertised from 1882 to 1927
    Refs: OS 6in 3 SE (1895); *Almanach for Crawley* (1895) (ex inf. Pat Bracher); Pike/Horsham (1903-10).

5   Brickfield on the north side of the railway at Snell Hatch
    NGR: TQ 258 367
    Date: Marked on the map of 1895 and as Brick Works in 1909
    Op.: Robert & Charles Gates advertised in 1903, Charles Gates in 1907 and Richard Easton from 1913 to 1927
    Refs: OS 6in 3 SE (1895, 1909); Kelly (1903-27).

6   Brickfield at West Green on the north side of Ifield Road
    NGR: TQ 266 368
    Date: Marked on the maps of 1895 and 1909
    Op.: J. Ockenden & Son advertised from 1907 to 1924
    Refs: OS 6in SE (1895, 1909); Kelly (1907-24).

IPING *see* TROTTON

ITCHINGFIELD

1   Tile kiln on Baystone farm in the NE of the parish
    NGR: TQ 141 298
    Date: Probably 2nd century
    Ref.: Green, 'Itchingfield', 23-38.

2   Brickyard on the south side of Five Oaks Road
    NGR: TQ 121 295
    Date: Listed on the tithe award of 1840 and mentioned in 1850
    Op.: In 1840 the owner/occupier was William Golds and in 1850 the tenant was James Nye
    Refs: TDW 72; Par. 113/30/8.

3   Brickfield SW of Barns Green between Valewood Lane and the railway
    NGR: TQ 122 263
    Date: In existence by 1925 and closed c1940
    Op.: L.C. Monier-Williams of the Shelley Brickfields advertised from 1925 to 1939; throughout this period Daniel Ireland was in charge of the yard
    Prod.: Hand-made clamp-fired bricks
    Refs: Pike/Horsham (1925-39); inf. Ron Ireland (1989).

KEYMER

1 Brickyard(s) on the common, north of present-day Queen Elizabeth Avenue
NGR: TQ 312 189
Date: A tile oast was mentioned in a survey of 1582 and two kilns were in existence in 1600. The western one went out of use c1670 but the other yard was extended northwards and eastwards in 1663 and continued in operation until c1703. The land was absorbed into adjoining brickyards in the 19th century
Op.: The earliest known brickmaker was John Pomfrey in 1588. Samuel Marten, the brickmaker from 1615, was succeeded by his son Samuel from 1636 to 1670 followed by Thomas Butcher and his son John until 1699, Thomas Bound(y) until 1702 and finally John Parker (cf site 5 and Clayton 4) in 1702-3
Refs: ESRO DAN 1126 & W/A48.297; H. Warne, *Heart of Burgess Hill: the History of its Brick and Tile Trade 1578-1855* (forthcoming).

2 Two brickyards on the site of present-day Dumbrells Close
NGR: TQ 314 201
Date: i. The northern and eastern portion of the site was in operation from c1642 to 1752
ii. The yard in the SW corner of the site was in operation from c1645 to 1659
Op.: i. The owners, who may also have been brickmakers, were called Jenner, Butcher (cf site 1) and Parker (cf Clayton 5)
ii. John Marten
Ref.: Warne (forthcoming).

3 Brickyard and pottery on the south side of present-day Station Road
NGR: TQ 313 188
Date: Known at different times as St John's Original Brickyard and Burgess Hill Pottery Works, the yard was opened in 1671 and closed in 1940. Additional land on the north side of the road was acquired in 1828 and a new brickfield opened to the east (314 189) by 1877
Op.: John Marten, the son of Samuel

Marten the younger (cf site 1) in 1671, followed by his son John and grandson Thomas. George Taylor, the son of George Taylor (cf Clayton 4) took over in 1736, followed c1785 by his son William, under whom the pottery side of the business was developed. In 1813 William Norman (cf Chailey 1) became the tenant, later going into partnership with William Shaw. Edward Harmes, a brickmaker, bought the yard in 1840 and William Chandler, probably his partner, advertised in 1845, followed by Harmes himself in 1851. In that year James Meeds took over the running of the yard and he became the owner in 1854. Meeds' sons William and Frederick were in charge by 1874 and the firm became known as Wm Meeds and Son from 1890 onwards
Prod.: Bricks, tiles, chimney pots, water pipes, terracotta and brown-ware pottery were listed on a bill head of the early 1900s
Refs: QDD/6/E3; TDE 77; OS 25in 39/6 (1874, 1897, 1910); ESRO W/A57.473; Kelly (1845-1938); Avery, *Burgess Hill*, 5-6; Baines, *Pottery*, 143-8; Warne (forthcoming).

4 Brickyard on Burgess Hill Farm at the eastern end of present-day Station Road
NGR: TQ 315 188
Date: c1690 to c1701; a brickyard in the same area was in use briefly c1851
Op.: i. Thomas Pockney
ii. F. King advertised in 1851
Refs: Kelly (1851); Warne (forthcoming).

5 Brickyard on the east side of Mill Road
NGR. TQ 317 194
Date: 1703-8
Op.: [ ] Parker
Ref.: Warne (forthcoming).

6 Brickworks and pottery on the corner of Station Road and London Road
NGR: TQ 308 188
Date: 1828 to 1909
Op.: William Shaw (cf site 3), who had been in partnership with William Norman for the previous 10 years, was granted the freehold of this site in 1828. His

widow was the owner in 1845, when the tenant was M. Longmer Daynes, who was in partnership with James Meeds (cf site 3). In 1854 the tenancy was taken over by John Gravett. By 1890 Gravett had been succeeded by his son Henry, who managed the works until it closed

Prod.: Bricks, tiles, drainpipes and pottery: an inventory taken in 1854 shows that bricks were both kiln- and clamp-fired

Refs: QDD/6/E3; TDE 77; OS 25in 39/5 (1877, 1898, 1910); Kelly (1845-1907); Avery, *Burgess Hill*, 5-6; Baines, *Pottery*, 141-3; inventory in the possession of F.M. Avery.

7   Brickworks and pottery on the east side of London Road
NGR: TQ 308 190
Date: 1828 to the early 1930s
Op.: William Norman (cf site 3) from 1828, followed in 1850 by his sons Richard and Nathan; thereafter the firm was known as R. & N. Norman
Prod.: Bricks, tiles, drainpipes, flowerpots and ornamental terracotta
Refs: QDD/6/E3; TDE 77; OS 25in 39/5 (1877, 1898, 1910); Kelly (1845-1934); Avery, *Burgess Hill*, 5; Baines, *Pottery*, 136-41.

8   Brickyard on the west side of Cant's Lane (now Junction Road)
NGR: TQ 317 189
Date: Listed on the tithe award of 1845; re developed by 1874, when a new brickfield had been opened to the north
Op.: James Ellis advertised in 1845 and 1851
Refs: TDE 77; OS 25in 39/6 (1874); Kelly (1845-51).

9   Brickfield on Valebridge Common
NGR: cTQ 32 21
Date: 1850s and 1860s
Op.: Ashdown & Wilkinson advertised in 1855 and William Ashdown (cf Cuckfield 7) in 1859 and 1862
Prod.: Clamp-burnt bricks, as appears from an advertisement in 1856, when the yard was to let
Refs: Kelly (1855-62); *SWA*, 4 Nov 1856.

10   Brickfield on the south side of Lye Lane (now Leylands Road)
NGR: TQ 316 199
Date: Marked as Oldstream Brickfield on the map of 1874; disused by 1897
Op.: William Berry advertised in the 1880s
Refs: OS 25in 39/6 (1874, 1897); Kelly (1882-7).

11   Brickfield on the north side of Birchwood Grove Road
NGR: TQ 322 186
Date: Marked only on the map of 1874
Ref.: OS 25in 39/6 (1874).

12   Brickfield on the east side of the railway north of Hassocks
NGR: TQ 307 162
Date: Marked on the map of 1875; Old Clay Pit in 1898
Refs: OS 6in 39 (1875) 39 SW (1898).

13   Brickfield on the east side of Mill Road
NGR: TQ 317 196
Date: Opened in the 1870s but marked only as Old Clay Pits on the map of 1897
Op.: Savage & Green advertised in 1878 and 1882
F.Inf.: Bricks were machine-moulded and an engine used to power the pugmill; 50-60 men were employed
Refs: OS 25in 39/6 (1897); Kelly (1878-82); C.D. Meads, *Historical Notes Of Burgess Hill 1828-1891* (1891), Ch 8.

14   Brickfield on the west side of Junction Road south of Wivelsfield station
NGR: TQ 321 198
Date: Late 1870s to 1890s marked 'disused' on the map of 1897
Op.: Ebenezer Geall in 1878; H. & E. Geall (cf Plumpton 7 & South Bersted 7) advertised in Junction Road in the 1890s
Refs: OS 25in 39/6 (1897); Kelly (1878, 1895-99).

15   Brick and tile works on Nye Road
NGR: TQ 323 193
Date: Opened in 1875 and still in operation as a tileworks (2001)
Op.: H. Johnson & Co. (cf Ditchling 2) from 1875 to 1883, when the works was destroyed by fire. In the 1890s the Keymer Brick & Tile Works Co. Ltd

was managed by A.P. Scrase. The firm was reconstituted as Keymer Brick & Tile Co. in 1904 under the management of Amos Ware (cf Uckfield 6). In the late 1920s the company was bought by the Maidenhead Brick & Tile Co. but continued to trade under its own name. It is now known as the Keymer Tile Company

Prod.: Some terracotta was made to begin with; in 1960 the works was making red and multi-coloured facing bricks and hand- and machine-made roofing tiles. At present only hand made tiles are produced

F.Inf.: No 1 works was surveyed prior to demolition in 2000

Refs: OS 25 in 39/6 (1897, 1910) 1:25,00 TQ 21/31 (1965); Kelly (1878-1938); Foster, *Mines* (1896-1901); *QMJ* (1927-59); Avery, *Burgess Hill*, 7-8; F.M. Avery, 'The Keymer Tile Works' and R.M. Martin, 'Keymer No 1 Brickworks' *SIH* **30** (2000), 29-39; inf. G. Bradley-Smith (1989).

16 Brickfield on the west side of Freek's Lane
NGR: TQ 313 201
Date: In existence by 1907 and closed c1915
Op.: The Burgess Hill Brick Co. advertised in 1907 and T.H. Scutt in 1915
Refs: OS 6in 39 NW (1912); Kelly (1907-15).

KINGSTON-BY-SEA

1 Brickfield south of the railway
NGR: TQ 226 051
Date: Marked on the map of 1873 only
Ref.: OS 6in 65 (1873).

2 Brickfield north of the railway
NGR: TQ 224 053
Date: Opened c1899 and marked on the map of 1912
Op.: Albert Henry Dearing, who gave his address as Ivydene, advertised from 1899 to 1924
Refs: OS 6in SW (1912); Kelly (1899-1924).

3 Brickfield on the south side of Middle Road
NGR: TQ 225 054
Date: In operation by 1903 and marked on the map of 1912

Op.: Hicks Bros, of Middle Road Brickfields, advertised in 1903 and 1907
Refs: OS 6in SW (1912); Kelly (1903-7).

4 Brickworks on the east side of Eastern Avenue
NGR: TQ 224 056
Date: 1920s and 1930s
Op.: W. Allfrey & Sons (cf West Grinstead 5) advertised from 1924 to 1933
Refs: Kelly (1924-30); *QMJ* (1927-33); inf. Geo. Elliott (1986).

KIRDFORD

1 Brickyard on the north edge of Ebernoe Common
NGR: SU 979 274
Date: In existence by 1693; marked on a map of Ebernoe manor of 1764; closed in the 1930s
Op.: Owned by the Peachey family from the mid-17th century and operated by the estate; sold to the Petworth estate in 1912. The brickmaker in the 1840s and 1850s was James Cole(s). From the 1860s to the 1880s Edward Phillips was the occupier of the brickyard and Ephraim & Robert Holden worked there before World War 1
F.Inf.: The kiln and shed were restored in 1983
Refs: PHA 10063; Add. MS. 2021; OS 6in 11 (1871) 11 NE (1896, 1910); Kelly (1859); Aldsworth, 'Ebernoe', 219-24; *West Sussex Gazette*, 1 Dec 1983.

2 Brickfield south of Marshalls Farm
NGR: TQ 013 242
Date Listed on the tithe award of 1845
Ref.: TDW 74.

3 Brickyard NW of Sparrwood Farm
NGR: SU 992 303
Date: Brick Field, Brick Mead and Old Kiln Field, all lying together between the footpath and the stream, were listed on the tithe award of 1845. Another Brick Field NE of Chilsfold Farm (987 302) may have acquired its name from its proximity to this operation
Ref.: TDW 74.

4 Brickyard in Shillinglee Park NW of Upper North Pond
NGR: SU 961 326
Date: In existence in 1836, marked on the tithe map of 1845 and as Brick Works on the map of 1871; disused by 1896
Op.: Owned by the Shillinglee estate
Refs: MS 2056; TDW 74; OS 6in 11 (1871) 11 NE (1896).

5 Brickfield at Foxbridge east of Plaistow
NGR: TQ 022 306
Date: In existence by 1876, closed c 1915
Op.: Frederick Wooldridge advertised from 1882 to 1903, followed by Samuel Mitchell in 1907 and 1915
Refs: OS 6in 12 (1876) 12 NW (1895, 1914); Kelly (1882-1915).

6 Brickyard on the edge of Ashpark Wood west of Plaistow
NGR: SU 993 315
Date: Said to have opened in the 1880s, closed during World War 2 and for a short time in the 1970s but revived in 1979 and still in operation in 2001
Op.: Owned by the Shillinglee estate: the tenant was Samuel Mitchell (cf site 5) who advertised from 1924 to 1938. c1970 the freehold was bought by the builders Chapman, Lowrie & Puttock of Haselmere but the yard closed shortly afterwards. It was revived in 1979 by Ron Ireland, the son of R.O. Ireland (cf Thakeham 3). Now owned by Cranleigh Brick & Tile Co.
Prod.: Kiln-fired bricks and tiles, as formerly produced by the yard, could be seen in the shed at the entrance in 1989. Two gas fired Scotch kilns were built in the 1970s, when a three-mould Berry brickmaking machine was also installed. In 1989 bricks were handmade and clamp-burnt, using gas. At the present time some red but a majority of yellow facing bricks, which contain added chalk, are made to imperial measurements and kiln-fired
Geol.: Weald Clay
Refs: Kelly (1924-30); *Brighton & Tun. Wells Tel. Dir.* (1936); *DBC* (1938); Thurrell et al, *Haslemere*, 50, 140; inf. R. Ireland (1989); inf. Colin Davies (2001).

LANCING

1 Brickyard at South Lancing
Exact location not known
Date: Early 19th century
Op.: Messrs Nevill & Steele up to 1804, when their partnership was dissolved; John Loader and William Sweetingham took over in 1805 but the yard was sold to pay the latter's creditors in 1810
Prod.: White bricks, kiln bricks, clamp bricks and tiles
Refs: *SWA*, 19 Nov & 3 Dec 1804; Par. 118/30/1; Add. MS. 2996.

2 Brick kiln near the site of Lancing College chapel
NGR: TQ 196 066
Date: In operation in 1868 when the chapel was under construction
Op.: Billy Woodard, third son of Nathaniel Woodard, founder of the college
F.Inf.: Half a million bricks were made for the core of the fabric
Ref.: *Country Life*, 11 May 1978.

3 Brickfield on the south side of Penhill Road
NGR: TQ 183 040
Date: In existence by 1874; abandoned c1900
Op.: James Sheirlock advertised from 1874 to 1887
F.Inf.: Peak production was 30,000 bricks per week
Refs: OS 64/12 (1874, 1896); Kelly (1874-87); *Weekend Review* (Worthing), 27 Feb 1988 (ex inf. K. Cosway).

4 Two brickworks on the south side of Ham Lane (Sompting Road)
NGR: TQ 176 044 & 178 044
Date: In operation by 1882; closed in the 1930s
Op.: i. John Bartlett advertised from 1882 to 1899
ii. Various members of the Gammans family advertised from 1882 to 1938; Charles R. Gammans also had brickmaking interests in Rustington and Shoreham in 1915 and J.W. Gammans had a depot in Shoreham in 1933
Refs: OS 64 SE (1909); Kelly (1882-1915); *QMJ* (1927); *DBC* (1938).

5 Brickyard at Ingleside, South Lancing
   NGR: cTQ 185 042
   Date: 1890s and early 1900s
   Op.: Frederick Young advertised as a market gardener and brickmaker from 1895 to 1907
   Ref.: Kelly (1895-1907).

EAST LAVANT

1 Brick kiln on the north side of Old Broyle Road
   NGR: SU 841 068
   Date: Listed as Brick Kiln Field on the tithe award of 1839
   Ref.: TDW 48.

EAST LAVINGTON see
WOOLAVINGTON

LINCHMERE

1 Tile kiln north of Shulbrede Priory
   NGR: SU 876 300
   Date: 14th century: the kiln, which was excavated in 1928, appeared to have been re-used for brickmaking in more recent times
   Prod.: Mainly paving tiles but some roof tiles were found
   Ref.: Ponsonby, 'Monastic Tiles', 34-5.

2 Brickworks at Hammer between Copse Road and the river Wey
   NGR: SU 878 324
   Date: Opened in the late 1890s and closed c1940
   Op.: Edmund Roe (cf Fernhurst 3) advertised at Shottermill in 1899, followed by Grover & Sons from 1903 to 1930. The works was then taken over by Nutbourne Brickworks (cf Westbourne 1)
   Geol.: Atherfield Clay
   Refs: OS 6in 10 NE (1910); Kelly (1899-1939); Thurrell et al, *Haslemere*, 72.

LINDFIELD

1 Brickyard near the southern edge of Town Wood
   NGR: TQ 343 260
   Date: Listed on a survey of 1844 and on the tithe award of 1848
   Op.: The tenant in 1848 was [ ] Riddles

Refs: Add. MS. 32977; TDE 21.

2 Two brickfields on opposite sides of High Street
   NGR: TQ 349 261 & 351 261
   Date: In operation by 1845 and listed on the tithe award of 1848
   Op.: Burrows Beckett advertised in 1845 and was the owner of both fields in 1848 although the western one was in the occupation of Haines and others. J.H. Ellis advertised from 1859 to 1867, possibly working on one of these sites
   Refs: TDE 21; Kelly (1845, 1859-67).

3 Brickworks on Sugworth Farm NW of Haywards Heath
   NGR: TQ 326 260
   Date: First marked on the map of 1899 and still in existence in 1938
   Op.: Thomas Bannister, estate agent and auctioneer, advertised as a brickmaker from 1899 to 1907
   F.Inf.: A kiln, shown on sale particulars of 1919, was not demolished until c1960
   Refs: OS 6in 26 NW (1899, 1912, 1938); Kelly (1899-1907); inf. David Clowes.

4 Brickfield on the west side of Bordehill Lane opposite the junction with Hanlye Lane
   NGR: TQ 326 258
   Date: Marked only on the map of 1899
   Ref.: OS 6in 26 NW (1899).

5 Brickfield on the south side of College Road, Haywards Heath
   NGR: TQ 333 250
   Date: Marked only on the map of 1899
   Op.: Finches, builders, of Haywards Heath
   Refs: OS 6in NW (1899); inf. C. Anscombe/ G. Thomerson (1986).

6 Brickfield on the site of present-day Hillcrest Close, Scaynes Hill
   NGR: TQ 365 230
   Date: Opened c1905: the pit and pond were marked on the map of 1910. The last bricks were made in 1936 although stocks were not cleared until 1946
   Op.: Owned by Mr Luckens: the brickmakers in the 1930s were Mr Setford and his sons Herbert and Ernest, formerly of Freshfield Lane (cf Horsted Keynes 5)
   Prod.: Hand-made, clamp-fired bricks

Refs: OS 25in 26/16 (1910); inf. E.E. Luckens (1989).

LITTLEHAMPTON

1   Brickyard on the north side of Church Street west of the junction with St Flora's Road
NGR: TQ 036 022
Date: Listed on the tithe award of 1841, in operation in 1845 but not marked on any subsequent maps
Op.: John Butt jun. was the tenant in 1841 and advertised as a builder and brickmaker in 1845. From 1874 onwards, the firm was known as John Eede Butt & Sons. They were also timber merchants, with depots in Littlehampton and Portslade and brickyards in Lyminster and Rustington (qv)
Refs: TDW 78; Kelly (1845, 1874-1907).

2   Brickworks on East Ham Road
NGR: TQ 026 024
Date: Marked only on the map of 1898
Op.: G. Brewer advertised from 1899 to 1915 although the site had apparently been re-developed by 1910
Refs: OS 6in 63 SW (1898); Kelly (1899-1915).

LODSWORTH

1   Brickyard on the south side of Lodsworth Common
NGR: SU 927 244
Date: In existence by 1761, marked as Brick & Tile Works in 1872 and survived until after World War 1
Op.: Thomas Perce, a brickmaker here in 1761, inherited the property under his uncle's will of 1782. The owner/ occupier in 1842 was Neale Hill. John Spooner & Son advertised from 1878 and Henry Spooner from 1895 to 1918
Geol.: Weald Clay
Refs: TDW 79; OS 6in 22 (1872) 22 NW (1898, 1910); Cowdray MSS. 1302-11; Kelly (1878-1918); *SRS* **32**, 177; Thurrell et al, *Haslemere*, 37, 140.

LOXWOOD *see* WISBOROUGH GREEN

LURGASHALL

1   Brick kiln on the north side of the road from Lickfold Bridge to Lurgashall
NGR: SU 928 266
Date: Bricks from Lickfold were available for use at Petworth in 1702; Brick Copse and Kiln Field were marked on a map of 1792
Refs: Mitford MS. 1007; PHA 6324 No 49 (ex inf. A. McCann).

LYMINSTER

1   Brickyard on the west side of Clay Lane
NGR: TQ 036 063
Date: Late 18th and early 19th centuries
Op.: George Hazelgrove supplied 20,000 bricks for Michelgrove House in 1767 and was living in Lyminster in 1781; a man of the same name was the tenant of Brickyard Field in 1838
Refs: TDW 81; G.W. Eustace (ed) 'The Tompkins Diary' *SAC* **71** (1930), 22; Daggett, *Toddington*, 89.

2   Brickyard east of Wick Street south of the railway
NGR: TQ 028 037
Date: In operation by 1861 and marked on the map of 1879
Op.: Probably owned by John Pepper, a farmer and builder who also advertised as a brickmaker, but operated by Stephen Bushby and other members of his family
Refs: OS 6in 63 (1879); Kelly (1862-90); Daggett, loc. cit.

3   Brickyard on the north side of Worthing Road adjacent to the Globe Inn
NGR: TQ 027 035
Date: In operation by 1861, marked on the map of 1879 and as Brick Works in 1899
Op.: Bernard and Robert West were brickmakers in Wick in 1861. John Gates, who was described as a brick merchant and publican in 1871, advertised as a brickmaker from 1866 to 1890, followed by the firm of Jas. Linfield & Son from 1895
Refs: OS 6in 63 (1876) 63 SW (1899); Kelly (1866-99); Daggett, loc. cit.

4 Brickworks east of Wick Street
NGR: TQ 028 032
Date: In operation by 1882; marked on the map of 1899 and as Brick Field in 1910
Op.: John E. Butt & Son of Littlehampton (qv), who advertised at Wick from 1882 to 1890, may have used this site, followed by John Pepper & Son (cf site 2)
Refs: OS 6in 63 SW (1899, 1910); Kelly (1882-1918); Daggett, loc. cit.

5 Brickfield on the south side of Worthing Road on the site of present-day Gladonian Road
NGR: TQ 027 034
Date: Marked only on the map of 1910
Op.: Probably Jas. Linfield & Son, after the clay at site 3 was exhausted
Refs: OS 6in 63 SW (1910); Kelly (1903-27).

6 Brickfield on the south side of Worthing Road south of Toddington
NGR: TQ 034 033
Date: In operation by 1910 and closed in 1940
Op.: Charman & Cleverley advertised in 1922 and W. Charman & Sons from 1927 to 1938
Prod.: A kiln was shown on the map of 1910 but from the 1920s only clamp bricks were made
F.Inf.: The late Ben Foreman of East Preston, who worked with his father at this brickfield in the 1920s, lived in one of the four houses built there by Charmans for their workers
Refs: OS 6in 63 SW (1910-38); Kelly (1922-38); inf. B. Foreman (1988).

7 Brickfield on the south side of Worthing Road east of site 6
NGR: TQ 030 033
Date: 1920s and 1930s
Op.: Jas. Lindfield & Sons Ltd (cf sites 3 & 5)
Refs: OS 6in 63 SW (1932, 1938); Kelly (1927-38).

UP MARDEN

1 Brickyard at Lye Common
NGR: SU 788 127
Date: Listed on the tithe award of 1843; the kiln was still standing but the yard

had ceased operation by 1880
Op.: The yard belonged to the Watergate Park estate, owned by the Crosbie family
Cond.: A 50ft-diameter brick-lined pond remains in the garden of Keeper's Cottage (formerly Kiln Cottages)
Refs: TDW 131; sale particulars of 1880 in the possession of F. Francis.

MIDDLETON see FELPHAM

MIDHURST

1 Brickworks NW of the former station
NGR: SZ 877 212
Date: Opened in 1913: closed in 1985
Op.: Originally owned and run by S. Pearson & Son, civil engineers, and bought by Benjamin Cloke in 1926. He was succeeded as Managing Director by his nephew George Cloke. The company advertised as the Midhurst Brick & Lime Co. Ltd in 1930 and as Midhurst Whites Ltd from 1938 onwards
Prod.: Red building bricks, superseded by white sand-lime bricks from the 1930s
Refs: Kelly (1930-38); *QMJ* (1944-60); 'Midhurst Whites Brickworks: George Cloke's Account', *SIH* **30** (2000), 24-8; inf. J.C.V. Mitchell.

MILLAND see CHITHURST

NORTH MUNDHAM

1 Brickyard on the south side of Bognor Road north of present-day Brick Kiln Farm
NGR: SU 883 041
Date: Marked on maps from 1825 to 1909
Op.: In 1848 the tenant of the farm, including Brick Kiln Plot, was Mary Field
Refs: *SRS* **72**, 174; TDW 91; OS 6in 61 (1875) 61 SE (1896, 1909).

NORTHCHAPEL

1 Brick kiln south of Mitchellpark Farm
NGR: SU 970 298
Date: Brick Kiln Field was marked on a Petworth estate survey of 1779

Ref.: PHA 3606/4.

2 Brickyard on Colhook Common on the west side of the Petworth road
NGR: SU 965 262
Date: In existence by 1779 and closed c1960
Op.: Owned by the Petworth estate: Holt & Knight were the brickmakers in 1805 and Thomas Holt the tenant in 1837. George Phillips advertised from 1874 to 1903 followed by Archibald Phillips in 1907 and Mrs Phillips in 1913 and 1915. The Colhook Brick & Tile Co. (proprietor: Major Sydney Vincent) advertised from 1924 to 1944. After World War 2 the yard was in the hands of R.G. Ward & Co. Ltd (cf Slaugham 5)
Prod.: Kiln-fired bricks and tiles: this may have been the brickyard near Petworth which was supplying bricks for the West Indies in the late 18th century
Geol.: Weald Clay
Cond.: The buildings were still standing in 1985
Refs: PHA 3606/6; TDW 89; OS 6in 22 (1875) 22 NE (1896, 1910) 1:25,000 SU 92 (1958); *SWA*, 18 Mar 1805; Kelly (1874-1938); *QMJ* (1927-59); A. Young, *General View of the Agriculture of the County of Sussex* (1813), 436; Thurrell et al, *Haslemere*, 38, 140.

PAGHAM

1 Brickfield on the east side of Honer Lane
NGR: SZ 880 998
Date: Field name on the tithe award of 1849
Op.: The tenant in 1849 was George Rusbridge
Ref.: TDW 94.

2 Brickfield at the junction of Hook Lane and Rose Green Road
NGR: SZ 899 993
Date: In operation by 1910; closed c1950
Op.: Rose Green Brick Co. Ltd advertised from 1927 to 1944
Refs: OS 6in 63 NE (1910, 1933, 1948); Kelly (1927-38); *QMJ* (1933-44).

3 Brickworks east of Lion Road, Nyetimber
NGR: SZ 894 988
Date: 1920s and 1930s
Op.: Lion Brick Works (proprietor: R.T.

Smart) in 1927 and 1930, (props: Edward Benton & Co.) in 1934 and 1938; Lion Brick Company in 1951
Prod.: Clamp-burnt bricks; post-war production was mainly of briquettes and fireplaces
Refs: OS 6in 63 NE (1933); Kelly (1927-38); *QMJ* (1951).

4 Brickworks on the north side of Nyetimber Lane
NGR: SZ 896 985
Date: Late 1930s to c1960
Op.: Harold Geall, son of Harry Geall (cf South Bersted 7)
Prod.: Clamp bricks
Refs: *Brighton & Tun. Wells Telephone Directory* (1936); Kelly (1938); *QMJ* (1951-9); inf. Eric Geall/David Hawes (1992).

PARTRIDGE GREEN *see* WEST GRINSTEAD

PETWORTH

1 Brick kiln WNW of Petworth House
NGR: SU 970 221
Date: Marked on an estate plan of 1706; bricks were supplied for building work on the house from at least 1574 when the banqueting house was built. A kiln was built, or re-built, in 1607, possibly on this site
Op.: Members of the Philp family were mentioned in accounts as brickmakers in 1595-6 and again in 1691-2 and 1702
Refs: PHA 6324 No 49 (ex inf. A. McCann); G. Batho, 'The Percies of Petworth' *SAC* **95** (1957), 12 & 'Petworth House 1574-1632' *SAC* **96** (1958), 132; G.H. Kenyon, 'Petworth Town and Trades' *ibid.*, 65.

2 Brickfield on the east side of the stream east of Hampers Green
NGR: SU 983 230
Date: Field name on the tithe award of 1837
Ref.: TDW 87.

PLAISTOW *see* KIRDFORD

POLING

1 Brickyard and pottery on the south side of Arundel Road west of Poling Corner
NGR: TQ 042 058
Date: A brickyard was in existence in 1630, probably in this area. The later yard, which was in operation by 1825, continued until the mid-1950s
Op.: John Philp up to 1630, followed by another John Philp, who died in 1643. In 1838 the yard was owned by the Arundel Castle estate. Between 1855 and 1890 the brickmakers were members of the Blunden family, followed by Pocock and Tompkins in 1895 and George Pocock from 1903 to 1918. George Gates advertised in 1922 and from 1927 onwards the business was called Poling Pottery, Brick & Tile Works Ltd
Prod.: Kiln-fired bricks and tiles; from the 1880s, pottery was added to the range of products, flowerpots being a speciality
F.Inf.: Photographs of craftsmen at work were published in 1950
Refs: *SRS* **72**, 174; TDW 98; OS 6in 63 (1875) 63 NW (1896, 1910, 1938, 1946); EpI/29/150/12 & 22; Kelly (1855-1938); *QMJ* (1951); *SCM* **24** (1950), 378; Baines, *Pottery*, 164-5.

EAST PRESTON

1 Brickyard now under the beach near the south end of Sea Lane
NGR: TQ 068 015
Date: Marked on a map of 1825 and still in operation in 1838
Op.: John Slater was the owner/occupier in 1825 and 1838
Refs: QDP/W 54; TDW 50.

2 Brickfields in the area between Sea Road, Manor Road and North Lane
NGR: cTQ 073 020
Date: Opened c1897, not marked on the map of 1913 but the Manor Road part of the site was still referred to as 'the brickyard' in 1921
Op.: Goodall & Son were the owners and advertised as brickmakers from 1899 to 1907. Their tenants Henry Reed and James Roberts also advertised, the former in 1899 and 1903 and the latter from 1899 to 1907 and it is said that he continued brickmaking until World War 1 and possibly later. Goodalls sold out in 1908 and in 1912 the Manor Road brickyard was owned by the Angmering-on-Sea Company, property developers
Prod.: Kiln-fired bricks and tiles and clamp bricks: a tile with the date Sept 28 1907 and the letters G(?) scratched on it, probably the last tile made for Goodall & Son, has been found in the nursery north of the site and 300,000 kiln bricks were advertised when their business was sold in the following April. A postcard of the early 1900s shows a large conical kiln
Refs: Kelly (1903-7); inf. Richard Standing (1983).

PULBOROUGH

1 Brick kiln east of Lee Place (now in the par. of Billingshurst)
NGR: TQ 054 237
Date: Brick Copse was listed on the tithe award of 1839
Ref.: TDW 99.

2 Brickfield to the east of the moated site NE of the town
NGR: TQ 056 190
Date: Listed as Brick Field in 1839
Ref.: TDW 99.

3 Brickyard on North Heath Common
NGR: TQ 066 213
Date: In existence by 1815, marked on the map of 1841 and as Tile Works from 1879; in operation until c1940
Op.: James Comper was the owner of the brickyard in 1815 and he and his successors advertised until 1867. In 1874 the yard was in the hands of Baker & Tidy (cf Washington 1) and George Pellett advertised from 1882 to 1918. North Heath Brickfields were listed in 1936, with Geo. C. Snead named as the brickmaker in 1938
Geol.: Weald clay with a fine sand bed running through it

Refs: QDD/16/W8; TDW 99; OS 6in 23 (1879) 23 SE (1896, 1909); Pigot (1832-9); Kelly (1851-1938); *Brighton & Tun. Wells Tel. Dir.* (1936); inf. Roger Bristow (1981).

4   Brickyard(s) on the west side of Stane Street at Codmore Hill
    NGR: TQ 058 206
    Date: A brick kiln was marked on the map of 1841 and the yard was in operation until c1870. A brickworks was opened in the same area in the 1930s and was still in existence in 1959
    Op.:   The tenant in 1839 was James Penfold, who advertised from 1851 to 1867. W.T. Lamb & Sons advertised at Codmore Hill from 1933 to 1938 and after World War 2 they operated both here and at Wamborough Brick & Tile Works
    Prod.:   Bricks, tiles, fireplaces, briquettes and paving bricks (1959)
    Cond.:   The pit (Weald clay) was partially filled but there were still some bricks lying around in 1981
    Refs: TDW 99; OS 6in 36 (1879); Kelly (1851-67, 1938); *QMJ* (1933-1959); inf. R. Bristow (1981).

5   Brickfield NE of Pulborough Station
    NGR: TQ 044 187
    Date: c1900 to c1930
    Op.:   Geo. Brewer (cf Littlehampton 2) advertised from 1903 to 1918 followed by Arthur Jones in 1922 and 1927
    Geol.:   Marehill clay, with a high silica content
    Cond.:   Site obliterated by a new warehouse built in 1980
    Refs: OS 6in 36 NW (1910); Kelly (1903-27); inf. R. Bristow (1981).

6   Brickworks at Stallhouse Farm, North Heath
    NGR: TQ 075 215
    Date: 1930s
    Op.:   W. Allfrey & Sons (cf West Grinstead 5) advertised from 1930 to 1936 and John Allfrey in 1938
    Geol.:   Weald clay with a fine sand bed running through it
    Refs: Kelly (1930-8); inf. R. Bristow (1981).

7   Brickworks at Black Gate, Toat
    NGR: cTQ 056 212

Date: Late 1930s
Op.:   Shelton Bros
Ref.:   Kelly (1938).

RACTON

1   Brickyard on the north side of the smaller of the two Brick-kiln Ponds
    NGR: SU 756 093
    Date: Marked on a map of 1785, when it was part of Brick Kiln Farm and listed in 1839 as Brick kiln & Pottery; in 1880 only the ponds remained
    Op.:   The tenant in 1785 was Richard Cathery and in 1839, Cleverly Stent. In 1867 and 1874 the Brick, Tile Drain Pipe & Pottery Works of Bosham (qv) had a pottery works at Stansted, probably on this site
    Refs: Add. MS. 2158; TDW 100; OS 6in 67 (1880); Kelly (1867-74).

2   Brickyard on the east side of the road south of Stansted Park
    NGR: SU 757 094
    Date: Marked on a map of 1785
    Op.:   The tenant in 1785 was Benjamin Turner of Sindalls Farm
    Refs: Add. MS. 2158; TDW 100.

ROGATE

1   Brickyard at Harting Combe on the east side of the road to Rake
    NGR: SU 803 267
    Date: Opened in the early 1780s: the kilns were shown on the map of 1813 and Combe Brick Yard was listed on the tithe award of 1843. It was in operation in 1874 but marked 'disused', on a site slightly to the north, in 1896. In 1920, when Harting Combe Farm was advertised for sale, the sheds were about to be removed
    Op.:   The land was owned by T.S. Joliffe Esq. and the brickmaker from 1784 to 1792 was William Wisdom, succeeded by William Newland until 1798, John Ayling to 1803, James Ayling to 1825 and William Bromham to 1831. Samuel Twyford was the owner/ occupier in 1843. Thomas Ayling advertised from 1845 to 1859 followed by George Berry from 1862 to 1874, Albert Kiln in 1878

and William Larcombe in 1887 and 1890

Refs: OS 1in 5 (1813) 6in 21 (1874) 10 SW (1896); TDW 101; LT Rogate 1782-1831; SP 347; Kelly (1845-90).

2 Brickfield SW of Combeland Farm
NGR: SU 815 270
Date: Marked on the map of 1910 and still in existence after World War 2
Op.: George Randall in 1907 followed by James Randall from 1913 to 1918
Refs: OS 6in 10 SW (1910) SU 82 NW (provis.); Kelly (1907-18).

3 Brickfield on the east side of the road south of Rake
NGR: SU 804 270
Date: Post-World War 2
Refs: OS 6in SU 82 NW (provis.); inf. J.C.V. Mitchell (1985).

see also: HARTING

RUDGWICK

1 Brickyard on Naldretts Farm
NGR: TQ 089 319
Date: Marked on a map of 1819 and listed on the tithe award of 1840
Op.: The tenant in 1840 was Michael Botting
Refs: Add. MS. 1994/31; TDW 102.

2 Brickyard east of Lynwick
NGR: TQ 076 338
Date: Listed as Brick Yard Plat on the tithe award of 1840; the outline of the claypit is marked on the map of 1965
Op.: The tenant in 1840 was Philip Butcher; J.Puttock advertised as a brickmaker at Woodsome Farm in 1855
Refs: TDW 102; OS 1:25,000 TQ 03 (1965); Kelly (1855).

3 Brickfield on the east side of Marles Lane
NGR: TQ 085 298
Date: Marked on maps from 1875 to 1914
Op.: Edward Sayers advertised in 1887 and Charles Pannell in 1895
Geol.: Weald Clay
Refs: OS 6in 12 (1875) 12 SE (1898, 1914); Kelly (1887, 1895); Thurrell et al, *Haslemere*, 58.

4 Brickworks on the west side of Lynwick Street
NGR: TQ 083 343
Date: Bricks for the tunnel on the Horsham to Guildford railway, opened in 1865, were said to have been made here but the yard was not marked on any of the early editions of the Ordnance Survey. It was revived in 1928, closed during World War 2, re-opened in 1947, re-built and re-equipped in 1963 and is still in production (2001)
Op.: Harold Tate, a local builder, bought the yard in 1928. After 1946 it was in the hands of the Fowke family, trading up to the 1960s as Rudgwick Clayworks Ltd and then as Rudgwick Brickworks Co. Ltd: owned since 1998 by Baggeridge Brick plc
Prod.: Hand-made, clamp-fired bricks at the outset, changing to kiln-fired bricks (Scotch kilns) between the wars. At the present time an Aberson moulding machine and gas-fired clamps are used to produce sand-faced stocks
Geol.: Weald Clay
Refs: OS 1;25,000 TQ 03 (1965); *QMJ* (1951 - 59); Thurrell et al, *Haslemere*, 61, 140; *West Sussex Gazette*, 2 Aug 1973; *Sussex Life*, Nov 1979, 33; *SIAS Newsletter* **53 & 56** (Jan & Oct 1987); inf. P.A. Laker, managing director (1986).

RUMBOLDSWYKE

1 Brickyard on the north side of Bognor Road
NGR: SU 881 043
Date: The land was called Brick-kiln Eight Acres in 1848, when it was probably associated with the brickyard on the opposite side of the road in North Mundham (qv). A brickfield in Whyke in 1913 may have been in the same area
Op.: P. & R. Habin advertised in 1913
Refs: TDW 103; Kelly (1913).

RUSPER

1 Brick kiln east of Nunnery Farm
NGR: TQ 189 363
Date: Brick Close was listed on the tithe schedule of 1842. The adjacent field in the parish of Horsham had the same name
Refs: TDW 104 & 68.

2 Brickyard NE of Rusper village
NGR: TQ 209 375
Date: Listed as Brick Burn Plat in 1842
Ref.: TDW 104.

3 Brickfield on the west side of Faygate Lane opposite Faygate (Caryll's Lea) Farm
NGR: TQ 217 349
Date: A kiln, which may have been either a brick or a lime kiln, was marked here on the tithe map. A brickfield was marked on the map of 1874
Op.: Thomas & Jesse Norman (cf Lower Beeding 4) advertised as brickmakers in Faygate in the 1870s
Refs: TDW 104; OS 6in 3 (1874); Kelly 1874-8).

4 Brickworks south of the railway at Faygate Station
NGR: TQ 217 343
Date: In operation by 1882 and marked on the map of 1896
Op.: Faygate Brickyards (C. Fraser, proprietor) advertised in 1882 and 1887 followed by James Innes in 1890 and Faygate Brickworks (James Weller, manager) from 1895 to 1903
Refs: OS 6in 14 NW (1899); Kelly (1882-1903).

5 Brickworks at Lambs Green
NGR: cTQ 220 368
Date: In operation by 1934; closed c1957
Op.: Rusper Clay Works Ltd advertised from 1934 to 1955
Refs: Kelly (1934-55); *VCH* **6** (3), 117.

RUSTINGTON

1 Brickyard on the east side of Ash Lane
NGR: TQ 055 025
Date: Marked only on the map of 1876
Ref.: OS 6in 63 (1876).

2 Brick and tile works on the north side of Worthing Road
NGR: TQ 052 031
Date: In operation by 1882 and closed c1940
Op.: Victoria Brick & Tile Works (Geo. Marshall, manager) advertised in 1882. By 1887 it was called Rustington Brick & Tile Works and had been taken over by Butt & Sons of Littlehampton (qv), whose manager in 1895 was John

Shepherd. In the late 1920s the works was in the hands of Chamberlains of Arundel (foreman: Bill Cornwall). George Baker & Son, of Worthing, advertised in 1930 and Rustington Brick Works in 1934 and 1938
Prod.: Pottery was also made in the 1880s
Refs: OS 6in 63 SE (1896, 1910, 1932); Kelly (1882-1938); *QMJ* (1933); Baines, *Pottery*, 171; inf. Ben Foreman (1989).

3 Brickfield at the corner of Worthing Road and Mill Lane
NGR: TQ 054 028
Date: Marked on maps from 1896 and closed c1940
Op.: Possibly C.R. Gammans (cf Lancing) in 1915, Zachariah Peskett of Angmering in the 1920s and Mill Brick Co. from 1930 to 1938
Refs: OS 6in 63 SE (1896, 1910, 1932); Kelly (1915, 1930-8); inf. B. Foreman.

4 Brickfields on the south side of Worthing Road
NGR: TQ 051 030
Date: Marked on the map of 1910 and, covering a wider area to the south and east, in 1932
Op.: James Linfield (cf Lyminster) advertised from 1915 to 1930 but by the late 1920s the works were in the hands of Major Baker (cf site 2) whose foreman was George Cornwall (brother of Bill cf site 2)
Refs: OS 6in 63 SE (1910, 1932); Kelly (1915-30); inf. B. Foreman.

5 Brickfield on the west side of North Lane
NGR: TQ 046 028
Date: Opened in the 1930s, revived after World War 2 and closed in the 1950s
Op.: North Lane Brick Co. Ltd; J.J. Louett was the manager in 1933
Refs: OS 6in 63 SW (1932); *QMJ* (1933-51); Kelly (1934-8).

SELSEY

1 Brickfield on the coast at the south end of Hillfield Road
NGR: SZ 850 923
Date: 1880s; marked 'disused' on the map of 1898

Ref.: OS 6in 81 NW (1898).

2 Brickfield on the east side of present-day Croft Road
NGR: SZ 855 931
Date: In existence by the 1890s and marked on the map of 1909
Op.: Probably Henry Arnell Smith, a builder, who advertised in 1895 and 1899
Refs OS 6in 81 NW (1909); Kelly (1895-99).

3 Brickfield on the east side of High Street behind the present-day British Legion Hall
NGR: SZ 856 936
Date: Marked only on the map of 1909
Op.: Possibly A. Jones, who gave his address as Poplars in 1899. The yard was later owned by Ralph Selsby, coal-merchant and contractor, who employed Bill Mariner as his brickmaker
Refs: OS 6in 81 NW (1909); Kelly (1899); V. Mitchell & K. Smith, *Branch Line to Selsey* (1983).

4 Brickworks on the west side of Chichester Road north of present-day St Peters Crescent
NGR: SZ 855 939
Date: In existence by 1925 when Roman coins were found in the brickfield; closed during World War 2 but re-opened afterwards and still in operation in 1960
Op.: Trojan Manufacturing Co. Ltd
Prod.: Stock bricks, briquettes and fireplaces
F.Inf.: A siding from the Selsey tramway led into the works, a photograph of which was published in 1983
Cond.: The site is now used as a caravan park
Refs: OS 6in 81 NW (1932); *SAC* **74** (1933), 149; Kelly (1927-38); *QMJ* (1951-59); Mitchell & Smith, *op. cit.*

5 Brickworks east of Chichester Road north of Norton
NGR: SZ 862 960
Date: 1930s
Op.: Ferry Brick & Tile Co. advertised in 1930 and again in 1938. Selsey Multi-stock Brick Co. Ltd also advertised in the 1930s, possibly operating in the same area
Refs: OS 6in 73 SE (1932); Kelly (1930-8); *DBC* (1938).

SHIPLEY

1 Brick kiln east of Shipley Road
NGR: TQ 157 243
Date: Brick Kiln Farm was first named on a map of 1795
Ref.: *SRS* **72**, 108.

2 Brick kiln north of Cow Barn in the south of the parish
NGR: TQ 141 182
Date: Brick Kiln Mead was listed on the tithe award of 1847
Ref.: TDW 108.

3 Brickyard NW of Knepp Castle
NGR: TQ 154 221
Date: Old Brick Yard on the tithe award of 1847 and Brickyard Wood in 1876
Refs: TDW 108; OS 6in 24 (1876).

4 Brickfield south of Hoes Farm east of Coolham
NGR: TQ 130 230
Date: Marked only on the map of 1876
Ref.: OS 6in 24 (1876).

5 Brickworks on the south side of Cross Lane north of Brooks Green
NGR: TQ 131 260
Date: Marked on the map of 1913
Ref.: OS 6in 24 NW (1913).

SHOREHAM

1 Brickfield between Gordon Road and Rosslyn Road
NGR: TQ 221 053
Date: Marked only on the map of 1898 but in use as a depot until c1933
Op.: C.R. Gammans (cf Lancing 4) advertised in Old Shoreham in 1899 followed by John William Gammans from 1903 to 1933
Refs: OS 6in 65 SW (1898); Kelly (1899-1930); *QMJ* (1927-33).

2 Brickfield on part of the site of the former Swiss Gardens
NGR: TQ 207 058
Date: 1820s and early 1830s: the brickfield was disused when the gardens were created c1835
Op.: James Britton Balley, a shipbuilder, who advertised as a brickmaker in 1828 and 1832
Refs: Pigot (1828-32); inf. Trevor Povey.

SIDLESHAM

1 Brickyard on the south side of present-day Lockgate Road
   NGR: SZ 846 996
   Date: Marked on maps of 1755, 1792 and 1848
   Op.: William Rusbridge was a brickmaker in Sidlesham in 1751. Thomas Hobgen was the owner of the yard in 1792 and John Hobgen the owner and Charles Hobgen the tenant in 1848
   Refs: Add. MS. 1990 & 5160; TDW 109; *SRS* **32**, 118.

2 Brickworks on Jury Farm
   NGR: cSU 847 002
   Date: 1930s
   Op.: Jury Brick Co. advertised in 1933 and as Jury Brick & Coal Co. in 1938; Duttons (Bricks) Ltd gave their address as Sidlesham Common from 1938 to 1951 but were brick merchants, not manufacturers
   Refs: Kelly (1934-8); *QMJ* (1933-51); *DBC* (1938); inf. V. Mitchell

SLAUGHAM

1 Brick kiln in the northern part of the parish
   Exact location not known
   Date: Listed on the Land Tax assessment for 1785
   Op.: The owner in 1785 was Thomas Harding. William Kensett, a tilemaker from West Grinstead, worked in Slaugham from 1793
   Refs: *SRS* **77**, 194; E. Kensett, *History of the Free Christian Church, Horsham* (1921).

2 Brickfield north of High Beeches Lane NE of Handcross
   NGR: TQ 272 311
   Date: Marked on the map of 1874; Old Brick Kiln and Old Clay Pit in 1898
   Op.: Charles Hyder advertised from 1887 to 1895
   Refs: OS 6in 14 SE (1874, 1898); Kelly (1887-95).

3 Brickfield on the east side of the Brighton Road south of Handcross
   NGR: TQ 263 290
   Date: Marked on the map of 1874, disused in 1898 but shown as Brick Works in 1912
   Op.: James Brewer (cf Lower Beeding 6)

advertised from 1903 to 1915
   Refs: OS 6in 14 SE (1874, 1898, 1912); Kelly (1903-7); Pike/Horsham (1903-15).

4 Brickfield north of Pease Pottage
   NGR: TQ 266 341
   Date: Marked only on the map of 1898
   Refs: OS 6in NE (1898).

5 Brickworks at Handcross
   NGR: cTQ 261 293
   Date: 1930s
   Op.: R.G. Ward & Co. Ltd advertised in 1933
   Ref.: *QMJ* (1933).

SLINDON *see* BINSTED, WALBERTON

SLINFOLD

1 Brickfield north of Hill House on the bank of the River Arun
   NGR: TQ 118 323
   Date: Field name on the tithe award of 1843
   Op.: The tenant in 1843 was John Briggs
   Ref.: TDW 112.

2 Brickyard north of Lower Lodge Farm
   NGR: TQ 097 308
   Date: Listed on the tithe award of 1843
   Op.: The owner/occupier in 1843 was John Turner
   Refs: TDW 112.

3 Brickfield on the eastern edge of Rookery Wood south of Five Oaks Road
   NGR: TQ 118 292
   Date: Marked on the map of 1880 but disused by 1896
   Op.: Peters and Parker, builders, of Horsham, advertised in 1882
   Refs: OS 6in 13 (1880) 13 SW (1896); Kelly (1882).

4 Brickfield SE of Slinfold station
   NGR: TQ 116 308
   Date: In operation by 1907 and still marked on the map of 1965
   Op.: Slinfold Railway Brick Co. (Chas. Lansbury, manager) advertised in 1907 and Duke & Ockenden from 1915 to 1927
   Refs: OS 6in 13 NW (1909) 1:25,000 TQ 13 (1965); Kelly (1907-1927).

SOMPTING

1 Brickyard
   Location not known
   Date: Mid-19th century
   Op.:   Francis Ide, a brickmaker and beer
          retailer, advertised from 1845 to 1855
   Ref.: Kelly (1845-55).

SOUTHWATER *see* HORSHAM

SOUTHWICK

1 Brickfield on the east side of present-day
   Kingston Lane
   NGR: TQ 238 054
   Date: Described as Brickground on railway
          plans of 1836 and listed on the tithe
          award of 1842
   Op.:   In 1836 the land, together with the
          right to make bricks, was let to George
          Cheesman, William Lambert, Thomas
          Wisden and John Field. Nathaniel
          Hall, the owner in 1836, exchanged the
          land with William Gorringe in 1842.
          John Faulkener advertised as a
          brickmaker in Southwick in 1845
   Refs: TDW 164; Add. MS. 27377; Brighton
          Ref. Lib. Sussex Pamphlet Box O No 8
          (ex inf. G. Mead); Kelly (1845).

2 Brickyard SE of Southwick Station
   NGR: TQ 244 051
   Date: 1880s
   Op.:   T. Vernon Marsh was the manager of
          Rock Brickyard in 1882
   Ref.: Kelly (1882).

3 Brickfield north of the railway at Fishersgate
   NGR: TQ 254 054
   Date: Brickmaking was taking place in
          Fishersgate in 1851. The brickfield was
          marked on the map of 1899
   Op.:   W. Nicholson was a brickmaker in
          Fishersgate in 1851; Edmund John
          Ockenden advertised from 1890 to
          1899 and H. Ockenden in 1903
   Refs: OS 6in 65 SE (1899); Kelly (1851, 1890-
          1903).

4. Brickfield on the north side of Fishersgate
   Road
   NGR: TQ 256 051
   Date: Marked on the map of 1912
   Refs: OS 6in 65 SE (1912).

STEDHAM

1 Brickfield east of Mill Lane
   NGR: SU 867 229
   Date: Upper and Lower Brick Fields were
          listed on the tithe award of 1845
   Ref.: TDW 117.

STEYNING

1 Brickyard in the NE of the parish
   Exact location not known
   Date: 17th and early 18th centuries
   Op.:   Brownings of Steyning were
          brickmakers and maltsters in 1659 and
          Thomas Ellis occupied, inter alia, a
          malthouse and a 'brickworks for
          making bricks and tiles' in 1700
   Refs: Par. 183/33 f12; PRO E1 34/11 & 12 (ex
          inf. T.P. Hudson).

2 Brick kiln north of Staplefields
   NGR: TQ 175 127
   Date: Brick Kiln Field was listed on the tithe
          award of 1840
   Op.:   Owned by the Wiston estate
   Ref.: TDW 118.

3 Brickyard on the west side of Horsham Road
   south of Wappingthorn
   NGR: TQ 170 128
   Date: In existence by 1882 and closed c1900;
          Old Brick Kiln was marked on the
          map of 1909
   Op.:   H.E. Hammond advertised as a
          farmer and brickmaker at
          Wappingthorn in 1882
   Refs: OS 6in 51 NE (1909); Kelly (1882).

4 Brickworks on the south side of Bostal Road
   NGR: TQ 177 105
   Date: Pre-1945
   Op.:   The Steyning Lime & Brick Works
   Prod.: Probably sand-lime bricks
   Ref.: Sale particulars of 1945 (copy supplied
          by Janet Pennington)

STOPHAM

1 Brickyard on the west bank of the Arun at
   Harwoods Green
   NGR: TQ 033 206
   Date: Marked on maps from 1820 to 1896 but
          as disused in 1910; re-opened in the
          1920s but shown as Works (Dis.) in 1959
   Op.:   Chripps & Son in 1839 and T. Cripps

in 1855 followed by James Pellatt in 1867 and 1874. Eli Holden advertised from 1890 to 1907 and from 1927 to 1938

Geol.: Atherfield clay

F.Inf.: Bricks were transported by barge to Pallingham Quay and to the wharf at Pulborough

Cond.: All the pits and tips have been levelled

Refs: QDP/W 41; TDW 119; OS 6in 36 (1876) 36 NW (1896, 1910) 1:25,000 TQ 02 (1959); Robson (1839); Kelly (1855-1907); *QMJ* (1927); *DBC* (1938); *A Brief Guide to Lower Street, Pulborough before the Great War* (ex inf. I. Lissamore); inf. Roger Bristow (1981).

STORRINGTON

1 Brick and tile works on the west side of Greyfriars Lane
NGR: TQ 084 136
Date: In operation by 1879 and apparently disused by 1896 although the Catholic church was said to have been built with bricks from the yard in 1905
Op.: F. Terry advertised in 1882 and 1887
F.Inf.: A photograph of the brickfield was taken in the 1880s
Refs: OS 6in 50 (1879) 50 NE (1896); Kelly (1882-7); Joan Ham, *Storrington in Pictures* (1979); *West Sussex History* **38** (Sept 1987), 34.

2 Tile works on the east side of Chantry Lane
NGR: TQ 093 137
Date: 1930s to c1960
Op.: The Marley Tile Co. (Storrington) Ltd advertised from 1934 to 1959
Prod.: Roofing tiles and concrete products
Refs: OS 1:25,000 TQ 01 (1959); Kelly (1934-8); *QMJ* (1959).

TANGMERE

1 Brickfield
Exact location not known
Date: Early 20th century
Op.: The Goodwood estate
Prod.: Clamp-burnt bricks
Ref.: Goodwood MS. E5488.

WEST TARRING

1 Brickfield between the railway and the south end of Princess Avenue
NGR: TQ 127 033
Date: In existence by 1893; marked as Tarring Brick Field on maps of 1896 and 1909, it was moved to the north side of Canterbury Road to make way for the goods yard
Op.: The company's offices were probably in Elm Grove, Heene, where George Greenfield advertised in 1899, followed by White & Peters from 1907 to 1915
Refs: OS 6in 64 SW (1896) 25in 64/14 (1909); Kelly (1899-1915); *SAC* **66** (1925), 232; White, *Brighton & Worthing*, 86.

2 Brickworks on the site of present-day Gerald Road
NGR: TQ 126 024
Date: Marked as West End Brick Works on maps of 1896 and 1909
Refs: OS 6in 64 SW (1896) 25in 64/14 (1909).

THAKEHAM

1 Brickyard on the east side of West Chiltington Road
NGR: TQ 104 188
Date: In existence by 1874 and still operating in 1887 but disused by 1898
Op.: Owned by G.C. Carew-Gibson Esq. in 1887
Prod.: Bricks and tiles; sale particulars of 1887 mentioned two brick kilns and a tile shed
Refs: OS 6in 37 NW (1878, 1898); SP 173, 30.

2 Brickworks between Goose Green Lane and Peacock's Lane
NGR: TQ 116 184
Date: Opened c1933, closed during World War 2, re-opened after the war but finally closed by 1957, when the site was acquired by the Laybrook Co. (site 4)
Op.: Robert Oliver Ireland, the son of Daniel Ireland (cf Itchingfield 3), and R.F. Wells traded as Goose Green Brickfields Ltd in the 1930s. Ireland's post-war partner was a Mr Lustig
Prod.: Hand-made clamp-fired bricks

Refs: OS 6in 37 NW (1939); Kelly (1938);
        QMJ (1933-44); inf. Ron Ireland (1989).

3   Tile works on Heath Common
    NGR: TQ 104 149
    Date: In existence by 1934 and still in
          operation in 1983
    Op.: Thakeham Tiles Ltd (manager: R.L.
          Sturtevant) advertised in the 1930s
    Prod.: Bricks, tiles and cement
    F.Inf.: A 2ft-gauge railway was used to
          transport materials within the works
    Refs: OS 6in 37 SW (1937); Kelly (1934-8);
          QMJ (1944); *VCH* **6** (2), 43; Chalkpits
          Mus., *Industrial Railways*.

4   Brickworks on the east side of Goosegreen
    Lane opposite Laybrook Farm
    NGR: TQ 115 188
    Date: Opened in 1935 and still in operation
          (2001)
    Op.: Owned initially by Deans, builders, of
          Storrington, whose first foreman was
          Ted Scutt; Laybrook Brick Co. Ltd
          advertised from 1938 to 1959. In 1961
          the company was acquired by
          Hudsons (cf West Hoathly 3) when the
          name Hudsons Laybrook was
          adopted. In 1976 this was changed to
          Ibstock Brick Hudsons and subse-
          quently Ibstock Brick Laybrook: now
          Ibstock Brick Ltd
    Prod.: Clamp-burnt multi-coloured stocks,
          machine-moulded using the soft mud
          process and a four-mould Berry
          machine (1981). Production of clamp
          bricks stopped at the beginning of
          1992 and the rebuilding of the works,
          including a new gas-fired tunnel kiln,
          was complaeted in 1995. 50 million
          kiln stocks a year are produced, using
          fully-automatic Aberson moulding
          and setting machinery
    F.Inf.: An industrial light railway engine
          formerly owned by the company now
          operates at the Chalkpits Museum,
          Amberley
    Refs: OS 6in 37 NW (1939); Kelly (1938);
          QMJ (1951-59); *SIAS Newsletter* **32** (Oct
          1981); inf. R. Ireland (1989) and
          I. Lissamore, Works Manager, (1989
          and 1992).

TILLINGTON

1   Brickyard north of Coxland Cottages
    NGR: SU 961 215
    Date: Brick Yard Field was marked on a
          Petworth estate survey of 1779
    Ref.: PHA 3606/10.

2   Brick kiln on the west bank of the stream NW
    of River
    NGR: SU 935 232
    Date: Brick Kiln Field was listed on the tithe
          award of 1837
    Ref.: TDW 127

TODDINGTON *see* LYMINSTER

TORTINGTON

1   Brickyard(s) on the south side of Arundel
    Road
    NGR: SU 998 073
    Date: A bricklayer/brickmaker was record-
          ed in Tortington in 1620 and 1665 and
          a brick kiln was marked on a map of
          1724 to the west of the site in use later.
          Brick kilns on the eastern site were
          shown on a map of 1772 and this yard
          continued in use until at least 1910
    Op.: Bricks were listed in John Rybread's
          inventory, taken in 1711. George
          Blunden was a brickburner in
          Tortington in the 1770s and '80s.
          Thomas Suter advertised from 1839 to
          1851 followed by William Jupp from
          1859 to 1874 and Mrs Ann Jupp in
          1878. Charles Chamberlain, who also
          ran Arundel Cement Works,
          advertised in 1882 and 1887, followed
          by Arthur Burrell (cf Arundel 3) from
          1890 to 1903. Burrell was still the
          tenant of the brickyard, by now
          owned by the Arundel Castle estate, in
          1910. David Suter advertised as a
          brickmaker in Tortington in 1899,
          possibly working as Burrell's manager
          on this site
    Refs: Arundel Castle MSS. FC 399 & H1/3
          (ex inf. T.P. Hudson); TDW 128; OS 6in
          62 (1876) 62 NE (1910); IR 19 f65 (ex
          inf. T.P. Hudson); EpI/29/198/26; *SRS*
          35, 320; Pigot (1839); Kelly (1845-1903).

TROTTON

1 Brickyard(?) on the west side of Milland Lane
   NGR: SU 832 281
   Date: Brick Lane Field was listed on the tithe
   award of 1840
   Ref.: TDW 130.

2 Brickworks at Ingrams Green in a detached
   portion of the parish (now Iping)
   NGR: SU 842 201
   Date: Opened c1827, marked on maps of
   1840, 1860 and 1873, advertised for
   sale in 1875, still in use in 1878 but
   disused by 1897
   Op.: Benjamin Challen in 1840, Benjamin &
   Shotter Challen in 1860, Job Challen in
   1874 and the exors of B. Challen in
   1878
   Cond.: In 1985 about half of the kiln remained
   and was visible from the road
   Refs: TDW 130; QDP/W126; OS 6in 34
   (1873) 34 NW (1897); SP 366; Kelly
   (1874-8); inf. J.C.V. Mitchell (1985).

TURNERS HILL *see* WORTH

TWINEHAM

1 Brickworks on Job's Lane, Hickstead
   NGR: cTQ 270 203
   Date: 1920s and 1930s
   Op.: The Job Brick Co. advertised from
   1927 to 1938
   Ref.: Kelly (1927-38).

WALBERTON

1 Brickyard south of The Street to the east of
   Walberton House
   NGR: SU 975 057
   Date: Probably in operation by the 1730s,
   marked Brick Kiln Field on a map of
   1756 and listed in the Land Tax from
   1780, the yard seems to have gone out
   of use c1810, although named as
   Brickyard Field on the tithe award of
   1846
   Op.: George Cartwright was a brickmaker
   in Walberton in 1733; William Hedger
   had been the occupier 'for many years
   past' in 1782; John Andrew was the
   tenant in 1787-8 followed by William
   Halsted from 1789 to 1809.

Refs: Add MSS 1802 & 7778; TDW 133; *SRS*
32, 18; LT Walberton.

2 Brickyard west of Mill Road on the edge of
   Slindon Common
   NGR: SU 968 072
   Date: In existence in 1832, marked as Brick
   Field in 1876 but disused by 1898
   Op.: William Halstead (cf. site 1) advertised
   in 1832 and 1839 and was the owner/
   occupier in 1846. By 1860 the owner
   was Sir John Anson of Avisford House
   Refs: TDW 133; OS 62/3 (1876, 1898); Pigot
   (1832-9); Hunt, *Mining Records*, 39.

WARNHAM *see* HORSHAM

WARNINGCAMP

1 Tile kilns on the east side of Blakehurst Lane
   NGR: TQ 047 064
   Date: Post-medieval: the remains of two
   kilns beside small water-filled claypits
   were observed in 1987
   Ref.: West Sussex Sites and Monuments
   Record No 4475.

WASHINGTON

1 Brickyard on the south side of Storrington
   Road near the present-day roundabout
   NGR: TQ 119 133
   Date: In existence by 1839 and marked on
   the maps of 1879 and 1896
   Op.: G. & J. Golds were the occupiers in
   1839 and John Golds advertised as
   farmer and brickmaker in 1845. Tidey
   & Baker had taken over by 1866 and in
   1874 they advertised as Baker & Tidey
   (cf Pulborough 3). Finally Henry Terry
   & Son advertised from 1878 to 1899
   Refs: TDW 137; OS 6in 51 (1879) 51 SW
   (1896); Kelly (1845, 1866-99).

2 Brick and tile works on Rock Common
   NGR: TQ 127 137
   Date: 1950s and 1960s
   Op.: West Sussex Tile & Brick Co. Ltd
   Ref.: *QMJ* (1959).

WESTBOURNE

1 Brickyard on the west side of Broad Road at Nutbourne

NGR: SU 786 056

Date: In operation by 1760, the kilns were shown on maps of 1778, 1795 and 1806 but in 1840 the site was listed only as Brickyard Meadow, although there was a pottery on an adjacent site from 1799 onwards; revived as a brickworks in the 1930s and still marked on the map of 1947

Op.: William Carter was a brickmaker in Westbourne in 1760, as was William Comb(es) in 1766. George Combes, a tilemaker, married Mary Hoar in 1781 and members of the Hoar family (cf Funtington 1) were potters and owners of the property in the late-18th and 19th centuries. Nutbourne Brickworks Ltd advertised from 1930 to 1938

Refs: *SRS* **72**, 91, 108; OS 1in (1806) 6in 60 NE (1932, 1947); TDW 138; *SRS* **32**, 171 & **35**, 330; LT Westbourne; Kelly (1930-8).

2 Brickyard on the east side of Mill Lane at Lumley

NGR: SU 754 064

Date: Opened in 1805; brick kilns were shown on the map of 1806 but in 1840 the site was listed as Brickyard Orchard

Op.: Edward Tollervey, a miller, was the owner/occupier in 1805, followed by Captain Hawker from 1822, his tenant from 1824 being Thomas Coates

Refs: OS 1in (1806); TDW 138; LT Westbourne.

3 Brick and tile works on Westbourne Common NW of Monks Farm

NGR: SU 752 085

Date: In existence by 1859 and marked on maps from 1874 to 1947

Op.: The yard belonged to the Stansted estate. H. Wild advertised as a brickmaker on the Common in 1859 and 1862 followed by William Stent in 1878, James Shilling in the 1880s and William Lock in 1899 and 1903

Prod.: Bricks, tiles and pottery: a pottery

shed was included in the buildings listed in sale particulars of 1913

F.Inf.: In 1983 the site was examined by Messrs Aldsworth, Allnutt and Rudkin, who interpreted the surviving circular kiln contained within a rectangular building as a pot kiln

Refs: OS 6in 67 (1874) 67 SW (1898, 1910, 1947); SP 2694; Kelly (1859-1903); inf. A. Allnutt (1983).

4 Brickfield on the west side of Cot Lane at Maybush, on the boundary with Chidham

NGR: SU 786 052

Date: In operation by 1932; closed in 1964

Op.: West Sussex Brick & Tile Co. advertised from 1933 to 1945. The owner in the 1960s was A.N.G. Pycroft

Prod.: Hand-made clamp-fired bricks

Refs: OS 6in 60 NE (1932, 1947); *QMJ* (1933-44); *Hand Brickmaking: Chidham Brickfield* (1974) – mss in Chichester Ref. Lib.

5 Brickyard on the west side of Thorney Road at the end of the former ropewalk

NGR: SU 755 055

Date: In existence by 1780, marked on a map of 1786 and listed in the land tax until 1798

Op.: The yard was owned by a Mr Cathery from 1780 until 1796, followed by Richard Barwell Esq of the Stansted estate

Refs: LT Westbourne; J.H. Mee, *Bourne in the Past* (1913), 264; inf. Peter Wilkinson

see also: RACTON

WESTHAMPNETT

1 Brickyards on Claypit Lane and Arundel Road

NGR: SU 883 063

Date: The first yard, opened in 1782, was on the west side of Claypit Lane (882 063). By 1838 this had been moved to the east side of the lane and a second yard opened on the south side of Arundel Road (884 062). Both were still in operation in 1875 but the northern one was disused by 1898 and the southern one closed c1915

Op.: Owned by the Goodwood estate and operated throughout by members of the Lillywhite family

Prod.: A series of ledgers and accounts gives details of the wide range of bricks, tiles and drainpipes produced and the prices charged at various times between 1782 and 1915

Refs: PM 4; TDW 143; OS 6in 61 (1875) 61 NE (1898, 1910); Goodwood MSS. E5402, 5408, 5476-82, 5487; Kelly (1878-1903).

WIGGONHOLT

1 Brick kiln on the east side of the Pulborough road opposite the turning to Wiggonholt Farm

NGR: TQ 064 168

Date: In operation from 1688 but out of use by 1837, when the site was named Brick and Kiln Croft

Op.: John Cook was the occupier in 1688. The tenant in 1837 was George Penfold

Refs: TDW 13; Parham Acc 9163/10 (ex inf. Annabelle Hughes).

WISBOROUGH GREEN

1 Brickyard on the edge of Homebushes Copse NW of Homebushes Farm

NGR: TQ 046 295

Date: 18th century; listed as Brick Kiln Field in 1842

Op.: Probably members of the Billinghurst family (cf Ditchling 2) including Edward, who died in 1749, and another Edward, who was working in Wisborough Green in 1785. The latter belonged to the General Baptists, who held a Meeting at 'Homebush'

Prod.: The first Edward Billinghurst's probate inventory listed kiln bricks, various kinds of tiles and also pots and crocks

Refs: TDW 149; EpI/29/210/258; *Records of the Old Meeting House, Ditchling* (transcript loaned by J.J. Goring).

2 Brickyard on Brickkiln Common NW of Rose Cottage

NGR: TQ 028 229

Date: In existence by 1766, marked as Brick & Tile Works on the map of 1879 and in operation until World War 1

Op.: John Westbrook was a brickmaker in Wisborough Green in 1766 and another John was the tenant of this yard in 1842 and advertised in 1845. Noah Mann advertised from 1887 to 1903 and Arthur John Keen and Frederick Phillips, who gave their address as 'Burdocks' in 1907 and 1915 respectively, probably worked on this site

Geol.: Weald Clay

Refs: TDW 149; OS 6in 23 (1879) 23 SW (1896, 1910); Kelly (1845, 1887-1915); Pike/Horsham (1903); *SRS* **32**, 231; Thurrell et al, *Haslemere*, 45.

3 Brickyard 1 mile NE of Loxwood, now known as Brickkiln Farm

NGR: TQ 055 326

Date: Brick Kiln Field and Brickyard Plat were named on the tithe award of 1842

Op.: The tenant in 1842 was Stephen Knight, who was also the tenant of a brickyard on Pephurst Farm (site 4)

Ref.: TDW 149.

4 Brickyard at Pephurst Farm on the north side of Loxwood Road

NGR: TQ 056 319

Date: In existence by 1842, shown as Brick Works in 1879 and in operation until the 1920s

Op.: Stephen Knight was the tenant in 1842. Alfred Phillips advertised at Bullhams in 1895 followed by William Mitchell from 1899 to 1925

Refs: TDW 149; OS 6in 12 (1879) 12 NE (1910); Kelly (1895-1907); Pike/ Horsham (1903-25).

5 Brickyard on the edge of Bittles Wood on the SW side of the road from Newbridge to Loxwood

NGR: TQ 053 278

Date: In operation in 1842, shown as Brick Field in 1879 and closed at the end of World War 1

Op.: Daniel Mann was the tenant in 1842. J. Thayre advertised from 1855 to 1867 followed by David Thayer from 1895 to 1899 and John Mitchell from 1903 to 1918

Refs: TDW 149; OS 6in 12 (1879) 12 SE (1895, 1910); Kelly (1855-1918); Pike/ Horsham (1903-10).

6 Brickyard on the east side of Fittleworth Road
NGR: TQ 038 245
Date: Kiln Plot on the tithe award of 1842; in 1879 Brickyard Cottages occupied the site, although the yard was no longer active
Refs: TDW 149; OS 6in 23 (1879).

7 Brickyard in Loxwood
Exact location not known
Date: Early 20th century
Op.: Child & Son advertised from 1913 to 1918
Ref.: Kelly (1913-18).

WISTON

1 Tile kiln north of Washington Road
NGR: TQ 157 136
Date: 2nd or 3rd century
Refs: West Sussex Sites and Monuments Record No 3477; W. Figg, 'A Roman Building Discovered at Wiston in 1848' *SAC* **2** (1849), 313-5.

2 Brickyard on Hook Farm
NGR: TQ 145 169
Date: The names Brickyard Coppice and Brickyard Field appeared on a map of c1800
Ref.: Wiston MS. 5601 (ex inf. T.P. Hudson).

3 Brick kiln SW of Frenchland House to the south of site 2
NGR: TQ 145 165
Date: Brick Kiln Wood was listed on the tithe award of 1839
Ref.: TDW 150.

4 Brickyard (?) NW of Wiston House
NGR: TQ 149 128
Date: Listed as Brick Piece on the tithe award of 1839
Ref.: TDW 150.

5 Brickyard on the south bank of the stream south of Brownhill
NGR: TQ 145 156
Date: Called Minty Field on the tithe award of 1839 but the layout of the buildings shown on the map is typical of a brickyard, which was probably the one mentioned in a valuation of the Wiston estate made in 1849
Refs: TDW 150; Wiston MS. 5143 (ex inf. T.P. Hudson).

6 Brick kiln east of Woodman's Farm in the north of the parish
NGR: TQ 154 174
Date: Brick Kiln Wood was marked on the map of 1879
Ref.: OS 6in 37 (1879).

WEST WITTERING

1 Brick kiln north of Cakeham Road
NGR: cSZ 785 980
Date: Great and Little Brick Kiln Fields were listed on the tithe award of 1848, possibly the site of brickmaking when a brick tower was added to the residence of the Bishop of Chichester at the beginning of the 16th century
Refs: TDW 147; Armstrong, *Sussex*, 32.

2 Brick kiln on the foreshore
NGR: SZ 774 992
Date: Probably 18th century: remains of a ki!n and brick wasters were observed in 1977
Ref.: West Sussex Sites and Monuments Record No 0025.

3 Tile works on the west side of Chapel Lane
NGR: SZ 795 990
Date: Marked on the map of 1879 only
Ref.: OS 6in 72 (1879).

WOOLAVINGTON (*now* EAST LAVINGTON)

1 Brick, tile and pottery kiln at Upper Norwood
NGR: SU 937 179
Date: 16th and 17th centuries
Op.: Bricks were mentioned in the will of John Phipp, made in 1557 and the inventory of Robert Champion, who died in 1617. They were followed by other members of the Champion and Philp families, who lived in the neighbouring parish of Graffham.
F.Inf.: A report on the site and plans of the kiln were published in 1990
Refs: *SRS* **45**, 417; EpI/29/215/3; F.G. Aldsworth & A.G. Down, 'Pottery in the Graffham Area' *SAC* **128** (1990), 117-122.

2 Brick and tile works north of the lane from Graffham to Upper Norwood Farm
NGR: SU 932 177
Date: Marked only on the map of 1880
Ref.:   OS 6in 35 (1880).

WOOLBEDING

1 Brick kilns near Tyeland Farm on the edge of Bepton Common
NGR: SU 864 205
Date: Land for the kilns was granted in 1587. The brick kilns were shown on a map of c1700 and listed on the land tax assessments until 1824. The property was called Brick Kiln House estate in 1724 (the modern name Tyeland may be a corruption of 'tile land')
Op.:   The land was granted to John Robynett in 1587. From the mid-17th century the yard was in the hands of several generations of the Denyer family, including Robert, who died in 1657, another Robert, who died in 1684, William, the owner of the freehold in 1724, Thomas, who died in 1730 and William in 1743. Christopher Croucher paid tax on the brick kilns from 1780, followed by William Philp from 1805 and John Grish from 1814 to 1824
Refs: Cowdray MSS. 1644 & 285; Add. MS. 13420; EpI/29/216/11,16 & 30; LT Woolbeding 1780-1824 (ex inf. J.C.V. Mitchell); *SRS* **32**, 76.

2 Brickyard on the west side of Linch Road at Redford
NGR: SU 862 262
Date: In operation by 1782, shown on the tithe map of 1838 and closed c1900
Op.:   Thomas Eames paid tax on Redford brick-kilns from 1782, followed by George Berry from 1793. He was still the tenant in 1838. J. Osgood advertised in 1851 and Mrs M. Osgood in 1855 followed by James Grist in 1862, Samuel Gale from 1867 to 1882 and Mrs Victoria Gale in 1887, Thomas Ramsey in 1890 and 1895 and A.G. West in 1899
F.Inf.:   The octagonal building which housed

the horse-driven pugmill was removed to the Weald and Downland Open Air Museum at Singleton in 1979
Refs: TDW 152; OS 6in 21 (1874) 21 NE (1898); LT Woolbeding (1782-1824); Kelly (1851-99); inf. J.C.V. Mitchell (1985).

WORTH

1 Brickyard (?) south of Tinsley Green
NGR: TQ 291 394
Date: The field name Brick Mead on the tithe award of 1842 suggests brickmaking when the ironworks were in operation in the 16th and 17th centuries
Ref.:   TDE 155.

2 Brickfield on the site of present-day Shelley Close, Pound Hill
NGR: TQ 291 375
Date: Listed as Brick Field Wood in 1842
Ref.:   TDE 155.

3 Brickfield on present-day Hazelwick Avenue NW of Three Bridges station
NGR: TQ 287 371
Date: Opened in 1838 to make bricks for the railway to Brighton and listed on the tithe award of 1842; closed c 1870
Op.:   Henry Michell, the Horsham brewer, owned the Plough Inn and the brickfield. He managed the yard himself in 1838-40 and again from 1850 for a few years. Edward Mitchell, listed as victualler and brickmaker in 1861, advertised as a brickmaker in 1859 and 1862, followed by Mrs Mitchell in 1867
Refs: TDE 155; census (1861); Kelly (1859-67); Neale, *Horsham*, 39-41, 49

4 Brickfield north of Paddockhurst Road
NGR: TQ 323 347
Date: Listed as Brick Field on the tithe award of 1842
F.Inf.:   Lime-burning also took place on the site. The 1899 map shows Old Lime Kiln in the NW corner of the field, which now forms part of Brickkiln Wood
Refs: TDE 155; OS 6in 4 SW (1899).

5   Brickyard on Tulleys Farm north of Turners Hill Road
    NGR: TQ 327 360
    Date: Listed on the tithe award of 1842
    Op.:   Owned in 1842 by the trustees of H.R. Willett
    Ref.: TDE 155.

6   Brick and tile works on the edge of Worth Forest east of the railway
    NGR: TQ 294 349
    Date: First marked in 1875; probably ceased work during World War 1, although the names Brick Field North and Brick Field South still appear on either side of the M23 on the map of 1982
    Op.:   Probably William Nightingale, who advertised as a brickmaker in Crawley from 1859 to 1903. A member of the Nightingale family, from Horley in Surrey, was said to have been a brickmaker in the Three Bridges area in 1864
    Refs: OS 6in 4 (1875) 4 SW (1899, 1912) 1:25,000 TQ 23/33 (1982); Kelly (1859-1903); inf. Mrs Joan Davy (1979).

7   Brickfield south of the former railway at Rowfant
    NGR: TQ 330 365
    Date: In existence by 1875; marked as Rowfant Brick Works from 1912 onwards and said to have closed in the early 1960s, although it was referred to as Hundred Acres Brickworks, Turners Hill in 1972
    Op.:   James Terry advertised from 1895 to 1907. George Wells (cf site 9) then took over the yard. After World War 2 it was run by W. Harbour & Sons, of Copthorne
    Prod.: Kiln-fired bricks and tiles. A brick made by Mr Terry dated 1877(9?) is in the possession of his granddaughter, Mrs Clarke, of Redhill and a paving brick of c1908 is in the East Grinstead Museum
    F.Inf.: The map of 1910 shows a railway line into the works and seven kilns: three circular and four rectangular
    Refs: OS 6in 4 (1874) 4 SW (1899, 1910, 1946); Kelly (1895-1907); Foster, *Mines* (1901); Bristow & Bazley, *Tunbridge Wells*, 36; inf. J. Hodgkinson (1990).

8   Brickfield at Withypitts south of Turners Hill
    NGR: TQ 343 350
    Date: 1870s and 1880s
    Op.:   William Bennett advertised in 1882 and 1887
    Refs: OS 6in 4 (1875); Kelly (1882-7).

9   Brickfield south of the former railway at Grange Road Station, Crawley Down
    NGR: TQ 347 374
    Date: A brickyard was in existence in 1853 on the site of the Prizefighters public house. This was destroyed when the railway was constructed. The brickfield alongside the railway was marked in 1875, extended to take in more land to the SE in 1897 and continued in operation until 1939
    Op.:   John Riddle (cf West Hoathly 2) in 1853. Bennett & Rapley advertised at Grange Road Station from 1881 to 1887, when William Bennett (cf site 8) alone leased the yard, followed in 1893 by Ambrose Bennett. Smith Bros of Norwood were granted a new lease in 1897 and continued until the outbreak of World War 1. From 1916 until 1939 the yard was in the hands of George Wells & Son
    F.Inf.: A steam engine, installed during World War 1 to cut timber, was later used to power the pugmill
    Refs: OS 6in 4 (1875) 4 SE (1895, 1912, 1938); Kelly (1881-1938); Foster, *Mines*, (1901); inf. Jeremy Hodgkinson (1986).

10 Brickfield behind Bowers Place, Crawley Down
    NGR: TQ 347 377
    Date: Marked only as Clay Pit in 1895 but as Brick Works on the map of 1912
    Op.:   The yard was known locally as Hall's or Gibb's. George T. Hall advertised as a brickmaker at Grange Road in 1899 and 1903 and three brickmakers gave their address as Bowers Road in 1916: Albert Philpott, T. Slator and E. Waite
    Refs: OS 6in 4 SE (1895, 1912); Kelly (1899-1903); inf. J. Hodgkinson.

11 Brickyard north of present-day Tiltwood Drive, Crawley Down
    NGR: TQ 351 380
    Date: c1900 until mid-1920s

Op.: Harry Nickalls (Nichall) advertised from 1903 to 1922. He was eventually bought out by George Wells (cf Site 9)

Refs: Kelly (1903-22); inf. J. Hodgkinson.

12 Brickyard SW of site 11

NGR: TQ 350 379

Date: Late 19th or early 20th century

Op.: A member of the Bennett family (cf site 9)

Ref.: Inf. J. Hodgkinson (1990).

WORTHING *see* BROADWATER, HEENE, WEST TARRING

YAPTON

1 Brickyard on the south side of the disused Chichester canal west of Bilsham Lane

NGR: SU 979 031

Date: Marked on the map of 1896 and as Brick Works in 1910

Op.: Mrs Sarah Sparks advertised from 1895 to 1903

Refs: OS 6in 62 SE (1896, 1910); Kelly (1895-1903).

2 Brickfield between Burndell Road and the canal

NGR: SU 982 032

Date: Opened c1901, marked on the map of 1910, advertised for sale as a going concern in 1924 and continued until 1938

Op.: The Sparks family (cf site 1); John Sparks advertised in 1927 and 1938

Prod.: The yard turned out about 800,000 clamp-burnt bricks per annum

Refs: OS 6in 62 SE (1910); SP 326; *QMJ* (1927); *DBC* (1938).

3 Brickfield on the site of Yapton Gardens

NGR: SU 980 025

Date: Late 1930s after the closure of the works in Flansham Lane (cf Felpham 3)

Op.: Raymond Brown, builder, of Felpham

Refs: *DBC* (1938); inf. G. Hardwell (1990).

BIBLIOGRAPHY

Aldsworth, F.G.	'An eighteenth-century brick kiln on Ebernoe Common, Kirdford' *SAC* **121** (1983), 219-224
Armstrong, J.R.	*A History of Sussex* (1961)
Avery, F.M.	*Development of Burgess Hill and its Potteries 1828-1978* (1979) – unpub. mss in ESRO and WSRO
Baines, J.M.	*Sussex Pottery* (1980)
Beswick, M.	*Bricks and Tiles: the story of a village industry* (Warbleton 1980)
Beswick, M.	'Brick- and Tilemaking on the Dicker in East Sussex' *SIH* **13** (1983), 2-10
Beswick, M.	'Battle Abbey Estate Brickworks 1853-1901' *SIAS Newsletter* **42** (Apr 1984), 4
Beswick, M.	'Bricks for the Martello Towers in Sussex' *SIH* **17** (1987) 20-27
Bristow, C.R. & Bazley, R.A.	*Geology of the Country around Royal Tunbridge Wells* (1972)
British Brick Society	'The Story of Brick' *Harrison Mayer Monthly Bulletin for the Ceramic Industry* **430-440** (1975-6)
Brodribb, G.	*Roman Brick and Tile* (1987)
Brunskill, R.W.	*Brick Building in Britain* (1990)
Chalkpits Museum	*Industrial Railways of the South East* (1984)
Cleere H. & Crossley D.	*The Iron Industry of the Weald* (1985)
Colvin, H.M. et al.	*The History of the King's Works* **4** (1982)
Cox, A.	*Survey of Bedfordshire: Brickmaking – a History and Gazetteer* (1979)
Daggett, I. & W.	*Toddington: its Past and its People* (1987)
Dobson, E.	*A Rudimentary Treatise on the Manufacture of Bricks and Tiles* (1850)
Draper, S. & Martin, D.	'The local brick-making industry' *Recologea Papers Vol 2 No 5* (Robertsbridge 1969), 54-8
Farrant, S.	'The Sources of Building Materials for Brighton' *SIH* **10** (1980), 23-7
Foster, C. le N.	*Reports of HM Inspector of Mines* (1896-1901)
Green, T.K.	'Roman Tileworks at Itchingfield' *SAC* **108** (1970), 23-38
Hammond, M.D.P.	*Bricks and Brickmaking* (1981)
Harmer, J.	'The Use of Clay at Ashburnham Brickworks' *SIH* **11** (1981),14-21 – reprinted in *Brick and Tile-making at Ashburnham* (Singleton 1991)
Hastings Area Local Studies Project (HALSP)	*How the Railways Came to Hastings* (1984)
Holt, M.	'Early Brickmaking in Sussex' *SNQ* **17** (1970), 164-5
Hunt, R.	*Mining Records* Memoir of the Geological Survey (1860)

Kenyon, G.H.	*Glass Industry of the Weald* (1967)
Lake, R.D. et al.	*Geology of the Country around Lewes* (1987)
Leslie, K.C.	'The Ashburnham Estate Brickworks 1840-1968' *SIH* **1** (1970/1), 2-22 – reprinted in *Brick and Tile-making at Ashburnham* (Singleton 1991)
Lusted, A.	'The Building of Glynde Place Stables and New Barn' *Glynde Archivist* **5** (Oct 1987)
Martin, R.	'Frederic Martin: Clayworker' *Hailsham Historian and Naturalist* Vol 2 No 2 (1991), 33-5
Mayhew, G.	*Tudor Rye* (1987)
Neale, K.	*Victorian Horsham (1975)*
Osborne, B.E.	'The Bakers: Brickmakers of Piddinghoe' *SIH* **12** (1982), 24-7
O'Shea, E.W.	'The Restoration of a Tile Kiln at Piddinghoe, East Sussex' *SIH* **12** (1982), 2-24
Paris, H.J.	'Recollections of Hillman's Brickyard, Partridge Green' *SIH* **12** (1982), 31-33
Ponsonby of Shulbrede, Lord	'Monastic Paving Tiles' *SAC* **75** (1934), 19-64
Reid, C.	*The Geology of the Country near Chichester* (1903)
Rudling, D.R.	'The Excavation of a Roman Tilery on Great Cansiron Farm, Hartfield, East Sussex' *Britannia* **17** (1986), 191-230
Rudling, D.R.	'The Excavation of a Roman Tilery at Dell Quay, West Sussex' *SAC* **125** (1987), 81-90
Salzman, L.F.	*History of the Parish of Hailsham, the Abbey of Otham and the Priory of Michelham (1901)*
Salzman, L.F.	*English Industries of the Middle Ages* (2nd ed. 1923)
Shephard-Thorn, E.R. et al	*Geology of the Country around Tenterden* (1966)
Streeten, A.	'The Ceramic Building Materials' in Hare, J.N., *Battle Abbey: The Eastern Range and the Excavations of 1978-80* (1985)
Thurrell, R.G. et al.	*Geology of the Country around Haslemere (1968)*
Vaisey, D. (ed)	*The Diary of Thomas Turner 1754-1765* (1984)
Venables, E.M. & Outen, A.F.	*Building Stones of Old Bognor* (Bognor Regis 1969)
White, H.J.O.	*Memoirs of the Geological Survey: Brighton and Worthing* (1924)
White, H.J.O.	*Memoirs of the Geological Survey: Lewes* (1926)
White, H.J.O.	*Geology of the Country near Hastings and Dungeness* (1928)
Whitehouse, M.S.	*Brickmaking near Warnham* (Warnham 1984)
Wight, J.A.	*Brick Building in England from the Middle Ages to 1550* (1972)
Woodforde, J.	*Bricks to Build a House (1976)*
Young, B. & Lake, R.D.	*Geology of the Country around Brighton and Worthing* (1988)

INDEX

Note. The index covers Part I (Brickmaking in Sussex). Parish names in Part II (Gazetteer of Brickmaking Sites) are also included. References to numbered illustrations are preceded by *illus.* Place names with two elements of which the first is East, Greater, High, Old, Upper, and so on, are indexed under the second element. For the 2nd edition, surnames of brickmakers mentioned in the gazetteer have been added.

245